75

Springer Series in So
Edited by M. Cardona

Springer Series in Solid-State Sciences

Editors: M. Cardona   P. Fulde   K. von Klitzing   H.-J. Queisser

Managing Editor: H. K. V. Lotsch

Volumes 1–49 are listed on the back inside cover

Marvin L. Cohen
James R. Chelikowsky

Electronic Structure and Optical Properties of Semiconductors

Second Edition

With 161 Figures

Springer-Verlag Berlin Heidelberg New York
London Paris Tokyo Hong Kong

Professor Marvin L. Cohen, PhD

Department of Physics, University of California,
and Materials and Chemical Sciences Division,
Lawrence Berkeley Laboratory, Berkeley, CA 94720, USA

Professor James R. Chelikowsky, PhD

Department of Chemical Engineering and Materials Science,
University of Minnesota, Minneapolis, MN 55455, USA

Series Editors:
Professor Dr., Dres. h. c. Manuel Cardona
Professor Dr., Dr. h. c. Peter Fulde
Professor Dr. Klaus von Klitzing
Professor Dr. Hans-Joachim Queisser

Max-Planck-Institut für Festkörperforschung, Heisenbergstrasse 1
D-7000 Stuttgart 80, Fed. Rep. of Germany

Managing Editor:
Dr. Helmut K. V. Lotsch

Springer-Verlag, Tiergartenstrasse 17
D-6900 Heidelberg, Fed. Rep. of Germany

ISBN 3-540-51391-4 2. Aufl. Springer-Verlag Berlin Heidelberg New York
ISBN 0-387-51391-4 2nd ed. Springer-Verlag New York Berlin Heidelberg

ISBN 3-540-18818-5 1. Auflage Springer-Verlag Berlin Heidelberg New York
ISBN 0-387-18818-5 1st edition Springer-Verlag New York Berlin Heidelberg

to Merrill,
Mark and Susan,
and Mitzy,
Bryan, Matthew and Todd

Preface

We began planning and writing this book in the late 1970s at the suggestion of Manuel Cardona and Helmut Lotsch. We also received considerable encouragement and stimulation from colleagues. Some said there was a need for instructional material in this area while others emphasized the utility of a research text. We tried to strike a compromise. The figures, tables, and references are included to enable researchers to obtain quickly essential information in this area of semiconductor research. For instructors and students, we attempt to cover some basic ideas about electronic structure and semiconductor physics with applications to real, rather than model, solids.

We wish to thank our colleagues and collaborators whose research results and ideas are presented here. Special thanks are due to Jim Phillips who influenced us both during our formative years and afterwards. We are grateful to Sari Yamagishi for her patience and skill with the typing and production of the manuscript. Finally, we acknowledge the great patience of Helmut Lotsch and Manuel Cardona.

Berkeley, CA   *M.L. Cohen*
Minneapolis, MN,   *J.R. Chelikowsky*
March 1988

Contents

1. Introduction

Semiconductors have played a major role in the current technological revolution. The enormous advances in electronics and computer science were made possible by a better understanding of the properties of semiconductors, and it is likely that the revolution has only just begun.

From the point of view of basic science and solid state physics in particular, semiconductors have been central and fundamental. Research on the properties of semiconductors has led not only to the transistor (Nobel Prize, 1956) but also to new insights into properties of matter such as tunneling (Nobel Prize, 1973 and 1986), disorder (Nobel Prize, 1977), and new quantum effects (Nobel Prize, 1985). In addition, studies of semiconductor band structures have had a vast impact on our understanding of the fundamental electronic structure of solids. Although most device applications focus on the minimum semiconductor band gap, which is generally around 1 eV, solid state physicists have been interested in a wider range of energy ~ 1 Ry. Research on electronic structure in this range has led to tests of the theories of quantum mechanics, optics, and electromagnetism.

For the past 50 to 60 years, a major aspiration of condensed matter physics has been to explain and predict the properties of solids knowing only the identities of the constituent atoms. Recently, this goal has been realized for many semiconductor properties. The successes are best illustrated by the progress made in understanding the electronic and optical properties of semiconductors. Recently, even crystal structures have been determined using accurate electronic calculations, but this area is in its infancy relative to the vast amount of experimental and theoretical work on optical properties.

The use of optical measurements to study a physical system is not a departure from traditional physics since it is probably true that more physics has been learned using photons as probes than by any other means. For example, the great advances of Heisenberg and Pauli were based on spectroscopic data. For many years, the major tests of quantum mechanics were almost synonymous with optical measurements in atoms (i.e., gases). However, in most areas, the transition from studying atoms to studying solids using optical probes came slowly. The standard argument was that the band spectra of solids were too broad to give useful detailed electronic structure data. It was obvious that the sharp, narrow line spectra associated with atoms lend themselves readily to interpretation in terms of electron transitions between narrow energy levels, but the band spectra of solids, although they also contain definitive structure capable of being interpreted, received far less attention. For solids, the experiments and theories require more sophistication, but the data are rich with clues, and a quantum mechanical theory can be constructed to unravel the mysteries.

Dozens of crystals have been analyzed, and the extent of the collaborative effort between experimentalists and theorists in this area has few parallels. The result is a detailed picture of the underlying mechanisms associated with optical processes. Some of the achievements are: accurate determinations of the electronic energy levels, wavefunctions for electrons in specific materials, interpretation of optical spectra in terms of electronic transitions between energy levels, theories giving gross trends for a wide variety of materials, and a variety of calculations related to properties not directly associated with optical probes. The approaches and techniques have allowed critical tests of the theory of electronic structure. These studies have resulted in the development of new approaches for electronic structure calculations, response theory, and so on.

The purpose of this volume is to review some of the highlights associated with the above studies and to provide information concerning the theoretical and experimental techniques. Another important objective is to supply some of the useful information which has been gathered in these studies. Sometimes references to the literature will be given in lieu of results.

Although some general aspects of electronic structure calculations will be reviewed, the focus will be on the pseudopotential approach. On the experimental side, emphasis will be on techniques which investigate band structure. In particular, those measurements which give information about the electronic structure over a large energy range ($\sim 1\,\mathrm{Ry}$) will be discussed in detail. The primary particle probe will be photons; reflectivity and photoemission measurements will be featured.

Our hope is that this volume can serve both as a coherent source for the underlying ideas relating electronic structure and optical properties and as a source of factual information about semiconductors. Because of the latter goal, we have included other relevant information about semiconductor properties which is not directly connected with the studies discussed, that is, lattice constants, effective masses, minimum band gaps, etc., and an attempt was made to include the most accurate and most current values. Hence, this volume is intended to lie somewhere between a textbook and a reference book. Numerous references to the literature are made, and it is hoped that these will serve as bridges to material beyond the scope of this book.

In most cases when discussing results, we have relied on a prototypical crystal. Having presented the general ideas and results for the prototype, extensions to other materials in the same class are described. Following this, other related classes of materials are discussed. For example, silicon will be used as one prototype. The band structure, optical response curves, density of states, and other properties will be described. Results for other diamond structure materials will then be given, and only those properties which differ from silicon will be discussed in any detail. The extensions to zinc-blende and other crystal types will then be made.

2. Theoretical Concepts and Methods

Of the many options for broadly classifying solids, electrical resistivity has proved to be the most useful. The grouping of materials into insulators, semiconductors, semimetals, and metals involves a parameter with a range of order 10^{30}. The resistivity boundaries between the classifications are not very sharp, but they are sharp enough to make the separation for most practical purposes. For the semiconductor regime, the resistivity is betwen 10^9 and 10^{-3} ohm-cm, but we will also discuss insulators with resistivities above 10^9 ohm-cm and doped semiconductors and semimetals with resistivities below 10^{-3} ohm-cm. The distinction at the boundary between semiconductors and insulators will be made on the basis of the size of the fundamental (minimum) band gap. Semiconductors are assumed to have band gaps from 0 to $\sim 4\,\mathrm{eV}$, insulators $> 4\,\mathrm{eV}$, and semimetals ≤ 0. Gray Sn (α-Sn) is an example of a borderline material which has zero band gap. It has been called a zero-gap semiconductor; it has also been called in ideal semimetal.

The wide range of resistivities of crystalline solids can be explained using band theory, which is one of the major successes of condensed matter theory. The existence of bands, gaps, overlap of bands, and the other important properties of band theory will be discussed later. These concepts and properties are the direct consequences of the model used to describe a solid. There are two conceptual models commonly used by theorists which are both useful and lead to a wealth of practical calculations.

The two popular models of solids are the interacting atoms model and the elementary excitation model. Since a solid is clearly a set of interacting atoms, the former model implies that the atoms retain their character and that perturbation theory on atomic properties will lead to a convenient description of solids. Only partial success has been achieved when this approach is taken too literally. The interacting atoms model has therefore evolved from describing a collection of individual atoms to a model of a solid composed of cores and valence electrons (Fig. 2.1). A core is composed of a nucleus and core electrons. In the frozen-core approximation, which is fundamental to the pseudopotential approach, the cores are taken to be inert with respect to the formation of the solid. Therefore, cores in solids are the same as the cores in isolated atoms, and only the valence electrons readjust when the solid is formed. For silicon, this implies that the electronic structure of the core is $(1s)^2(2s)^2(2p)^6$. Thus sodium, magnesium, and alu-

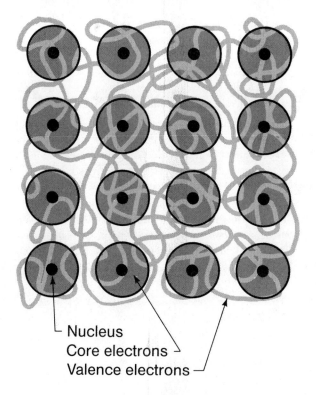

Fig. 2.1. Model of a solid with cores and valence electrons

Nucleus
Core electrons
Valence electrons

minum all have the same core electrons as silicon, but the core charges, because of the nuclei involved, are $+1$ for sodium, $+2$ for magnesium, $+3$ for aluminum, and $+4$ for silicon. The valence electrons are $(3s)^1$, $(3s)^2$, $(3s)^2(3p)^1$, and $(3s)^2(3p)^2$ respectively for these elements.

The interacting atoms model for silicon consists of cores with charge $+4$ arranged in a regular array with the four valence electrons per core moving more or less freely through the core lattice. Interactions exist between the cores, between the cores and valence electrons, and between the valence electrons themselves. The Coulomb interaction dominates, and the many-body problem involving around 10^{23} particles per cm^3 can, in principle, be solved using quantum mechanics.

For the elementary excitation model, the excitations of the solid are considered to be decomposed into normal modes, and the responses of the solid to external probes are described in terms of these modes or collective excitations. A similar approach is used for describing electromagnetic radiation in terms of photons using the formalism of quantum electrodynamics. An example of an analogous description for solids would be the concept of phonons. We begin with a description of the vibrations of atomic cores. The simplest models involve masses connected by springs [2.1]. The dispersion curve, i.e., the wavevector dependent frequency, $\omega(q)$, describes the motion of the cores in real space. The next step uses the language of quantum electrodynamics to describe the energy in the vibrational mode using the harmonic oscillator energy levels $E_n = (n + 1/2)\hbar\omega(q)$. A sound mode can be viewed as n quanta or phonons excited above the ground state. The phonons are a particular type of elementary excitation. They are collective excitations which do not resemble the constituent particles which are atomic cores and valence electrons holding the core together. Other examples of collective excitations are plasmons and magnons which result from collective motions of electrons or spins. Collective excitations are usually bosons.

There is another class of elementary excitation which consists of quasi-particles. Quasi-particles are fermions which resemble their constituent particles. Electrons excited by an external probe in a solid are quasi-particles. An electron or quasi-electron in a solid is strongly coupled to other electrons and to the lattice of atomic cores. When an electron is probed with an electromagnetic field, it does not usually respond as an individual particle. The interactions can manifest themselves in a number of ways.

One way of including these interactions is by associating an effective mass, m^*, with the electron. This concept is common in solid state physics, and it represents a convenient way of describing an interacting fermion. If the effective mass correction arises primarily from the interaction between an electron and the periodic core potential, the resulting effective mass is usually called the band mass. If the mass correction arises from electron-electron or electron-phonon interactions, then the effective mass correction is considered to be a many-body correlation correction. An example of the former is the small conduction band effective mass of InSb which arises from the interaction of electrons in the conduction band with the periodic potential. This is a band structure effect, and it will be discussed later. An example of the latter is the polaron in an ionic crystals. In this case, the electron polarizes the ionic lattice and carries a strain field with it as it moves through the crystal. The combined electron plus strain field or optical phonon cloud is a quasi-particle, a polaron, which behaves like an electron with an increased mass.

The elementary excitation picture describes a solid as a gas or liquid of excitations which can be created by external probes. The collective excitations are bosons, and they can interact with each other. An important component of this approach is based on the Landau theory of Fermi liquids. This theory demonstrates that there is a one-to-one correspondence between the excitations of a strongly coupled electron system (electron liquid) and single particles states, that is, quasi-electrons. For many applications, this important approach allows one to view the interacting electron system in terms of single particle excitations.

To make contact with experimental measurements, the concepts embodied in the interacting atoms or elementary excitation models need to yield predictions which can be tested. The usual approach is to compute a response function appropriate to the experimental probe. In the case of phonons, the approach would be as follows: The interacting atoms picture would be used to obtain the lattice vibration dispersion curves. Second quantization techniques would be used to introduce the phonon description. Interactions between phonons and other excitations could be included, and finally a response function is computed. A convenient response function in this case would be the heat capacity $C(T)$. The probe is temperature, T, and the measured $C(T)$ could be compared with the caluclated function.

For electrons, a convenient response function is the wavevector- and frequency-dependent complex dielectric function $\varepsilon(q,\omega) = \varepsilon_1(q,\omega) + i\varepsilon_2(q,\omega)$. The approach would be similar to the one just described for phonons. First the dispersion curve, or electron energy band structure $E_n(\boldsymbol{k})$ for electrons in band n and state $\boldsymbol{k}$, is determined. Then the dielectric function is computed as a response function to electromagnetic radiation and compared with experiment. In practice, experimental measurements yield a variety of optical constants [2.2] such as reflectivity, absorption, transmission, etc.; however, these can all be obtained from $\varepsilon(q,\omega)$. Other experiments, such as photoemission studies, require different response functions, but the scheme is the same.

Our object here is to compute the energy band structure as accurately as possible and use it to determine response functions to make comparisons with experiment. The scheme is sometimes more complicated because interactions must be considered. For example, electrons can interact with holes to form excitons; electron-phonon interactions produce polarons and so on. Some of these effects will be discussed, but even without these added features, the single-electron picture contains a vast amount of information and there is a great deal of interesting physics associated with it.

2.1 The One-Electron Model and Band Structure

Several simplifications and approximations are necessary before a useful scheme can be obtained for calculating the electronic dispersion curves or band structure, $E_n(\boldsymbol{k})$. The total Hamiltonian for a solid described by the cores plus valence electrons model consists of the kinetic energies of the electrons and the cores; the core-core, electron-electron, and electron-core Coulomb interactions; and relativistic effects. The Born-Oppenheimer approximation allows a decoupling of the core and electron parts of the total Hamiltonian. Since our object is to find $E_n(\boldsymbol{k})$, we will ignore the core vibrations and assume fixed cores in calculating the band structure. The resulting Hamiltonian has the form

$$H = \sum_i \frac{p_i^2}{2m} + \frac{1}{2}\sum_{i \neq j} \frac{e^2}{|\boldsymbol{r}_i - \boldsymbol{r}_j|} + \sum_{n,i} V_n(\boldsymbol{r}_i - \boldsymbol{R}_n) \qquad (2.1)$$

which represents the kinetic energy of the electrons, their mutual Coulomb interaction, and the Coulomb interaction V_n between the electrons and the cores. The position r, momentum p, and indices i and j refer to electron coordinates while R and n refer to the cores. This many-body problem is still too difficult to solve. The next step is to use the Hartree (mean field) approximation which assumes that each electron moves in the average field created by all the other electrons. The appropriate electronic wavefunctions are products of one-electron wavefunctions, and the Pauli principle requires that the quantum numbers for each one-electron state be distinct.

The above approximations have simplified the problem considerably. The new Hamiltonian can now be written as a sum of one-electron Hamiltonians

$$H = \sum_i H_i \tag{2.2}$$

$$H_i = \frac{p_i^2}{2m} + V(r) \quad , \tag{2.3}$$

where $V(r)$ possesses the symmetry of the lattice and contains both the electron-electron and electron-core interactions. The interactions have been averaged, and the electron moves in this average potential. The next steps involve a determination of the potential and a solution of Schrödinger's equation for $E_n(k)$ and $\psi_n(r)$. This task can be greatly simplified if one takes advantage of the symmetry properties of the solid. These are briefly reviewed below.

The periodic nature of an ideal crystal lattice is described in several elementary texts. For our purpose, the principal points to recall are that an electron feels the same potential at r and r' if $r' = r + R_l$, where $R_l = l_i a_i$ is a lattice vector, and the a_i's are the minimum translation vectors (l_i are integers and we sum over repeated indices). The primitive or "minimum volume" unit cell has a volume $\Omega_c = |a_1 \cdot a_2 \times a_3|$. The corresponding reciprocal lattice can be generated by the reciprocal lattice vectors, $G_m = m_i b_i$, where m_i are integers and the b_i are obtained from

$$b_i = 2\pi \frac{a_j \times a_k}{|a_1 \cdot a_2 \times a_3|} \tag{2.4}$$

and cyclic permutations.

To take advantage of the translational symmetry of the lattice, we use Bloch's Theorem and Bloch wavefunctions. The one-electron Schrödinger equation

$$\left[\frac{p^2}{2m} + V(r) \right] \psi(r) = E\psi(r) \quad , \tag{2.5}$$

subject to the boundary condition

$$V(r) = V(r + R_n) \quad , \tag{2.6}$$

has solutions

$$\psi_k(r) = e^{ik\cdot r} u_k(r) \quad \text{where} \tag{2.7}$$
$$u_k(r) = u_k(r + R_n) \quad . \tag{2.8}$$

Since $u_k(r)$ has the periodicity of the lattice, it can be expanded in a Fourier sum

$$u_k(r) = \sum_j a_j(k)\exp(iG_j \cdot r) \quad , \tag{2.9}$$

and our objective is to solve (2.5) for the $\psi_k(r)$ or equivalently the $u_k(r)$. The corresponding equation for $u_k(r)$ is obtained using (2.5) and (2.7):

$$\left[\frac{(p + \hbar k)^2}{2m} + V(r)\right] u_k(r) = E_n(k)u_k(r) \quad . \tag{2.10}$$

Since the electrons are confined more or less to cells, we expect $\overset{due\ to\ (2.6)}{\text{bands}}$ of states and band gaps just as in the case of an electron in a small box. In anticipation of this result, we add the band index n to $E_n(k)$ and $\psi_{nk}(r)$ to label the energy levels or bands.

Because of the translation symmetry of a perfect crystal, it is always possible to choose eigenfunctions and energy bands such that

$$E_n(k + G) = E_n(k) \tag{2.11}$$
$$\psi_{n,k+G}(r) = \psi_{n,k}(r) \quad . \tag{2.12}$$

This limits the k vectors needed to describe $E_n(k)$ and $\psi_{n,k}(r)$ and is the basis for the use of Brillouin zones. Details about Brillouin zones are given in [2.1]. The required region of k-space can be reduced further by using the other symmetry properties of the lattice. If, for example, the lattice is invariant under a rotation operation, θ, i.e., if it is unchanged when $r \to r'$ where $r' = \theta r$, then by applying this operator to (2.10) it is easy to show that $E_n(k) = E_n(k')$ where $k' = \theta k$. Hence, $E_n(k)$ possesses the rotational symmetry of the lattice, and time reversal symmetry requires that $E_n(k) = E_n(-k)$ if no fields or spin-orbit interactions are considered. As a result the computational complexity is reduced. For example, only 1/48 of the Brillouin zone need be considered when calculating $E_n(k)$ for a fcc lattice.

To avoid the effects of surfaces, the concept of periodic boundary conditions (PBC) can be used. For a finite one-dimensional crystal, this approximation can be viewed as bending a crystal into a circle so that the last cell is next to the first. In three dimensions, PBC for a crystal with N_1, N_2,

9

and N_3 cells in the x, y, and z directions require that

$$\psi(R + N_i a_i) = \psi(r) \quad i = 1,2,3 \qquad \text{(2.13)}$$

a_i also in x, y directions ?

Using the Bloch condition

$$\psi(r + N_i a_i) = \exp(ik \cdot N_i a_i)\psi(r) \quad , \qquad \text{(2.14)}$$

therefore

$$\exp(ik \cdot N_i a_i) = 1 \quad . \qquad \text{(2.15)}$$

For any choice of a_i,

$$k \cdot N_i a_i = 2\pi S_i \quad S_i = 0, 1, 2, \ldots \quad . \qquad \text{(2.16)}$$

This limits the acceptable k states. If

$$k_i = w_i b_i \quad , \qquad \text{(2.17)}$$

where the w_i are not necessarily integers, then

$$k_i \cdot N_i a_i = 2\pi N_i w_i = 2\pi S_j \qquad \text{(2.18)}$$

and the allowed k states are

$$k_i = S_j \frac{b_i}{N_i} \quad .$$

Since $|b| \sim 1/|a|$, $k_i \sim S_j/L$ and the spacing in reciprocal space is of the order of the inverse crystal size ($L \sim Na$). The mesh for k is very fine if the sample is large. This allows sums over states to be replaced by integrals:

$$\sum_k g(k) = \frac{\Omega}{(2\pi)^3} \int g(k) d^3 k \qquad \text{(2.19)}$$

where Ω is the crystal volume, that is, $\Omega = N\Omega_c$ where $N = N_1 N_2 N_3$ is the number of cells in the crystal. Equation (2.19) can be used to count the number of states in a Brillouin zone,

$$\sum_k = \frac{\Omega}{(2\pi)^3} \Omega_{BZ} = \frac{\Omega}{(2\pi)^3} \frac{(2\pi)^3}{\Omega_c} = N \quad . \qquad \text{(2.20)}$$

Thus, there are N orbital states in a Brillouin zone.

possible k choices

10

2.2 Properties of $E_n(k)$

The previous section sets up the problem for calculating $E_n(k)$ and provides schemes for doing sums and integrals (e.g. PBC) over the Brillouin zone. The existence of energy bands can be demonstrated using the Kronig-Penney model. This is a soluble one-dimensional model that illustrates the existence of band gaps or forbidden energy regions. The results exhibit the expected properties for one-dimensional bands; one finds for example: $E_n(k) = E_n(k + G)$, where $G = 2\pi/a$ and a is a lattice constant; $E(k = 0)$ is a maximum or minimum; and $E(k = \pi/a)$ is a maximum or minimum. These properties are just consequences of translational and inversion symmetry. For example, since $E(k) = E(-k)$,

$$\left. \frac{dE(k)}{dk} \right|_{k=0} \equiv \lim_{\Delta k \to 0} \frac{E(\delta k) - E(-\delta k)}{\Delta k} = 0 \quad , \tag{2.21}$$

and thus $E(k)$ is a maximum or minimum at $k = 0$.

We will assume that the Kronig-Penney demonstration of the existence of energy bands is sufficient and discuss some properties and uses of $E_n(k)$. A powerful concept in band structure theory is $k \cdot p$ perturbation theory. We introduce it here in its simplest form by assuming that we know the energy levels at a specific k-point, that is, we know $E_n(k_0)$. Assuming that these levels are nondegenerate, it is possible to obtain the energy levels at a neighboring point k' where

$$k' = k_0 + k \quad . \tag{2.22}$$

Starting with (2.10) for $u_{nk'}$, we get

$$\left[\frac{(p + \hbar k_0)^2}{2m} + V(r) + \frac{\hbar k \cdot (p + \hbar k_0)}{m} + \frac{\hbar^2 k^2}{2m} \right] u_{nk'} = E_n(k') u_{nk'} \quad . \tag{2.23}$$

The first two terms of (2.23) give the energy levels at k_0; the third term or "$k \cdot p$" term can be used as a perturbation, and the fourth term is just a constant. Another method for finding $E_n(k_0 + k)$ from $E_n(k_0)$ is to use a Taylor expansion. If the terms in the Taylor expansion are compared with the "$k \cdot p$" perturbation terms, the first term linear in k gives

$$v_{ink_0} = \frac{1}{\hbar} \frac{\partial E_n(k_0)}{\partial k_{0i}} \tag{2.24}$$

where v_{ink_0} is the electron velocity in band n, at k_0, in the i direction. Equating second order terms in k yields the "f-sum" rule,

$$\frac{m}{m_{ijn}} = \delta_{ij} + \sum_{n' \neq n} f_{nn'ij} \tag{2.25}$$

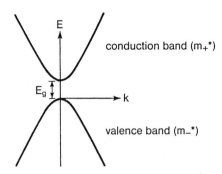

Fig. 2.2. Two band isotropic model for a semiconductor. The effective masses m_+^* and m_-^* refer to the conduction and valence bands at $k = 0$

conduction band (m_{+}^*)

E

E_g

k

valence band (m_{-}^*)

$$f_{nn'ij} = \frac{1}{m} \frac{\langle n'\boldsymbol{k}_0|p_i|n\boldsymbol{k}_0\rangle\langle n\boldsymbol{k}_0|p_j|n'\boldsymbol{k}_0\rangle + (i \leftrightarrow j)}{E_n(\boldsymbol{k}_0) - E_{n'}(\boldsymbol{k}_0)} \qquad (2.26)$$

where m_{ijn} is the ij component of the effective mass tensor for band n and $\langle n'\boldsymbol{k}_0|$ represents a Bloch state for band n' at $\boldsymbol{k}_0$.

The velocity expression and f-sum rule are very useful. Given a set of energy bands $E_n(\boldsymbol{k})$, the velocity throughout each band can be computed, and the effective masses of the bands are related to dipole matrix elements. A simple example of the use of the f-sum rule is the two-band isotropic model (Fig. 2.2) with constant momentum matrix elements $|P|$. Assuming one conduction and one valence band separated by a gap E_g, (2.25) and (2.26) yield the conduction and valence band masses, m_+^* and m_-^*,

$$\frac{m}{m_{\pm}^*} = 1 \pm \frac{2}{m} \frac{|P|^2}{E_g} \quad . \qquad (2.27)$$

If E_g is small, then $|m_+^*| \approx |m_-^*| \ll m$. The conduction (valence) band mass is positive (negative). It is clear from this model why small gaps imply small masses.

The "$\boldsymbol{k} \cdot \boldsymbol{p}$" method can also be used as a computational method for band structure calculations of real materials. A parametrization of the bands at a given point in the Brillouin zone is used as a starting point; a full zone calculation is then possible. This method is used often as an interpolation scheme along with an ab initio band structure calculation.

We now approach the problem of calculating $E_n(\boldsymbol{k})$. Two methods which serve as prototypes are the tight-binding method (TBM) [which is also called the linear combination of atomic orbitals method (LCAO)] and the nearly free-electron model (NFEM). These approaches are based on opposite views of electron states in solids. The TBM emphasizes the atomic-like nature of the electron states while the NFEM views the valence electrons as a perturbed gas of completely free electrons. Both methods are described in textbooks and in the literature. Since our emphasis will be on pseudopotential calculations which are often based on the NFEM, a description of this method is included here.

In the NFEM, we assume that the potential in the one-electron Hamiltonian of (2.5) is much smaller than the kinetic energy. This assumption allows an expansion of $E(\mathbf{k})$ (we suppress the band index temporarily) using perturbation theory. The potential term is the perturbation to be used on a completely free-electron system with cell volume Ω where the electron energy and wavefunctions are given by

$$E^0(\mathbf{k}) = \frac{\hbar^2 k^2}{2m} \tag{2.28}$$

$$\psi_{\mathbf{k}}^0(\mathbf{r}) = \frac{1}{\sqrt{\Omega}} e^{i\mathbf{k}\cdot\mathbf{r}} \quad . \tag{2.29}$$

To second order one finds

$$E(\mathbf{k}) = E^0(\mathbf{k}) + V_{\mathbf{k}\mathbf{k}} + \sum_{\mathbf{k}'\neq\mathbf{k}} \frac{|V_{\mathbf{k}\mathbf{k}'}|^2}{E^0(\mathbf{k}) - E^0(\mathbf{k}')} \tag{2.30}$$

$$V_{\mathbf{k}\mathbf{k}'} = \frac{1}{\Omega} \int e^{i(\mathbf{k}'-\mathbf{k})\cdot\mathbf{r}} V(\mathbf{r}) d\mathbf{r} \tag{2.31}$$

$$V_{\mathbf{k}\mathbf{k}} = \frac{1}{\Omega} \int V(\mathbf{r}) d\mathbf{r} = V_0 \tag{2.32}$$

where V_0 is a constant representing the average potential; it can be absorbed into $E^0(\mathbf{k})$ where it will just shift all the energy levels by a constant amount.

Since $V(\mathbf{r})$ has the periodicity of the lattice, it can be expanded in a Fourier sum (assuming one atom per unit cell):

$$V(\mathbf{r}) = \sum_{\mathbf{G}} V(\mathbf{G}) e^{i\mathbf{G}\cdot\mathbf{r}} \tag{2.33}$$

$$V(\mathbf{G}) = \frac{1}{\Omega} \int e^{-i\mathbf{G}\cdot\mathbf{r}} V(\mathbf{r}) d\mathbf{r} \quad . \tag{2.34}$$

This expansion simplifies the expressions for $V_{\mathbf{k}\mathbf{k}'}$ and $E(\mathbf{k})$

$$V_{\mathbf{k}\mathbf{k}'} = \sum_{\mathbf{G}} V(\mathbf{G}) \int e^{i(\mathbf{k}'-\mathbf{k}+\mathbf{G})\cdot\mathbf{r}} d\mathbf{r} = \sum_{\mathbf{G}} V(\mathbf{G}) \delta_{\mathbf{k},\mathbf{k}'+\mathbf{G}} \tag{2.35}$$

$$E(\mathbf{k}) = E^0(\mathbf{k}) + V_0 + \sum_{\mathbf{G}\neq 0} \frac{|V(\mathbf{G})|^2}{E^0(\mathbf{k}) - E^0(\mathbf{k}+\mathbf{G})} \quad . \tag{2.36}$$

The last term is usually small, and $E(\mathbf{k})$ is free-electron-like. However, this scheme fails when $E^0(\mathbf{k}) \approx E^0(\mathbf{k}+\mathbf{G})$. These points define the Brillouin zone boundary and the Bragg condition $2\mathbf{k}\cdot\mathbf{G}+G^2 = 0$. A solution for $E(\mathbf{k})$ near the Brillouin zone boundary requires the use of degenerate perturbation theory.

13

As an example, we expand the wavefunction in terms of the degenerate eigenstates

$$\psi_{\boldsymbol{k}} = a\psi_{\boldsymbol{k}}^0 + b\psi_{\boldsymbol{k}+\boldsymbol{G}}^0 \quad . \tag{2.37}$$

Taking matrix elements and solving the 2×2 secular equation yields

$$E(\boldsymbol{k}) = E^0(\boldsymbol{k}) \pm |V(\boldsymbol{G})| \quad \text{where} \tag{2.38}$$

$$V(\boldsymbol{G}) = V_{\boldsymbol{k},\boldsymbol{k}+\boldsymbol{G}} = V_{\boldsymbol{k}+\boldsymbol{G},\boldsymbol{k}} \quad . \tag{2.39}$$

The formerly degenerate levels are split by $2|V(\boldsymbol{G})|$. Solving for the eigenstates, (2.37) yields two solutions

$$\psi_1 \propto \cos \tfrac{1}{2}\boldsymbol{G}\cdot\boldsymbol{r} \tag{2.40}$$

$$\psi_2 \propto \sin \tfrac{1}{2}\boldsymbol{G}\cdot\boldsymbol{r} \quad . \tag{2.41}$$

The lower energy state $E^0(\boldsymbol{k}) - |V(\boldsymbol{G})|$ corresponds to ψ_1 with probability density $|\psi_1|^2$ peaked near $\boldsymbol{r} = 0$, and $\boldsymbol{r} = n\boldsymbol{R}$ where n is an integer (Fig. 2.3). This state puts charge on the atomic core sites. The upper state corresponds to a probability density which localizes charge between the cores. The energy difference between these two configurations causes the gap at the zone boundary $\sim 2|V(\boldsymbol{G})|$ (see Fig. 2.4).

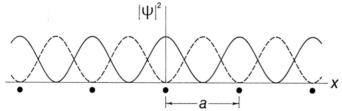

Fig. 2.3. Probability density $|\psi|^2$ for bands at the bottom of a band gap (*solid line*) and at the top of the band gap (*dashed line*) near the Brillouin zone edge (see text)

The central features of the NFEM are: weak potential, plane-wave basis set, free-electron bands except near the Brillouin zone boundaries, and small band gaps of order $2|V(\boldsymbol{G})|$. Calculated $E(\boldsymbol{k})$ curves for real systems using the NFEM do not resemble simple parabolas because the band structure is projected onto a particular section of the Brillouin zone. To determine how similar the results are to a free-electron model, a comparison should be made with the free-electron bands mapped into the appropriate part of Brillouin zone. The free electron energy levels are given by

$$E(\boldsymbol{k}) = \frac{\hbar^2}{2m}(\boldsymbol{k} + \boldsymbol{G})^2 \quad , \tag{2.42}$$

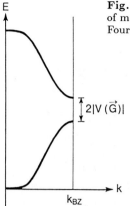

E

$2|V(\vec{G})|$

k_{BZ}

k

Fig. 2.4. Nearly free electron model band structure with band gap of magnitude $2|V(G)|$ at the Brillouin zone edge k_{BZ}; $V(G)$ is the Fourier component of the crystal potential

in addition a band indexing scheme can be chosen. A free-electron band structure of this kind is called an "empty lattice" band structure. Empty lattice calculations are simple to compute, and they are available in the literature for most common structures.

The NFEM and TBM can be used to perform band calculations for real materials. However, these methods represent extreme views of the electronic structure of solids. The dilemma faced by band structure calculations is that the potential felt by an electron is strong and atomic-like near the cores and weak between the cores. Most modern band structure techniques attempt to resolve or compromise between these two extremes. The Augmented Plane Wave (APW) method [2.3], which can also be cast in a Green function form, uses basis states with plane waves matched to solutions of the radial wave equation. It is common to use a simple radial potential, the muffin-tin potential, in the APW approach. The method has been particularly successful for calculating properties of metals, especially transition metals since this potential is a reasonable approximation for these systems.

Another useful method for band structure calculations is the Orthogonalized Plane Wave (OPW) method [2.4]. This method has been used successfully for semiconductors, insulators, and metals. The basis states are constructed from a set of plane waves which have been orthogonalzed to the atomic core states. The plane wave component has the virtue of being appropriate for the weak, almost constant potential between the atomic cores. Near the cores, the orthogonalization terms require that the wavefunction resemble the next highest core state wavefunction since it is orthogonal to all the lower core functions. Only a few OPW's are needed in the expansion; this illustrates the fact that these basis states provide a good description of the solid wavefunction.

An important byproduct of the OPW approach is its use to demonstrate the features and properties of the pseudopotential method. This application of the OPW method will be described in the next chapter.

3. Pseudopotentials

The pseudopotential method will be used throughout the remainder of this text to calculate $E_n(k)$ and other properties of semiconductors. The major virtue of this approach is that only the valence electrons need be considered. The cores are assumed to be frozen in an atomic-like configuration, and the valence electrons move in a net, weak one-electron potential.

The pseudopotential was introduced by *Fermi* in 1934 [3.1] to study high lying atomic states. In the following year, *Hellmann* [3.2] proposed that a pseudopotential approach could be used to obtain energy levels of alkalai metal atoms. Several other suggestions [3.3] appeared in the solid state literature and in other areas of physics concerning the use of effective potentials. However, it was in the late 1950's when activity began to accelerate, and this area of condensed matter theory has continued to expand at a rapid rate since that time.

A useful place to start our discussion is the OPW-type derivation of the Phillips-Kleinman cancellation theorem [3.4]. This theorem demonstrates that the expansion coefficients used to ensure that the plane wave part of an OPW wavefunction is orthogonal to the core states can be grouped to construct an orthogonality potential. This potential is repulsive because its effect is to keep the valence electrons out of the core which, indeed, was the purpose of the orthogonalization. If this repulsive potential is added to the attractive core potential, they almost "cancel" leaving a net weak potential or pseudopotential. This pseudopotential can then be treated using the NFEM or other standard techniques to solve Schrödinger's equation.

The mathematical formulation of the above description is presented next. We begin by expressing the true wavefunction ψ as the sum of a smooth wavefunction ϕ and a sum over occupied core states ϕ_t,

$$\psi = \phi + \sum_t b_t \phi_t \quad . \tag{3.1}$$

If the wavefunction is forced to be orthogonal to the core states as in the OPW scheme, that is, $\langle \phi_t | \psi \rangle = 0$, then solving for b_t yields

$$\psi = \phi - \sum_t \langle \phi_t | \phi \rangle \phi_t \quad . \tag{3.2}$$

Operating on ψ with the Hamiltonian, $H = p^2/2m + V_c$ (where V_c is the attractive core potential) gives the correct energy eigenvalue E times ψ.

Why ψ is not exactly the next core state?

Therefore, substituting (3.2) into $H\psi = E\psi$ yields

$$H\phi - \sum_t \langle \phi_t | \phi \rangle E_t \phi_t = E\phi - E \sum_t \langle \phi_t | \phi \rangle \phi_t \qquad (3.3)$$

which can be rearranged to give

$$H\phi + \sum_t (E - E_t)\phi_t \langle \phi_t | \phi \rangle = E\phi \quad . \qquad (3.4)$$

Equation (3.4) can be written

$$(H + V_R)\phi = E\phi \quad \text{where} \qquad (3.5)$$

$$V_R \phi = \sum_t (E - E_t)\phi_t \langle \phi_t | \phi \rangle \quad . \qquad (3.6)$$

This term acts like a short-ranged non-Hermitian repulsive potential.

Equation (3.5) is the new wave equation for ϕ, the pseudowavefunction. However, it is important to note that the energy eigenvalue E is not a "pseudo" energy but the true energy corresponding to the true wavefunction ψ. If H is separated into a kinetic energy and attractive core potential V_c, then (3.5) becomes

$$\left(\frac{p^2}{2m} + V_c + V_R \right)\phi = \left(\frac{p^2}{2m} + V \right)\phi = E\phi \qquad (3.7)$$

where V is the pseudopotential. Because V is the sum of the attractive long-ranged potential V_c and a short-range repulsive potential V_R, V becomes weak with long-ranged attractive regions away from the core and weakly repulsive or attractive regions near the core (Fig. 3.1). The cancellation can be fairly complete, and the potential is relatively weak compared to a Coulomb potential. Hence, it is possible to use the NFEM to solve

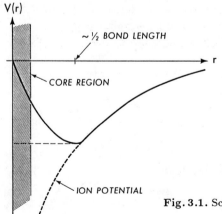

Fig. 3.1. Schematic plot of pseudopotential in real space

Schrödinger's equation [now (3.7)] using plane waves in the basis set expansion for ψ. This calculation was a feature of the pseudopotential proposed by *Phillips* and *Kleinman* [3.4]. The cancellation effect was demonstrated in detail by *Cohen* and *Heine* [3.5] and is often referred to as the Phillips-Kleinman cancellation theorem [3.6].

There are several features of pseudopotentials and pseudowavefunctions that are worth describing. The pseudopotential is, in general, spatially nonlocal and depends on r and r'. To see the explicitly, (3.6) can be written as

$$V_{\mathrm{R}}(r, r') = \sum_t (E - E_t) |\phi_t(r)\rangle\langle\phi_t(r')|\rangle \tag{3.8}$$

where the empty "ket" will contain a function of r. The expression "nonlocal" is usually reserved for the angular momentum or l-dependence of the pseudopotential. Since V_{R} involves a sum over the t occupied core states, it can be broken down into angular momentum components by summing over the various core states according to their orbital angular momentum symmetry. Hence, sums over $l = 0, 1, 2$ will result in s-, p-, and d-components for V_{R} and therefore for V we can write

$$V = V_s + V_p + V_d + \cdots \; . \tag{3.9}$$

If the core does not contain electrons of a certain angular momentum involved in the sum, there is no repulsive potential for that component. As an example, the core of carbon is $(1s)^2$, and therefore carbon will not have a p-repulsive potential. This will affect the properties of the $(2s)^2(2p)^2$ valence electrons. In particular, it is expected that the $2p$ electrons will have a higher probability of being closer to the core than in Si and Ge where the repulsive p-core potential pushes the valence p-electrons away from the core.

The Phillips-Kleinman form [3.4] of the pseudopotential allows several interesting analytic investigations of pseudopotentials in addition to the one given above. Some of these features are not completely general and depend on the form of the potential. Although some of these features are not important aspects of the Empirical Pseudopotential Method which is the main theme of this volume, they do illustrate interesting properties, and we include two of these here, normalization and uniqueness.

If the true wavefunction ψ is normalized to unity, then ϕ is only approximately normalized in the Phillips-Kleinman scheme. The condition $\langle\psi|\psi\rangle = 1$ together with (3.2) gives

$$1 = \langle\phi|\phi\rangle - 2\sum_t \langle\phi_t|\phi\rangle\langle\phi|\phi_t\rangle + \sum_t |\langle\phi_t|\phi\rangle|^2 \; . \tag{3.10}$$

Therefore

$$\langle \phi | \phi \rangle = 1 + \sum_t |\langle \phi_t | \phi \rangle|^2 \tag{3.11}$$

where the last term is of the order of 0.10. In modern schemes involving pseudopotentials, ϕ is explicitly normalized.

The non-uniqueness of the Phillips-Kleinman pseudopotential can be illustrated as follows. Let $\phi \to \phi + \delta\phi$ where $\delta\phi = \sum_t \alpha_t \phi_t$, that is, the change in the wavefunction can be represented as a sum over core states. The true wavefunction (3.2) then becomes

$$\psi = \phi + \sum_t \alpha_t \phi_t - \sum_t \langle \phi_t | \phi \rangle \phi_t - \sum_t \alpha_t \langle \phi_t | \phi_t \rangle \phi_t \tag{3.12}$$

which reduces to (3.2), i.e., it is unchanged. Hence, adding core states to ϕ or the corresponding term to V_R leaves the eigenvalues and wavefunctions unchanged (see for example the formalism of *Austin* et al. [3.7]).

The cancellation theorem and analytic proofs based on the Phillips-Kleinman pseudopotential served as a basis for explaining why the electronic structure of real physical systems could be described using the NFEM and weak potentials. However, the Phillips-Kleinman approach did not have wide application as a computational tool for obtaining electronic band structures for materials. Instead, model and empirical potentials were used to fit some observed properties and then used to solve a host of problems. In some cases, the model potential is fit to atomic data such as atomic energy levels and then the potential is used for calculations of the electronic structure of the solid.

The simplest models consist of a Coulomb potential at large distances and a simple constant potential in the core region. The matching point r_c can be taken as the core radius. One form of the potential is

$$V(r) = \begin{cases} -\dfrac{Ze}{r} & , \quad r > r_c \\[2mm] -\dfrac{Ze}{r_c} & , \quad r \le r_c \end{cases} \tag{3.13}$$

where Z is the valence of the atomic species of interest, e.g. $Z = 4e$ for Si. The one adjustable parameter r_c can be used to fit atomic data. Another similar form which was used extensively is the empty core potential [3.8]

$$V(r) = \begin{cases} -\dfrac{Ze}{r} & , \quad r > r_c \\[2mm] 0 & , \quad r \le r_c \end{cases} . \tag{3.14}$$

Heine and *Abarenkov* (3.9) introduced more flexibility for fitting atomic data through the use of a variable A for the constant potential in the core region

$$V(r) = \begin{cases} -\dfrac{Ze}{r} \ , & r > r_c \\ A \ , & r \leq r_c \end{cases} \ . \tag{3.15}$$

The potential could be made nonlocal (angular momentum dependent) by chosing a different constant in the core for each l. Energy dependence could also be included by allowing $A = A(E)$. The relevant coefficients were fit [3.10–12] for many elements in the periodic table.

For band structure calculations, the quantity $V(G)$ is required, hence $V(q)$ is the relevant potential. The Fourier transforms of the model potentials (3.13–15) behave (for $Z = e$) approximately as

$$V(q) \sim \frac{-4\pi e^2}{q^2} \cos qr_c \ . \tag{3.16}$$

For metals, if Fermi-Thomas screening arising from the free electrons is included, then we find

$$V_{\text{screened}}(q) \sim \frac{-4\pi e^2}{q^2 + K_s^2} \cos qr_c \tag{3.17}$$

where K_s is the Thomas-Fermi screening wavevector. Hence, for metals, $V(q \to 0) = -2E_F/3$. This is the same limit as in the case of a screened Coulomb potential. However, an added feature of the pseudopotential is that $V(q)$ becomes positive (repulsive) for $q > q_c$ where $q_c \sim \pi/2r_c$. This arises because of the repulsive "orthogonality potential" for short distances.

Once the model atomic potential parameters are determined, the screening for metallic electron densities can be evaluated by means of an appropriate q-dependent dielectric function. The resulting q-dependent pseudopotential can be used to compute the band structure for the metal. In addition, the predicted Fermi surface can be compared with measured values, and this provides a test of the potential and the method. The results are in fairly good agreement [3.13] with the measured values.

3.1 The Empirical Pseudopotential Method

Another approch involves a direct fit of the $V(G)$'s to the experimental band structure. At first, Fermi surface data were used for metals, but photoemission and reflectivity results later became the main sources of relevant information. The method was not used extensively for metals, but it was applied to dozens of semiconductors with surprisingly good results. The scheme is called the Empirical Pseudopotential Method (EPM). The first successful applications were to Ge and Si [3.14, 15], but the method was soon extended to other commonly studied semiconductors [3.16].

The EPM involves the fitting of the atomic form factors $V_a(G)$ to experiment. The solution for the energy band structure $E_n(k)$ (n is the band index) is an extension of the NFEM which was described earlier by (2.28–36). The crystal potential $V(r)$ is assumed to be represented by a linear superposition of atomic potentials ~~pseudo (not the same as in last section)~~

$$V(r) = \sum_{R,\tau} V_a(r - R - \tau) \qquad (3.18)$$

where R is a lattice vector and τ is a basis vector. If we expand the potential in the reciprocal lattice

$$V(r) = \sum_G \underbrace{V_a(G)S(G)}_{V(G)} e^{iG \cdot r} \qquad V_a(G) = \int V_a(r) e^{-iG \cdot r} d^3r \qquad (3.19)$$

where the structure factor

$$S(G) = \frac{1}{N_a} \sum_\tau e^{-iG \cdot \tau} \qquad (3.20)$$

and where $V_a(G)$ is the form factor for the atomic potential and N_a is the number of basis atoms. The pseudowavefunctions $\psi_{n,k}(r)$ and the band energy values $E_n(k)$ are then a solution of

$$\left[\frac{p^2}{2m} + V(r) \right] \psi_{n,k}(r) = E_n(k)\psi_{n,k}(r) \qquad (3.21)$$

where $V(r)$ is given by (3.19). The $\psi_{n,k}(r)$ have the Bloch form, and they can be expanded in a set of plane waves. The expansion coefficients are obtained by solving the relevant secular equation. Perturbation techniques are often used [3.13]. Hence, the necessary inputs to this calculation are the atomic form factors and the structure via $S(G)$.

Typical schematic pseudopotentials in r- and q-space are shown in Figs. 3.1 and 3.2. The values of the $|G|$ vectors shown in the schematic drawing Fig. 3.2 are appropriate for a semiconductor having the diamond structure. As this figure illustrates, the potential $V(q)$ becomes very weak

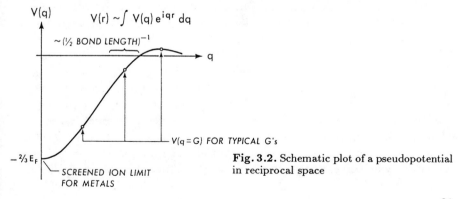

Fig. 3.2. Schematic plot of a pseudopotential in reciprocal space

21

for q's larger than the third G vector. This is a consequence of the cancellation of the strong core potential. Hence, three $V_a(G)$'s are usually sufficient for each element comprising a diamond or zinc-blende semiconductor. To illustrate the approach, it is useful to show explicitly how the structure factor manifests itself in the calculation using diamond and zinc-blende as examples.

The diamond lattice is composed of two interpenetrating fcc lattices displaced from one another by $(\frac{1}{4}, \frac{1}{4}, \frac{1}{4})a$, where a is a lattice constant. If the origin is taken half way between the two fcc lattices, then $\tau = \pm(\frac{1}{8}, \frac{1}{8}, \frac{1}{8})a$ and $S(G) = \cos G \cdot \tau$. Omitting the $G = 0$ term which gives a constant average potential, the structure factor $S(G)$ is only nonzero for G's in the diamond lattice, the first three of which are given by $G^2 = 3, 8, 11$, in units of $(2\pi/a)^2$. Hence, we require $V(G^2 = 3, 8, 11)$ to specify the pseudopotential for diamond structure semiconductors such as C (actually an insulator), Si, Ge and α-Sn.

For the zinc-blende lattice which is common for III-V and II-VI semiconductors, the two elements involved each occupy one of the two interpenetrating fcc lattices. Hence, zinc-blende is just like diamond except that the two atoms in the unit cell are different species. If this feature is included in (3.19), the extension is simple, and the resulting potential has the form

$$V_S(G) \cos G \cdot \tau + iV_A(G) \sin G \cdot \tau \quad . \tag{3.22}$$

The symmetric and antisymmetric form factors, $V_S(G)$ and $V_A(G)$ are the sums and differences of the form factors for the atoms in the primitive cell. For example, for GaAs

$$2V_S(G) = V_{Ga}(G) + V_{As}(G)$$
$$2V_A(G) = V_{Ga}(G) - V_{As}(G) \quad . \tag{3.23}$$

In the case of diamond structure semiconductors, $V_A = 0$, and the structure factor reduces to $\cos G \cdot \tau$. The antisymmetric structure factor $\sin G \cdot \tau$ is nonzero for $G^2 = 3, 4, 11, \ldots$ in units of $(2\pi/a)^2$.

Hence, an EPM calculation proceeds as shown in the block diagram in Fig. 3.3. First starting $V(G)$'s for the elements involved are chosen; a model potential based on atomic term values is a good starting point. Next the structure is included via $S(G)$, and the Schrödinger equation is solved for the energy eigenvalues and wavefunctions. Using these eigenvalues and wavefunctions, it is possible to solve for response functions such as the reflectivity R, the modulated reflectivity R'/R or the density of states $N(E)$. A discussion of the theory related to these functions will be given in the next chapter. These functions are compared with experiment, and the $V(G)$'s can be altered if good agreement is not achieved. The process is repeated until satisfactory agreement between experiment and theory is obtained. Usually,

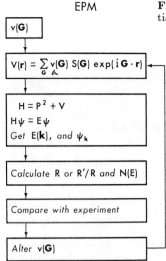

EPM

Fig. 3.3. Block diagram for the Empirical Pseudopotential Method

only a few cycles lead to agreement within a few percent between theory and experiment for the optical properties, density of states, and band structure. Generally, just three form factors are sufficient to determine each atomic potential.

It is impressive that the EPM works so well considering the limited input. The results will be discussed later, but it is interesting to emphasize at this point that this approach yields accurate calculated properties and a determination of the origin of the optical structure of the semiconductors involved. Often the potentials used to describe semiconducting compounds can be applied individually to study the properties of the constituent elements. For example, in the case of InSb, the In and Sb potentials extracted from optical studies of InSb [3.13] give accurate band structures and Fermi surface topology for the metal In and the semimetal Sb. In fact, the In potential can be used to calculate electron-phonon interactions and even the superconducting transition temperature of In [3.17].

The previous discussion of the EPM and the relevant techniques involved used a local pseudopotential to illustrate the procedures. In practice, a nonlocal potential is used. The extension is reasonably straightforward, but it does involve some extra computation. The detailed improvements obtained can be significant. The nonlocal pseudopotential is used to account for variations in the pseudopotential for electrons with different angular momentum, l. This situation may occur, as discussed previously, in first row elements, for example, C or O where the $2s$ electrons experience a much weaker attractive potential than the $2p$ electrons. The effect is also important elsewhere: for example, in d-metals, where the $l = 0, 1$ components of the potential are much weaker than the $l = 2$ component.

To describe this l-dependence, the atomic pseudopotential can be expanded in angular momentum components $V_l(\boldsymbol{r})$ together with projection operators P_l which project out the lth angular momentum component of the wavefunction,

$$V(\boldsymbol{r}) = \sum_{l=0}^{\infty} P_l^+ V_l(\boldsymbol{r}) P_l \quad . \tag{3.24}$$

While this sum is in principle over all l-values, for most cases only the first few l components are significant, that is, $l = 0, 1, 2$. In addition for many semiconductors the $l = 0$ and $l = 1$ potentials are quite similar, and (3.24) simplifies

$$V(\boldsymbol{r}) = V_{l=0,1}(\boldsymbol{r}) + P_2^+ [V_{l=2}(\boldsymbol{r}) - V_{l=0,1}(\boldsymbol{r})] P_2 \tag{3.25}$$

Here we explicitly separate out the nonlocal potential for $l = 2$. The $V_{l=0,1}(\boldsymbol{r})$ part of the potential can be included using the techniques discussed previously.

As in the local pseudopotential approach, we can construct the nonlocal potential from atomic structure calculations or parameterize the potential using the EPM. Because of the nonlocal character, it is not possible to rely on just a few form factors as in the local potential case. Instead a model potential is chosen. Two simple, yet accurate, forms for the model potential are commonly used; these are the square well and Gaussian model potentials. In both cases, radial symmetry is assumed and two parameters are introduced, the well depth and the spatial range.

Because of the nonlocal nature of the potential, the form factors $V(\boldsymbol{G})$, are no longer simple functions of $\boldsymbol{G}$ but also depend on the wavevector $\boldsymbol{k}$. This can be illustrated using a plane wave basis set by investigating the matrix element of the nonlocal potential $V_l(\boldsymbol{r})$ taken between plane waves $\langle \boldsymbol{k} + \boldsymbol{G}|$ and $|\boldsymbol{k} + \boldsymbol{G}'\rangle$. First the plane wave is decomposed into a sum of standard functions in the usual way

$$\exp[i(\boldsymbol{k} + \boldsymbol{G}) \cdot \boldsymbol{r}] = \sum_{l=0}^{\infty} (2l + 1) i^l P_l(\cos \gamma) j_l(|\boldsymbol{k} + \boldsymbol{G}|r) \tag{3.26}$$

where $P_l(x)$ is a Legendre polynomial, $j_l(x)$ is a spherical Bessel function and γ is the angle between the vectors $\boldsymbol{r}$ and $\boldsymbol{k} + \boldsymbol{G}$. The projection operator P_l is now easy to use since the l part of the wavefunction is readily obtained using (3.26). The matrix elements for a radially symmetric potential may then be written as

$$\langle \boldsymbol{k} + \boldsymbol{G}|V_l|\boldsymbol{k} + \boldsymbol{G}'\rangle = \frac{4\pi}{\Omega}(2l + 1) P_l(\cos \theta_{\boldsymbol{k}+\boldsymbol{G}, \boldsymbol{k}+\boldsymbol{G}'})$$

$$\times \int_0^{\infty} dr\, r^2 V_l(r) j_l(|\boldsymbol{k} + \boldsymbol{G}|r) j_l(|\boldsymbol{k} + \boldsymbol{G}'|r) \quad . \tag{3.27}$$

For the square well or Gaussian well, analytic expressions have been obtained for these matrix elements [3.18]. Hence, the nonlocal corrections can be handled easily and included in the secular equation. In general, these corrections are reasonably small for semiconductors, but they can change the topology of the dispersion relation for some bands and also the size of the band gap.

3.2 Self-Consistent and Ab Initio Pseudopotentials

Although the EPM is the major theoretical tool in electronic structure calculations related to optical properties of solids, variations of the pseudopotential method have been developed to assist in the solution of other problems in electronic structure. The extent of the direct applicability of these developments to the study of optical properties is not yet clear. There is hope that future research will yield a universal approach for calculating almost all electronic properties using one form of the pseudopotential. We explore two advances in pseudopotential theory which are characteristic of the recent developments.

One aspect of the pseudopotential which is necessary for studying surface electronic structure is self-consistency. In the EPM, it is assumed that the $V(G)$'s represent the total one-electron potential for a valence electron. This potential is composed of an ionic (or atomic core) component plus potential arising from the valence electrons themselves. To achieve a truly self-consistent potential, the wavefunctions obtained in an electronic structure calculation can be used to construct a new valence electron potential which in turn is used to compute the wavefunctions. When no changes occur in a feedback loop of this kind, the solution is considered to be self-consistent.

An early check on the self-consistency of the EPM potentials [3.19] was made using a calculated dielectric function based on wavefunctions and energy eigenvalues obtained in an EPM study. The wavevector-dependent dielectric function was then used to screen the ionic pseudopotential, and the resulting potential was compared with the original empirical potential. It was found that the pseudopotential was reasonably self-consistent which substantiated the "physical reasonableness" of the early EPM form factors.

A more direct approach to self-consistent pseudopotentials arose in connection with surface and interface studies. At an interface, since there is rearrangement of electronic charge, the electronic components of the potential change. This change has to be evaluated self-consistently if the interface electronic structure is to be calculated accurately. To achieve this the electronic potentials are expressed as a function of the electronic density and the variations in the density are calculated self-consistently [3.20–23].

A block diagram illustrating the approach is shown in Figure 3.4. The empirical potential may be used to start the calculation. Solution of

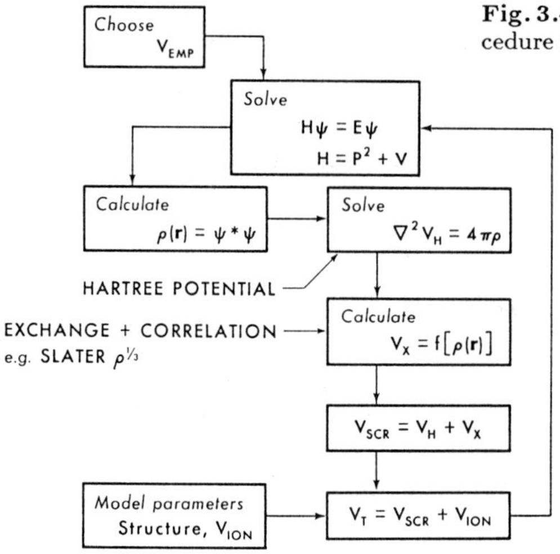

Fig. 3.4. Block diagram illustrating the procedure for obtaining self-consistent potentials

Schrödinger's equation yields the wavefunctions and charge density. The one-electron Hamiltonian now has the form

$$H = \frac{p^2}{2m} + V_{\text{ion}} + V_{\text{H}} + V_{\text{XC}} \; . \tag{3.28}$$

The total ionic pseudopotential is taken to be a linear superposition of spherical potentials as in (3.18). The potential itself can be fit to atomic data. A common form using four parameters a_1, a_2, a_3, a_4 is given below:

$$V_{\text{ion}}(q) = \frac{a_1}{q^2}[\cos(a_2 q) + a_3]\exp a_4 q^4 \quad . \tag{3.29}$$

The electronic contributions to the potential are the Hartree screening potential V_{H} and the exchange-correlation potential V_{XC}. If it is assumed that these potentials depend only on the local density, we obtain the following

$$\nabla^2 V_{\text{H}}(\boldsymbol{r}) = -4\pi e^2 \varrho(\boldsymbol{r}) \tag{3.30}$$

and

$$V_{\text{XC}}(\boldsymbol{r}) = -3(\tfrac{3}{8})^{1/3}\alpha e^2 [\varrho(\boldsymbol{r})]^{1/3} \tag{3.31}$$

where we have chosen a Slater form for an exchange-correlation potential (with a parameter α) to illustrate the method. The parameter can be adjusted to account partially for correlation, and a commonly used value is $\alpha \approx 0.8$. The potential can be written to include explicitly the effects of electron correlation, and several good local density approximations are available [3.24–29].

The self-consistent pseudopotential calculation then proceeds in a similar manner to the EPM. The wavefunction is expanded in plane waves

$$\psi_{n,k}(\mathbf{r}) = \sum_{\mathbf{G}} a_{n,k}(\mathbf{G}) \exp[\mathrm{i}(\mathbf{k}+\mathbf{G}) \cdot \mathbf{r}]$$ (3.32)

and the expansion coefficients are obtained by solving a secular equation

$$\sum_{\mathbf{G}} (H_{\mathbf{GG'}} - E\delta_{\mathbf{G},\mathbf{G'}}) a_{n,k}(\mathbf{G'}) = 0 \quad .$$ (3.33)

The matrix elements $H_{\mathbf{GG'}}$ involve the form factors for the Hartree and exchange potentials given in (3.30) and (3.31). These form factors become

$$V_{\mathrm{H}}(\mathbf{G}) = \frac{4\pi e^2 \varrho(\mathbf{G})}{|\mathbf{G}|^2}$$ (3.34)

$$V_{\mathrm{XC}}(\mathbf{G}) = -\frac{3}{2\pi}(3\pi^2)^{1/3} \frac{\alpha e^2}{\Omega} \int [\varrho(\mathbf{r})]^{1/3} e^{-\mathrm{i}G \cdot \mathbf{r}} d\mathbf{r}$$ (3.35)

where $\varrho(\mathbf{G})$ is the Fourier transform of the crystalline charge density $\varrho(\mathbf{r})$ and Ω is the cell volume.

The self-consistency procedure illustrated in Fig. 3.4 requires a model structure which is included via the structure factor $S(\mathbf{G})$. For surface and interface calculations, a slab geometry is used, but this is not essential to the method. Finally, the new potential is used to initiate the calculation again. When input and output screening potentials agree, the potential is considered to be self-consistent. In practice, this requires several iterations for a surface or interface. Self-consistent pseudopotential calculations have also been done for the bulk electronic states. Depending on how V_{ion} [Eq. (3.29)] is constructed, the results are comparable with the EPM. We will return to this question later.

A more recent variation of the pseudopotential is called either the "*ab initio*" pseudopotential, the "first principles" pseudopotential or the "density functional" pseudopotential, and there are other names. The primary application of these potentials was made in the study of total energies and structural properties of solids. The approach grew out of the studies associated with self-consistent pseudopotentials. In fitting the ionic potential (3.29), various schemes had been tried. One variation involved the construction of a pseudopotential which would reproduce atomic wavefunctions very accurately outside the core region but would not reproduce the nodes characteristic of an all-electron wavefunction. The new pseudowavefunction was constrained to be normalized. Hence, there is no change in normalization in going from all-electron to pseudowavefunctions. A comparison of the pseudowavefunction and the corresponding all-electron radial wavefunction is given in Fig. 3.5. The parameter which determines the pseudopotential is the radius at which the pseudo and all-electron wavefunctions are allowed to deviate. This is usually taken to be inside the first wavefunction maximum and before the first node encountered coming in from large distances.

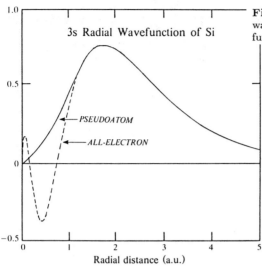

3s Radial Wavefunction of Si

PSEUDOATOM

ALL-ELECTRON

Radial distance (a.u.)

Fig. 3.5. All-electron and pseudoatom wavefunction for the 3s radial wavefunction of Si

There are several proposals for potentials which produce the desired wavefunctions. *Starkloff* and *Joannopoulos* [3.30] proposed a local potential, *Zunger* and *Cohen* [3.31] a hard core potential; soft core potentials were constructed by *Hamann* et al. [3.32] and by *Kerker* [3.33]. The potentials generated for a given atomic configuration yield excellent results for other configurations [3.34, 35]. The important feature of these potentials is their ability to reproduce the atomic energy eigenvalues and wavefunctions to a high degree of accuracy. The potentials which are now accurate in the atomic limit can be used for detailed calculations of solid state properties. In particular, the total energy of the system can be computed with high precision and direct comparisons can be made between the atomic and condensed phases to determine the cohesive energies. Other properties which can be evaluated with these potentials include crystal structure, lattice constants, bulk moduli, lattice vibrational spectra, and properties of solid-solid phase transitions [3.36].

Despite the dramatic successes of the ab initio potentials, their applicability to optical and photoemission properties is limited. The limitations are not caused by the pseudopotential approach, i.e., the elimination of the core states, but by the use of the local density functional approach [3.29]. As in all-electron calculations, the use of local density functional potentials [3.30–35] are appropriate for calculating ground-state properties. Excited-state properties such as energy gaps are not given accurately in this theory. For example, the calculated indirect gap for Si is approximately one-half of the measured value. Direct gaps are also generally reduced [3.37]; however, valence band features are in fairly good agreement with experiment.

Since our major focus here is optical properties, the results of the EPM will be featured. This approach deals with excited-state spectra and allows an accurate analysis of optical and other data related to electronic transitions. Perhaps future developments will extend the ab initio approaches to encompass excited states. The EPM results can then serve as a test of these theories.

4. Response Functions and Density of States

The experimental input to the EPM is achieved through a comparison of measured and calculated spectra. Only a few pseudopotential form factors are required to determine accurate energy eigenvalues and wavefunctions. The method requires a calculation of a response function to compare with experimental data. Two major sources of measured spectra are optical reflectivity and photoemission data for the energy distribution curves (EDC) of the emitted electrons. The reflectivity spectra can be analyzed in terms of a frequency-dependent complex dielectric function, while the photoemission EDC can be compared with calculated density of states curves. The details and methods regarding the use of the measured spectra will be discussed elsewhere in this volume. Here we describe the theoretical calculations of the response functions.

The reflectivity, modulated reflectivity, and related spectra can be expressed in terms of the other frequency-dependent optical constants. In the frequency range of interest for band structure determination, the photon wavevector is much smaller than a Brillouin zone size, and hence, except for indirect minimum gaps, only direct transitions are considered and the photon wavevector is ignored. The complex dielectric function, $\varepsilon(\omega) = \varepsilon_1(\omega) + i\varepsilon_2(\omega)$, complex index of refraction $N(\omega) = n(\omega) + ik(\omega)$, and reflectivity $R(\omega)$ are the most common optical functions used. They are related to one another as follows:

$$N^2 = \varepsilon_1 + i\varepsilon_2 \quad , \tag{4.1}$$

$$\varepsilon_1 = n^2 - k^2 \quad , \tag{4.2}$$

$$\varepsilon_2 = 2nk \quad , \tag{4.3}$$

$$R = \left| \frac{N-1}{N+1} \right|^2 = \frac{(n-1)^2 + k^2}{(n+1)^2 + k^2} \quad . \tag{4.4}$$

Hence, a knowledge of $\varepsilon(\omega)$ yields all the other response functions. In fact, because of the Kramers-Kronig relation

$$\varepsilon_1(\omega) = 1 + \frac{2}{\pi} P \int_0^\infty \frac{\omega' \varepsilon_2(\omega')}{\omega'^2 - \omega^2} d\omega' \tag{4.5}$$

only a knowledge of $\varepsilon_2(\omega)$ [or $\varepsilon_1(\omega)$] is needed to specify completely the full dielectric function. However, it is necessary that $\varepsilon_2(\omega)$ [or $\varepsilon_1(\omega)$] be known over a wide frequency range.

There are useful sum rules which can be applied to test the accuracy of response functions. One obvious example is to use the $\omega \to 0$ limit of (4.5):

$$\varepsilon_1(0) = 1 + \frac{2}{\pi} \int_0^\infty \frac{\varepsilon_2(\omega)}{\omega} d\omega \quad . \tag{4.6}$$

Another sum rule is

$$\int_0^\infty \omega \varepsilon_2(\omega) d\omega = \frac{\pi}{2} \omega_p^2 \tag{4.9}$$

where ω_p is the electron plasma frequency.

The imaginary part of the dielectric function for cubic semiconductors for transitions between i and j band states can be expressed [4.1] in terms of an integral containing the dipole matrix element, $M_{ij}(\boldsymbol{k})$, and an energy conserving delta function

$$\varepsilon_2(\omega) = \frac{4\pi^2 e^2 \hbar}{3m^2 \omega^2} \sum_{ij} \frac{2}{(2\pi)^3} \int_{BZ} \delta[\omega_{ij}(\boldsymbol{k}) - \omega] |M_{ij}(\boldsymbol{k})|^2 d^3k \quad . \tag{4.10}$$

The integral is over all states in the Brillouin zone where $|M_{ij}(\boldsymbol{k})|^2 = |\langle u_i \boldsymbol{k} | \nabla | u_j \boldsymbol{k} \rangle|^2$, $\hbar \omega_{ij}(\boldsymbol{k}) = E_j - E_i$, and the u's are the periodic parts of the Bloch wavefunctions. The transitions are assumed to take place between initial valence band (i) states and final conduction band (j) states. The real part of the dielectric constant can be evaluated using a Kramers-Kronig transform on (4.10) or directly [4.2, 3]. Since the reflectivity of semiconductors in the visible and ultraviolet range is dominated by $\varepsilon_2(\omega)$, we concentrate on this function here.

Usually the dipole matrix element in (4.10) is smoothly varying and reasonably constant except at points of high symmetry. It is therefore useful to remove the matrix element and constants and isolate that part of $\varepsilon_2(\omega)$ which produces the major structure. The resulting function is called the joint density of states

$$J_{ij}(\omega) = \frac{2}{(2\pi)^3} \int_{BZ} \delta[\omega_{ij}(\boldsymbol{k}) - \omega] d^3k \quad , \tag{4.11}$$

since it represents the counting of states for transitions between occupied valence bands and empty conduction bands separated by an energy $\hbar \omega_{ij}(\boldsymbol{k})$. The integral in (4.11) can be written as

$$J_{ij}(\omega) = \frac{2}{(2\pi)^3} \int_{\omega_{ij}=\omega} \frac{ds}{|\nabla_k \omega_{ij}(\boldsymbol{k})|} \tag{4.12}$$

where ds is the surface element in wavevector space defined by $\omega_{ij}(\boldsymbol{k}) = \omega$. This function is similar to the usual density of states for single energy states $E(\boldsymbol{k})$

$$D(\omega) = \frac{2}{(2\pi)^3} \int \frac{ds}{|\nabla_{\boldsymbol{k}} E(\boldsymbol{k})|} \quad . \tag{4.13}$$

In both (4.12) and (4.13), the sharp structure in the density states arises from the zeros of the denominators. For $D(\omega)$ the zeros occur when bands are flat in k-space. These give peaks and structure in $D(\omega)$. This structure can give detailed information about the band structure. For the joint density of states $J_{ij}(\omega)$. The major structure occurs at the critical points in k-space where $|\nabla_{\boldsymbol{k}}\omega_{ij}(\boldsymbol{k})| = 0$. This condition requires that

$$\nabla_{\boldsymbol{k}} E_i = \nabla_{\boldsymbol{k}} E_j \quad . \tag{4.14}$$

Hence the slopes of the ith and jth bands or the velocities of the electron and hole in these bands are equal. These critical points dominate the joint density of states and $\varepsilon_2(\omega)$.

The structure in the response functions and the relation to critical point structure has been studied in general [4.4, 5]. This theory has been used in studies of phonon and electron densities of states, optical properties, superconducting energy gap spectra, etc. It has been applied to optical response functions in the following way.

At a critical point, the band energy difference can be expanded to second order in $(\boldsymbol{k} - \boldsymbol{k}_{\mathrm{cp}})$ where $\boldsymbol{k}_{\mathrm{cp}}$ is the point in k-space where (4.14) is satisfied

$$\omega_{ij}(\boldsymbol{k}) = \omega_{ij}(\boldsymbol{k}_{\mathrm{cp}}) + \sum_{n=1}^{3} \alpha_n(\boldsymbol{k} - \boldsymbol{k}_{\mathrm{cp}})_n^2 \quad , \tag{4.15}$$

where $\boldsymbol{k}$ and $\boldsymbol{k}_{\mathrm{cp}}$ is expressed in components along the principal axes. The critical points are classified according to how many of the expansion coefficients α_1 are negative. For α_1, α_2, α_3 all positive,, the energy difference $\omega_{ij}(\boldsymbol{k})$ increases in all three directions, hence this function is a minimum at $\boldsymbol{k} = \boldsymbol{k}_{\mathrm{cp}}$. For all three α's negative, $\omega_{ij}(\boldsymbol{k})$ decreases in all directions and the function is a maximum at $\boldsymbol{k} = \boldsymbol{k}_{\mathrm{cp}}$. For mixed values, the function has a saddle-point behavior.

The four possibilities are called M_0, M_1, M_2, and M_3 critical points where the subscripts refer to the number of negative α's. The minimum M_0 and maximum M_3 are also called parabolic critical points while the M_1 and M_2 critical points are often referred to as saddle critical points. A similar density of status analysis can be made for the one-particle electron energy states $E(\boldsymbol{k})$ or for the phonon dispersion relation.

There are several theorems related to the number and character of the critical points. One useful theorem gives a limit on the minimum number of critical points. Its states that a function of N variables which is periodic in all of them must have at least C_n^N critical points of type M_n in each N-dimensional primitive cell where C_n^N is the binomial coefficient

$$C_n^N = \frac{N!}{n!(N-n)!} \quad n \leq N \quad .$$ (4.16)

For example, in one dimension ($N = 1$), $C_0^1 = 1$ and $C_1^1 = 1$, that is, there is at least one minimum and one maximum. In two dimensions, there are at least four critical points consisting of one minimum, one maximum, and two saddle points. For three dimensions, there are at least eight critical points containing a minimum M_0, a maximum M_3, three saddle M_1 critical points, and three saddle M_2 critical points. This implies that in a typical response function such as reflectivity at least eight critical points must be present.

If we label the frequencies for the energy values of the gaps at the critical points by the corresponding class subscripts, then it can be shown that

$$\omega_0 < \omega_1 < \omega_2 < \omega_3 \quad .$$ (4.17)

However, the various M_1 or equivalently the M_2 critical points can all have the same energy. So there are at least four distinct energy positions of interest in three dimensions. In practice, there are often many more.

Once the critical-point structure is set by determining the class, that is, the number of negative α's, it is straightforward to determine the structure of the density of states $D(\omega)$ or joint density of states $J_{jj}(\omega)$ near the critical point. In practice, this is done using a computer to sample energy bands or energy differences, and the spectrum for $D(\omega)$ or $J_{ij}(\omega)$ is given using (4.12) or (4.13). Close to the critical point, it is possible to solve analytically for the structure in the response function. We will sketch this procedure.

Near the critical point (4.15) can be written as

$$\omega - \omega_c = \alpha_1 k_1^2 + \alpha_2 k_2^2 + \alpha_3 k_3^2$$ (4.18)

where we measure the k's from $\mathbf{k}_{\mathrm{cp}}$. We can choose α_1 and α_2 to have the same sign and scale k_2 so that $\alpha_1 = \alpha_2$. using cylindrical coordinates

$$r = (k_1^2 + k_2^2)^{1/2}$$
$$\theta = \arctan(k_2/k_1) \quad \text{we have}$$ (4.19)

$$\omega - \omega_c = \alpha_1 r^2 + \alpha_3 k_3^2 \quad .$$ (4.20)

In the case of an M_0 critical point $\alpha_1 > 0$ and $\alpha_3 > 0$. For $\omega > \omega_0$, the frequency surface in k-space is an ellipsoid. for $\omega < \omega_0$, there is no surface.

33

For an M_1 critical point, $\alpha_1 > 0$ and $\alpha_3 < 0$. Hence the surface for $\omega < \omega_1$ is a hyperboloid of two sheets while the corresponding surface for $\omega > \omega_1$ is a hyperboloid of one sheet. In a similar fashion, an M_2 critical point has $\alpha_1 < 0$ and $\alpha_3 \gtrless 0$. For $\omega < \omega_2$ the surface is a hyperboloid of one sheet while $\omega > \omega_2$ yields a hyperboloid of two sheets. Finally, for an M_3 maximum, $\alpha_1 < 0$ and $\alpha_3 < 0$. For $\omega < \omega_3$, the surface is an ellipsoid while for $\omega > \omega_3$ there is no surface.

Using geometric arguments, it can be shown that

$$\frac{ds}{|\nabla_{\boldsymbol{k}}\omega_{ij}(\boldsymbol{k})|} = \pi \frac{dk_3}{|\alpha_1|} \ . \tag{4.21}$$

Hence

$$J_{ij}(\omega) = \frac{A}{8\pi^2|\alpha_1|} \int dk_3 \ , \tag{4.22}$$

where A is a scale factor. In other words, $J_{ij}(\omega)$ is proportional to the extent of the surface in the k_3 direction. Using (4.20) and the analysis of the critical point energy surface geometry, it is now possible to determine the structure of $J_{ij}(\omega)$ near a critical point.

For an M_0 critical point the k-space surface extends from $k_3 = -[(\omega - \omega_0)/\alpha_3]^{1/2}$ to $k_3 = [(\omega - \omega_0)/\alpha_3]^{1/2}$. Hence, $J_{ij}(\omega) \propto (\omega - \omega_0)^{1/2}$ rising from $\omega = \omega_0$ with infinite slope. The structure in $J_{ij}(\omega)$ arising from an M_0 critical point is shown in Fig. 4.1. The analysis for an M_1 critical point is similar. The surface extension in the k_3 direction is from $-\infty$ to ∞ except for a gap from $k_3 = -[(\omega_1 - \omega)/\alpha_3]^{1/2}$ to $k_3 = [(\omega_1 - \omega)/\alpha_3]^{1/2}$. For $\omega > \omega_1$ there is no gap (hyperboloid of one sheet). The infinite extent of the hyperboloid is not relevant since we are only expanding near the critical point. In fact, this analysis is only valid close to the critical point. The outer portions of the surface are finite and smoothly varying. Hence, $J_{ij}(\omega)$ comes into ω_1 from below with infinite slope and leaves with finite slope as shown in Fig. 4.1.

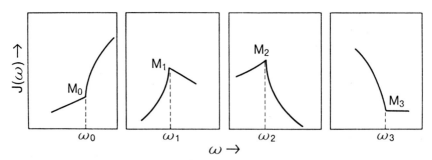

Fig. 4.1. Joint density of states $J(\omega)$ near the four types of critical points

The M_2 critical point analysis follows from the above discussion for M_1. In this case, the $J_{ij}(\omega)$ curve has a finite slope as ω approaches ω_2. It then drops with infinite slope (Fig. 4.1). Similarly for the maximum M_3, we can use the analysis of the M_0 but reverse the structure. Therefore, $J_{ij}(\omega) \propto (\omega_3 - \omega)^{1/2}$ below ω_3 and is zero above (Fig. 4.1).

Hence, the structure of the four critical points in k-space determines the spectral structure of the response function of interest. In the case of interest here, $J_{ij}(\omega)$ has a structure dictated by the properties of the M_0, M_1, M_2, and M_3 critical points. A similar analysis can be made for $D(\omega)$ where the surface of interest in k-space is the energy band structure $E(\boldsymbol{k})$ itself where, as for $J_{ij}(\omega)$, we investigate the energy differences $\omega_{ij}(k)$. Although the matrix elements $M_{ij}(\boldsymbol{k})$ in (4.10) will weight the critical-point structure and distort the shape from the ideal structure, the critical points will still give rise to sharp Van Hove singularities, and these will be evident in $\varepsilon_2(\omega)$, $R(\omega)$, and the other optical constants.

Since there is a minimum set of critical points, there is a simplest possible response function spectrum. For three dimensions, there are at least eight critical points and a minimum of four critical-point energies ω_0, ω_1, ω_2, ω_3. For the spectrum shown in Fig. 4.2, the three M_1 saddle points are put at the same energy ω_1 and similarly for the three M_2's at ω_2. Figure 4.2 therefore represents the simplest possible spectrum for a three-dimensional response function. An exception should be mentioned. In constructing the density of states for phonons, the acoustic branch is not quadratic at small wavevectors. As the wavevector approaches zero, the resulting density of states is proportional to ω^2. This is the famous Debye model. The minimum in the band therefore is not an M_0.

Critical-point analyses resulting from inspections of Van Hove singularities in response functions are very useful. For $J_{ij}(\omega)$ or $\varepsilon_2(\omega)$ or $R(\omega)$, an analysis of this type tells us a great deal about the energy-band structure since band topologies near critical points are determined. This approach is greatly aided by investigations of modulated reflectivity spectra. In these

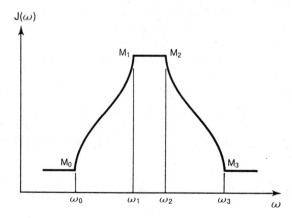

Fig. 4.2. Simplest $J(\omega)$ in three dimensions with the minimum number of critical points. The M_1 and M_2 saddle points are each triply degenerate

35

experiments, the Van Hove singularities are in a sense differentiated as a function of frequency. The "derivative" spectroscopies reveal sharp structure because of the nonanalytic behavior of the derivative near a critical point. This can easily be seen by investigating the frequency dependence of $J_{ij}(\omega)$ described above, for example, $J_{ij} \propto (\omega - \omega_0)^{1/2}$ and the derivative of this function is singular near ω_0.

Through the use of reflectivity, modulated reflectivity, absorption and other optical measurements, the energies and shapes (classes) of the critical points can be determined. In practice, the number greatly exceeds the minimum number of eight, and the analysis is further complicated by the fact that there are several bands involved giving many possible interband transitions. Examples of the use of this approach for determining electronic structure will be given later.

Another important source of band structure information is photoemission. If the energy distribution curves for the emitted electrons are taken to be proportional to the band density of states, a critical-point analysis of this spectrum together with $D(\omega)$ can yield direct information about $E(\boldsymbol{k})$. Reflectivity and photoemission measurements are the major sources of input data for the EPM, and analyses based on critical-point theory are essential for isolating the important interband transitions which determie the measured spectra.

As discussed earlier, optical probes in the visible and UV involve photons with wavevectors significantly smaller than a Brillouin zone. Hence, the frequency-dependent dielectric function for zero wavevector (long wavelength limit) suffices for these band structure analyses. However, there are many important problems in solid state physics which require a knowledge of the wavevector-dependent electron screening functions. Some examples are the screening of impurities by valence electrons, phonon spectra, and the determination of the pseudopotential itself.

The first attempts to calculate optical response functions for semiconductors involved model band structures and the calculations were done for zero frequency [4.6]. The first calculations based on accurate band structure results [4.7] were done for Si, Ge, GaAs, and ZnSe. The method was later extended to include frequency and wavevector dependence [4.8, 9]. These calculations yield insight into bonding and give interesting conceptual models for the relationships between semiconductors, insulators, and metals [4.8].

The formalism is based on a straightforward extension of the standard random phase approximation or self-consistent field [4.1] dielectric function. However, the calculation, which in principle is similar to the $q \rightarrow 0$ dielectric function cases described above, is fairly complex. The defining equation for the longitudinal $\varepsilon(\boldsymbol{q}, \omega)$ describes the response of the crystal to an electric field parallel to $\boldsymbol{q}$ and varying sinusoidally in time

$$\boldsymbol{D}\mathrm{e}^{\mathrm{i}(\boldsymbol{q} \cdot \boldsymbol{r} - \omega t)} = \varepsilon(\boldsymbol{q}, \omega)\boldsymbol{E}\mathrm{e}^{\mathrm{i}(\boldsymbol{q} \cdot \boldsymbol{r} - \omega t)} \quad . \tag{4.23}$$

Using the expression given by *Ehrenreich* and *Cohen* [4.1], we obtain

$$\varepsilon_1(\boldsymbol{q}, \omega) = 1 + \frac{4\pi e^2}{\Omega q^2} \sum_{\boldsymbol{k},c,v} |\langle \boldsymbol{k}, c | \boldsymbol{k} + \boldsymbol{q}, v \rangle|^2$$

$$\times \{ [E_c(\boldsymbol{k}) - E_v(\boldsymbol{k} + \boldsymbol{q}) - \hbar\omega]^{-1} + [E_c(\boldsymbol{k}) - E_v(\boldsymbol{k} + \boldsymbol{q}) + \hbar\omega]^{-1} \} \quad .$$

$$(4.24)$$

The matrix element is the inner product between the periodic parts of the Bloch functions; $\boldsymbol{k}$ is summed over the first Brillouin zone; v labels the valence bands; c labels conduction bands, and Ω is the crystal volume. For computational purposes, the summation is done over a finite grid of points in the Brillouin zone. The wavefunctions and energies are obtained using the EPM.

Results for ε_1, ε_2, and $\mathrm{Im}(\varepsilon^{-1})$ are given in (Figs. 4.3–5). A comparison between Si and a free-electron gas, which was modeled using a Lindhard

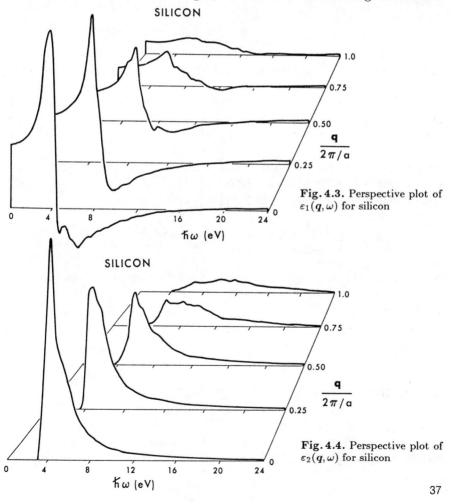

Fig. 4.3. Perspective plot of $\varepsilon_1(\boldsymbol{q}, \omega)$ for silicon

Fig. 4.4. Perspective plot of $\varepsilon_2(\boldsymbol{q}, \omega)$ for silicon

37

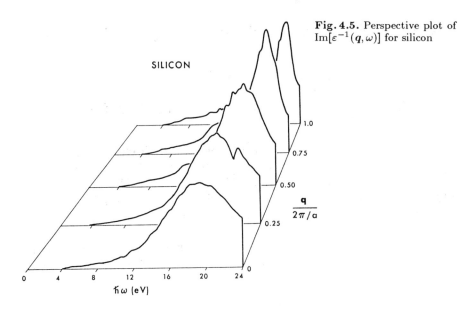

SILICON

Fig. 4.5. Perspective plot of $\mathrm{Im}[\varepsilon^{-1}(q,\omega)]$ for silicon

dielectric function [4.8], illustrates the important role of the semiconductor gap. At high ω, ε_1 for Si resembles that of a free-electron gas. For low frequency, the presence of a semiconductor gap gives rise to a lower zero in $\varepsilon_1(\omega)$ and a positive value for $\varepsilon_1(\omega)$ even as $q \to 0$. This lower zero and an associated peak occur at around 4 to 5 eV which is taken to be the average optical gap. The function $\varepsilon_2(\omega)$ peaks near this value, and if a one-oscillator model is used for $\varepsilon_2(\omega)$, it should be centered at this average gap. A model of this kind can be used to determine the static dielectric function $\varepsilon_1(0)$. This function has the form

$$\varepsilon_1(0) = 1 + \left(\frac{\hbar\omega_{\mathrm{p}}}{E_{\mathrm{g}}}\right)^2 \tag{4.25}$$

where $\hbar\omega_{\mathrm{p}}$ is the plasma frequency and E_{g} is the average optical gap.

This simple expression for $\varepsilon_1(0)$ can be derived from (4.24), and it is implicit in model dielectric functions [4.6]. Equation (4.25) is also basic to the theory of ionicity and structural phase transitions developed by Phillips and Van Vechten. This theory will be discussed in Chap. 8.

4.1 Charge Density and Bonding

Until recently, theorists have fared much better with electronic and optical properties than with structural and bonding properties. Most of the calculations described thus far involve the computation of functions in k-space.

In particular, spectral response functions often involve a determination of dispersion curves such as $E_n(\boldsymbol{k})$. On the other hand, structural chemists have concentrated on bonding properties using real space descriptions of bond-orbitals and empirical bond lengths (e.g. Pauling [4.10]).

By the early 1970s, the EPM band structures and related response functions had become refined, and the results were shown to be consistent with many experiments. It was at this point that theorists became sufficiently confident of the calculational results to consider the direct use of the "pseudowavefunctions" [4.11, 12]. Since core states are not included in pseudopotential calculations, the results were expected to be accurate only outside the core region. However, it is precisely this region which is of interest in determining bonding properties. Although experimental tests of the wavefunctions and electron probability density were not available at that time, more recent x-ray analyses have verified the pseudopotential predictions [4.13].

The probability function for the electrons in a spatial region of volume $d\Omega$ is given by $|\psi_{n,\boldsymbol{k}}(\boldsymbol{r})|^2 d\Omega$ for electrons in valence band n and state $\boldsymbol{k}$. When many $\boldsymbol{k}$-states are considered, a charge density or distribution can be described. In particular, the charge density for each valence band can be written as

$$\varrho_n(\boldsymbol{r}) = \sum_{\boldsymbol{k}} e |\psi_{n,\boldsymbol{k}}(\boldsymbol{r})|^2 \tag{4.26}$$

where the summation is over all states in the Brillouin zone for a given band n.

To obtain adequate convergence for $|\psi_{n,\boldsymbol{k}}(\boldsymbol{r})|^2$, it is necessary to expand the wavefunction in a large number of plane waves and to evaluate the function at a large grid of points in the Brillouin zone. Later on, we illustrate an alternative method.

The total charge density for a semiconductor or insulator can be obtained by adding the charge density from all the valence bands, that is

$$\varrho(\boldsymbol{r}) = \sum_{n} \varrho_n \tag{4.27}$$

where the sum is over all occupied bands. The function $\varrho_n(\boldsymbol{r})$ yields information about the properties of individual bands and can be used to determine the role of each band in the bonding nature of the crystal. The total charge density $\varrho(\boldsymbol{r})$ represents the electronic distribution in a direct manner. As will be shown in the results section of this volume, $\varrho(\boldsymbol{r})$ clearly demonstrates the peaking of the charge density in the covalent bond halfway between the atoms in C, Si, Ge, and gray Sn. For ionic systems, $\varrho(\boldsymbol{r})$ can be used to demonstrate charge transfer. In general, the relationship between the topology of $\varrho(\boldsymbol{r})$ and bonding is almost immediately obvious from an investigation of this function. Hence, it is convenient to display $\varrho(\boldsymbol{r})$ in a two-dimensional plane using constant charge density contour lines. The plane chosen usually contains the atoms and the bond. For example, for the diamond and zinc-blende structures, a (110) plane is convenient. Examples of $\varrho_n(\mathbf{r})$ and $\varrho(\mathbf{r})$ for many semiconductors will be given later in this volume.

As stated above, early calculations of the charge density involved compoutations at a large number of $\mathbf{k}$-points in the Brillouin zone. However, it was soon realized that by using one $\mathbf{k}$-point [4.14] or several representative or "special" $\mathbf{k}$-points [4.15], a very accurate determination of $\varrho(\mathbf{r})$ can be made.

The special point scheme can be used to determine the average over the Brillouin zone of a periodic function of wavevector (e.g. energy bands, charge density, dipole matrix elements, etc.). The method is particularly useful for calculating $\varrho(\mathbf{r})$ when this function is used for evaluating self-consistent pseudopotentials as described earlier. The computational effort is significantly reduced when this method is used. An example of a systematic way of choosing special points is given here. There are variations on this method, but the concept remains the same.

If the Bloch function $\psi_k(\mathbf{r})$ for a specific band is expressed in terms of (real space) Wannier functions $a(\mathbf{r} - \mathbf{R}_m)$, we have

$$\psi_k(\mathbf{r}) = \frac{1}{\sqrt{N}} \sum_m \exp(\mathrm{i}\mathbf{k} \cdot \mathbf{R}_m) a(\mathbf{r} - \mathbf{R}_m) \tag{4.28}$$

where $\mathbf{R}_m$ is a lattice vector. The charge density for this state is

$$\varrho_k(\mathbf{r}) = \frac{1}{N} \sum_{mn} \exp[\mathrm{i}\mathbf{k} \cdot (\mathbf{R}_m - \mathbf{R}_n)] a(\mathbf{r} - \mathbf{R}_m) a^*(\mathbf{r} - \mathbf{R}_n) \tag{4.29}$$

and the total charge density is

$$\varrho(\mathbf{r}) = \sum_k \varrho_k(\mathbf{r}) = \sum_m |a(\mathbf{r} - \mathbf{R}_m)|^2 \quad . \tag{4.30}$$

Equation (4.29) can be rewritten as

$$\varrho_k(\mathbf{r}) = \frac{1}{N} \sum_m |a(\mathbf{r} - \mathbf{R}_m)|^2 + \frac{1}{N} {\sum_j}' \sum_m \exp(\mathrm{i}\mathbf{k} \cdot \mathbf{R}_j)$$
$$\times a(\mathbf{r} - \mathbf{R}_m) a^*(\mathbf{r} + \mathbf{R}_j - \mathbf{R}_m) \tag{4.31}$$

where the prime in the sum over j omits the $\mathbf{R}_j = 0$ term. The first term in (4.31) is proportional to the total charge density (4.30) for a band and is, in fact, the average charge density for that band. Hence, if it were possible to choose a $\mathbf{k}$-point sampling scheme to minimize the second term in (4.31), then a good approximation to the total charge density could be obtained.

Consider a wavevector $\mathbf{k} = (2\pi/a)(k_1, k_2, k_3)$. By performing all possible symmetry operations T on $\mathbf{k}$, up to 48 different $\mathbf{k}$ vectors can be generated. Similarly, all $\varrho_k(r)$ corresponding to each k can be generated from knowing one of them. Hence, the sum is given by

$$\sum_T \varrho_{Tk}(r) = \frac{1}{N} \sum_T \sum_m |a(r - R_m)|^2$$
$$+ \frac{1}{N} \sum_j' \sum_m \sum_T \exp[i(Tk) \cdot R_j] a(r - R_m) a^*(R + R_j - R_m) \quad .$$
(4.32)

The sum over T of the first term in (4.32) just gives a factor of 48 while the second sum denoted by $F(r)$ becomes

$$F(r) = \frac{1}{N} \sum_j \exp(ik \cdot R_j)$$
$$\times \sum_m \sum_T a(r - R_m) a^*(r + TR_j - R_m) \quad .$$
(4.33)

Since $|TR_j| = |R_j|$ the sum in (4.33),

$$s(r) = \sum_m \sum_T a(r - R_m) a^*(r + TR_j - R_m) \quad ,$$
(4.34)

remains constant over all sign changes and permutations of R_j. Hence, the condition that $F(r) = 0$, that is, that the first term in (4.32) represents the charge density, requires that the k vector satisfy the set of equations:

$$\sum_{|R_j|=c_m} \exp(ik \cdot R_j) = 0 \quad m = 1, 2, 3, \ldots$$
(4.35)

where c_m is the nearest neighbor distance corresponding to index m. When two lattice vectors have the same magnitude but are not related by permutations or sign changes, then (4.35) must be satisfied for each set of lattice vectors separately.

As an example, for the fcc lattice the first three nearest neighbor lattice vector R_j give

$$\cos k_1 \cos k_2 + \cos k_1 \cos k_3 + \cos k_2 \cos k_3 = 0 \quad ,$$
(4.36)

$$\cos 2k_1 + \cos 2k_2 + \cos 2k_3 = 0 \quad ,$$
(4.37)

$$\cos 2k_1 \cos k_2 \cos k_3 + \cos k_1 \cos 2k_2 \cos k_3$$
$$+ \cos k_1 \cos k_2 \cos 2k_3 = 0 \quad .$$
(4.38)

Baldereschi [4.14] showed that (4.36) and (4.37) could be satisfied with only one k-point

$$k = \left(\frac{2\pi}{a}\right)(0.622, 0.295, 0) \quad . \tag{4.39}$$

It is not possible to satisfy all three equations using only one k-point, but by using several points, a larger number of conditions given by (4.35) can be satisfied.

As an example, if we limit ourselves to symmetry points $k = 0(\Gamma)$, $k = (2\pi/a)(1,0,0)(X)$, and $k = (2\pi/a)(1/2,1/2,1/2)(L)$ for the fcc Brillouin zone the charge density given by

$$\varrho(\boldsymbol{r}) = \tfrac{1}{8}\varrho_\Gamma(\boldsymbol{r}) + \tfrac{3}{8}\varrho_X(\boldsymbol{r}) + \tfrac{1}{2}\varrho_L(\boldsymbol{r}) \tag{4.40}$$

satisfies conditions of the type (4.35) for the first three nearest neighbors. One can satisfy the conditions for the first seven nearest neighbors by using a weighted sum of charge densities for the k-points $k = (2\pi/a)(1/2,0,0)$ $k_2 = (2\pi/a)(1,1/2,0)$, and $k_3 = (2\pi/a)(1/2,1/2,0)$ with weighting factors 1/4, 1/4, and 1/2 respectively.

Hence the special point scheme allows a computationally efficient scheme for accurately estimating charge densities from a limited set of k-points. This approach has had a significant impact on calculations of electronic potentials and on analyses of bonding properties of solids.

5. Low Energy Probes of Semiconductors

Since most transport processes involve states at or near the valence- and conduction-band edges, it is useful to have probes which characterize the electronic structure within this energy region. The energy region of interest corresponds to photons having energies of a few hundredths to a few tenths of an electron volt, that is, the radio to infrared frequency region of the spectrum.

5.1 Band Gap Measurements

One of the most obvious infrared experiments is to measure the size of the band gap and to ascertain concurrently whether the band gap is direct or indirect. These measurements in their simplest form consist of measuring the absorption edge. In Fig. 5.1, the absorption spectrum of InSb [5.1] is displayed; the band threshold is clearly visible. As shown in Fig. 5.2, InSb is a direct band gap material with the conduction- and valence-band edges both occurring at the zone center. This accounts for the rather abrupt absorption threshold at the band gap energy of 0.23 eV. For a material such as silicon, the conduction band edge occurs near the X point while the valence band edge occurs at the zone center. (High symmetry points for the zinc-blende Brillouin zone are shown in Fig. 9.4). In such a situation, the lowest threshold transition cannot be achieved for a process which involves photons alone. Photon initiated transitions require a k-conserving process in order that the initial and final states have equal momentum. However, for indirect transitions in which the k-vectors for initial and final states are different, phonon assisted transitions can still conserve momentum. Thus, for an indirect gap material such as silicon, lattice vibrational modes are required to play a role in electronic transitions involving the conduction and valence band edges. Since three particles are involved in an indirect transition, that is, electron, photon, and phonon, the matrix elements for indirect transitions are much weaker than for direct transitions. Consequently, the band edge absorption is less distinct in indirect gap materials; the absorption threshold may exhibit a long tail into the optical gap region. By examining the line shape of the absorption threshold, it is possible to determine whether a gap is direct or indirect. Moreover, for indirect gaps, we can obtain information on phonon-related propeties. For example, at very low temperatures only

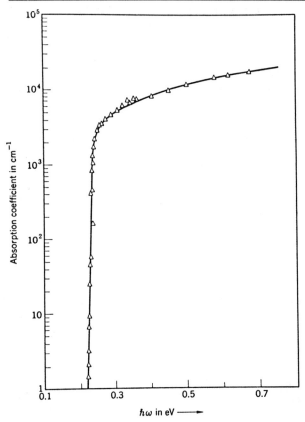

Fig. 5.1. Optical absorption coefficient of InSb near the absorption edge. The band gap of InSb is 0.23 eV and is direct [5.1]

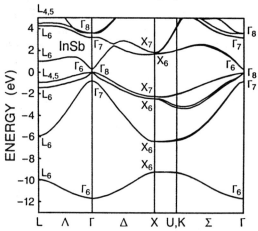

Fig. 5.2. Electronic band structure of InSb along several symmetry points in the Brillouin zone

Table 5.1. Energy band gaps for selected semiconductors. In several cases, the nature of the gap in terms of whether it is direct (d) or indirect (i) is given. The data is from [5.1–3]

Semiconductor	Energy Gap (eV) 0 K	300 K		Semiconductor	Energy Gap (eV) 0 K	300 K	
AgCl (rs)		3.2	i	HgSe (zb)	−0.24		d
AgI (w)		2.8		HgTe (zb)	−0.3		d
AlN (w)		6.02		InAs (zb)	0.43	0.35	d
AlP (zb)		2.5	i	InN (w)		2.0	
AlAs (zb)	2.3	2.16	i	InP (zb)	1.42	1.35	d
AlSb (zb)	1.65	1.52	i	InSb (zb)	0.24	0.18	d
BN (zb)		~4	i	PbS (rs)	0.29	0.35	d
BP (zb)		~6	i	PbSe (rs)	0.17	0.27	d
C (diam)	5.4		i	PbTe (rs)	0.19	0.3	d
CdGeAs₂	0.53			Se (trig)		1.8	d
CdGeP₂	1.8			Si (diam)	1.17	1.14	i
CdS (w)	2.58	2.42	d	SiC (hex)	3.		
CdSb (orth)	~0.5			SiC (zb)	1.9		i
CdSe (w)	1.84	1.74	d	Sn (diam)	0.00	0.00	d
CdSiP₂ (chalc)	2.2			SnTe (rs)	0.3	0.18	d
CdSnAs₂ (chalc)	0.26			Te (trig)		0.33	d
CdSnP₂ (chalc)	1.5			ZnGeAs₂ (chalc)		0.85	d
CdTe (zb)	1.61	1.45	d	ZnGeP₂ (chalc)	2.2		d
CdTe (w)		1.50	d	ZnO (w)		3.2	d
CuBr (zb)		2.94		ZnS (zb)		3.54	d
GaAs (zb)	1.52	1.43	d	ZnS (w)		3.67	d
GaN (w)		3.34		ZnSe (zb)	2.80	2.58	d
GaP (zb)	2.32	2.26	i	ZnSiAs₂ (chalc)		1.7	d
GaSb (zb)	0.81	0.78	d	ZnSiP₂ (chalc)		2.3	d
GaSe (l)		2.05	d	ZnSnAs₂ (chalc)		0.65	d
GaTe (l)	1.80	1.66		ZnTe (zb)		2.26	d
Ge (diam)	0.774	0.67	i				

phonon emission processes are possible, but at higher temperatures phonon absorption may occur.

The band gaps for a number of semiconductors are presented in Table 5.1.

5.2 Excitonic Effects Near Band Edges

Determining the precise nature of the electronic states near band edges can be complicated by the existence of excitons. Excitons consist of electron-hole pairs bound by Coulombic interactions. The chief condition for exciton formation is that the group velocity of the electron and hole be equal. In this fashion, the hole and electron traverse the crystal together and can remain bound. All semiconducting or insulating crystals can exhibit exciton formation.

Excitons were first proposed by *Frenkel* [5.4] who made an analogy between atomic or molecular excitations and solid state excitations. If we consider a solid to be composed of weakly interacting molecular species, then we might associate an optical excitation of the solid with the corresponding excitation of the molecular species. In molecular species such as anthracene excitonic effects are well known, and they are observed in the corresponding solid state. Unfortunately, the analogy Frenkel made between molecular and solid state excitons is not applicable to most semiconducting solids. The interactions in semiconductors are not strongly localized to molecular-like species; they are spread over a number of lattice constants.

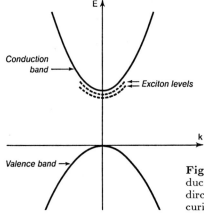

Fig. 5.3. Schematic band structure of a semiconductor illustrating exciton levels. The band gap is dirct with valence and conduction band edges occuring at $k = 0$

Excitons in semiconductors can be described by theories developed by *Mott* [5.5] and *Wannier* [5.6]. Their theories can be described qualitatively by introducing a screened Coulomb potential to replicate the electron-hole interactions. If we take a potential of the form $V = -e^2/\varepsilon r$, where ε is an appropriate dielectric constant, then the excitonic states will exhibit discrete energy levels within the band gap as indicated in Fig. 5.3. The energy levels will have spacings of the form $E_n = E_g - E_b/n^2$, where E_g is the energy band gap with no exciton and E_b is the binding energy of the exciton given by $E_b = e^4 m^*/2\varepsilon^2\hbar^2$. If we assume a typical dielectric constant, $\varepsilon = 15$, and a reduced band mass, $m^* = 0.1$, then we would obtain an exciton energy of about 5 meV. Some representative binding energies of excitons are Si (14.7 meV), Ge (~ 4 meV), and GaAs (3.5 meV). The line intensities associated with the excitonic states decrease as $1/n^3$. Eventually the excitonic states will merge into the continuum of valence to conduction band transitions. At transition energies away from the band edge, the absorption edge will assume the line shape associated with no excitonic interactions. In Fig. 5.4, we display the absorption coefficient for GaAs [5.7]. The threshold value of the absorption is considerably enhanced by the presence of the excitonic transition.

While excitons at band gap edges are well understood, excitonic effects elsewhere are not. It has been postulated by *Phillips* [5.8] that excitons

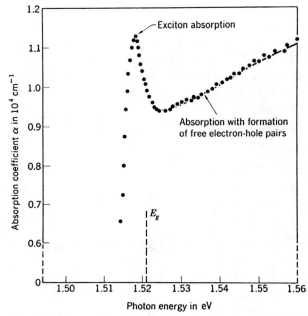

Fig. 5.4. Absorption coefficient near the band edge of GaAs. Note the exciton absorption level below the band gap E_g. the band gap occurs at 1.521 eV and the exciton binding energy is 3.4 meV [5.7]

can exist at critical points away from the band gap edges. Specifically, at so-called hyperbolic critical points (M_1 or M_2) one might have an enhanced transition probability. The existence of hyperbolic excitons is fairly well accepted; however a quantitative description has yet to be presented.

5.3 Cyclotron Resonance

By combining magnetic fields with radio frequency radiation, it is possible to measure the dynamical masses associated with the band edges in semi-conductors. Electrons or holes will traverse helical orbits in the presence of a static magnetic field. The angular rotation frequency of the electrons or holes can be measured by resonance experiments and determine an effective mass. In the simplest form, where we assume isotropic bands, the frequency is related to the mass via $\omega_c = eB/m^*c$. We can improve upon this simple relationship through the inclusion of directional effects. Specifically, we can determine the band edge dispersions by measuring the effective mass tensor, $1/m^*_{\mu\nu}$:

$$\frac{1}{m^*_{\mu\nu}} = \frac{1}{\hbar^2} \frac{\partial^2 E(\boldsymbol{k})}{\partial k_\mu \partial k_\nu} \tag{5.1}$$

where E is the band energy.

47

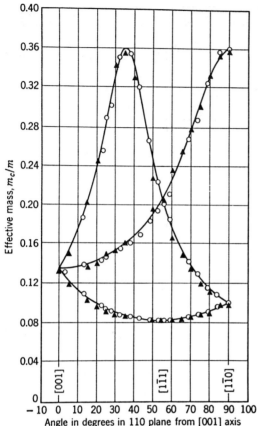

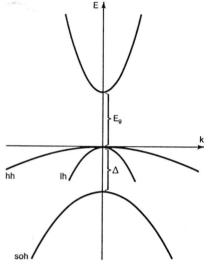

Fig. 5.5. Cyclotron resonance effective mass for germanium at 4 K. The magnetic field is oriented in a (110) plane with the angle measured from the [001] axis

Fig. 5.6. Schematic band structure for a direct gap semiconductor

If we decompose the band energy dispersion as

$$E(\boldsymbol{k}) = \frac{\hbar^2 k_1^2}{2m_1} + \frac{\hbar^2 k_2^2}{2m_2} + \frac{\hbar^2 k_3^2}{2m_3} \tag{5.2}$$

where (m_1, m_2, m_3) are the mass components along the principal axes $(1,2,3)$, then the effective mass m can be determined by the angles of the respective components of the static magnetic field. If we measure the effective mass using various orientations of the B field, then it is fairly routine to extract the effective mass tensor. An example of such a procedure [5.9] is given in Fig. 5.5.

A simplified picture of the band edge structure for a direct gap semiconductor, for example GaAs, is given in Fig. 5.6. In this picture, it is possible to extract four characteristic masses: the conduction band mass m_c; the heavy hole band mass m_{hh}; the light hole mass m_{lh}; and the split-off hole mass m_{soh}. The parameter Δ in Fig. 5.6 is the spin-orbit splitting of the valence band at the Brillouin zone centers. (See Chap. 11 for more details on

48

spin-orbit effects in solids). Spin-orbit interactions in solids scale roughly as the corresponding interactions in the isolated atoms [5.1]. In terms of these masses, the conduction band may be described by

$$E_c = E_g + \frac{\hbar^2 k^2}{2m_c} \tag{5.3}$$

and the valence bands by

$$E_v(hh) = \frac{-\hbar^2 k^2}{2m_{hh}} \qquad E_v(lh) = \frac{-\hbar^2 k^2}{2m_{lh}}$$

$$E_v(soh) = -\Delta - \frac{\hbar^2 k^2}{2m_{soh}} \quad . \tag{5.4}$$

Values for the band masses are given in Table 5.2.

Table 5.2. Energy band masses for selected semiconductors. The data is from [5.1–3]. Values in parentheses are estimated

Semiconductor	m_c	m_{lh}	m_{hh}	m_{soh}	Δ
AlSb*		(0.11)	0.9	(0.22)	0.75
GaAs	0.07	0.12	0.68	0.20	0.34
GaP*		(0.11)	(0.86)	(0.24)	0.13
GaSb	0.047	0.06	0.3	(0.14)	0.8
Ge*		0.043	0.34	0.08	0.3
InAs	0.026	0.025	10.41	0.08	0.43
InP	0.015	0.021	0.39	(0.11)	0.82
Si*		0.16	0.52	0.25	0.04

* Indirect gaps

Finally, we note that some fundamental differences exist between cyclotron resonance measurements on semiconductors and those performed on metals. In semiconductors, the carrier density is orders of magnitude lower than metals and as a consequence, the radio frequency field used to achieve resonance with the spiraling electrons or holes permeates the entire semiconductor. Thus, the special geometries used for cyclotron resonance measurements in metals need not be employed. However, owing to the lower carrier concentration in semiconductors, the resonance signal may be very small. To overcome the low carrier concentration, electron-hole pairs are often created in the semiconducting specimen by illuminating the sample with an incandescent lamp.

5.4 Doping Effects in Semiconductors

The technological importance of semiconductors stems from the ease with which their electrical properties can be altered through the controlled introduction of impurities. We can measure the electrical properties as a function of impurity additions and obtain information on the electronic structure of the semiconductor.

Dopants in semiconductors can be classified by their chemical valence. For a tetrahedral elemental semiconductor, impurities with valence less than four are acceptors and impurities with valence more than four are donors. Thus, for an elemental semiconductor such as silicon, elements such as boron, or aluminum are acceptors and elements such as arsenic or phophorous are donors. The general distinction is that elements which form fewer bonds than necessary to saturate the elemental crystalline environment are acceptors and those which form more bonds than is necessary for saturation are donors. The additional electron associated with a donor is relatively free to move throughout the crystal as it does not participate in a normal bonding state. For acceptors, the situation is reversed. An acceptor lacks sufficient electrons to complete the bonding and the unsaturated bond may migrate throughout the crystal. The unsaturated bond may be thought of as a hole.

Acceptor states are located near the valence band edge and reside within the band gap. Donor states are also located within the band gap, but these states are near the conduction band edge. Acceptor states which reside close to the edge, for example within 0.1 eV, are called shallow, and those away from the edge are called deep. Similar nomenclature is also used to describe donor states.

We may use properties of these states to alter the position of the Fermi level of a semiconductor. If we introduce a large number of donor dopants into a semiconductor, the carrier concentration may induce a metallic behavior. The donors will form band-like states near the conduction edge, and the Fermi level will reside within this band. Such a semiconductor will become a "degenerate semiconductor". We can move the Fermi level throughout the forbidden band gap and by measuring the electrical properties, determine the existence of states within the band gap.

6. Optical and Electronic Spectra of Semiconductors

Optical studies of semiconductors have concentrated on reflectivity measurements as opposed to transmission or absorption measurements. It is possible to measure absorption spectra, but the penetration depth of optical radiation is fairly low in semiconductors. Thus, absorption measurements require the use of thin films which can be difficult to prepare and to calibrate. Reflectivity measurements do not require films, and these measurements are relatively easy to perform: the ratio of the incident photon flux to the reflected photon flux is measured as a function of photon energy. In principle, the only tools required for this procedure are the sample, a light source, a monochrometer, and a detector.

Reflectivity experiments have two distinct advantages over other probes. First, they are not overly sensitive to surface conditions. Typically, the photon sampling length in semiconductors is of the order of a few thousand angströms. Since intrinsic surface perturbations in semiconductors heal within tens of angströms, optical measurements are insensitive to surface states. Secondly, reflectivity measurements have better resolution than other techniques with respect to band structure features which lie in or above the optical region. In some cases, this resolution may approach a few meV.

The chief drawback of reflectivity work is that only relative energy differences can be measured for the energy levels of interest as opposed to an absolute energy placement for each level. A second disadvantage of reflectivity work or optical work in general is that for the solid state the measured spectra are not rich in structure when compared with atomic spectra, which consist of sharp discrete lines. Solid state spectra consist of a broad continuum with some critical point structure superposed. One goal of solid state spectroscopy is to ascertain the energy position and location of these critical points within the Brillouin zone. In order to accomplish this goal, modulation spectroscopies have been developed.

Reviews of the optical spectra of semiconductors are given in [6.1–8].

6.1 Modulation Spectroscopy

To date, modulation spectroscopies are the most powerful tools available to study the optical spectra of solids. Modulation techniques accomplish the enhancement of critical-point structure by taking a derivative of the reflectivity spectrum with respect to an external or internal parameter.

We can demonstrate the basic principle of modulation spectroscopy by examining the dielectric function in the vicinity of a critical point [6.4]. Suppose we have

$$\varepsilon_2(\omega) = a(\omega - \omega_0)^{1/2} + \text{const.} \tag{6.1}$$

where the constant term represents the background and the leading terms represents ε_2 near an M_0 critical point (similar arguments would hold for an M_1, M_2, or M_3 critical point). Usually, the critical-point structure is small, and the nearly constant background dominates ε_2. To remove the obscuring background, we consider the derivative of ε_2 with respect to some parameter ξ:

$$\frac{d\varepsilon_2}{d\xi} = \frac{a}{2}(\omega - \omega_0)^{-1/2}\frac{d(\omega - \omega_0)}{d\xi} \quad . \tag{6.2}$$

Clearly, the differentiation process removes the background, and in this case as ω approaches ω_0, the derivative becomes singular. In practice, the measured derivative is never singular owing to broadening effects, but the enhancing effect is retained. In Fig. 6.1, derivatives of the real and imaginary parts of the dielectric function are presented for the vicinity of a three-dimensional critical point. Each term yields a characteristic imprint which makes it possible to identify the nature of the critical-point symmetry.

Another positive aspect of modulation spectroscopy is the implementation of phase sensitive detection. If we modulate the probing parameter with some specific frequency and the detector is fixed only to respond to that frequency, then we reject any spurious signal. For the modulating parameter, we may employ temperature, pressure, or electric field. We may

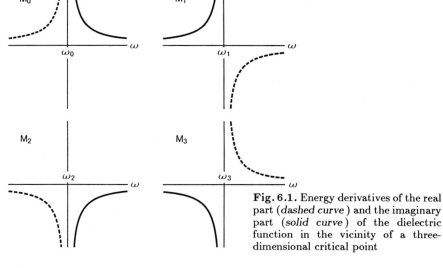

Fig. 6.1. Energy derivatives of the real part (dashed curve) and the imaginary part (solid curve) of the dielectric function in the vicinity of a three-dimensional critical point

also modulate the wavelength or energy of the incident photon flux. The former techniques are known as thermoreflectance, piezoreflectance, and electroreflectance respectively; the latter technique is known as wavelength modulation.

6.1.1 Wavelength Modulation

The essence of wavelength modulation is to alter the incident photon frequency and to measure the corresponding change in reflectivity; that is, we take

$$\Delta R = R(\omega + \Delta\omega) - R(\omega) \tag{6.3}$$

and in the limit of $\Delta\omega \to 0$, we have a $dR/d\omega$ spectrum. Modulation of the incident photon energy can be accomplished by a vibrating mirror, slit, or grating of the monochromator. Synchronous detection is achieved by setting a lock-in detector to the vibrating frequency. In this way, great sensitivity to spectral variations can be achieved.

The chief advantage of wavelength modulation lies in its ease of interpretation; the resulting spectrum is rigorously the derivative of the reflectivity spectrum. In fact, some workers have bypassed direct modulation altogether. They have achieved a "modulation" spectrum by measuring the reflectivity spectrum directly and numerically differentiating it. While it would appear that such a procedure does not have the noise rejection feature of phase sensitive detection, it is nonetheless very effective. First, the noise rejection feature of wavelength modulation is not required provided care is taken in the construction of the spectrometer. Second, the modulation feature itself can in any case reduce the incident photon flux and introduce noise into the system. Third, data handling techniques via computational devices can be extremely effective in noise removal and in taking numerical derivatives of the spectra.

The principal disadvantage of wavelength modulation is that such a technique can yield structure in the spectrum from the source, monochromator, detector, and the sample. However, systematic errors can be eliminated by interchanging the sample with a reference specimen which differs in a small but systematic way from the original. This procedure is called compositional modulation. Another concern with wavelength modulation relates to the light source. If R is the reflectivity coefficient, I_0 the incident photon intensity, and I the reflected intensity, then we have

$$\frac{dR}{d\omega} = \frac{1}{I_0}\left(\frac{dI}{d\omega} - \frac{I}{I_0}\frac{dI_0}{d\omega}\right) \quad . \tag{6.4}$$

If our light source is highly structured, then $dR/d\omega$ is not simply related to the sample signal $dI/d\omega$ but also contains contributions from structure in

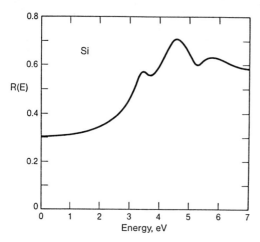

Fig. 6.2. Reflectivity spectrum for Si [6.9]

the source $dI_0/d\omega$. This is a problem, but it can be eliminated by the use of synchrotron radiation.

In Fig. 6.2, we display the reflectivity spectrum for silicon as measured by *Philipp* and *Ehrenreich* [6.9]. The spectrum is not overwhelming with respect to structure; three broad peaks occur between aproximately 3 and 6 eV. however, if we examine the wavelength modulation spectrum for Si [6.10] presented in Fig. 6.3, the spectrum is considerably enriched. This enhancement of structure is not limited to wavelength modulation; other forms of modulation spectroscopy would yield similar spectra for Si.

Some work on semiconductors with wavelength modulation is reported in [6.10, 11].

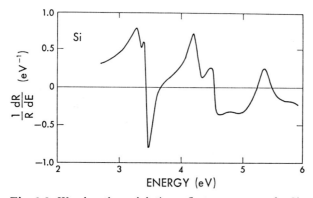

Fig. 6.3. Wavelength modulation reflectance spectra for Si measured at 5 K [6.10]

6.1.2 Temperature Modulation

In this technique, the reflectivity of the sample is measured at a series of neighboring temperatures, T and $T + \Delta T$. Hence, one measures a ΔR of

$$\Delta R = R(T + \Delta T) - R(T) \quad , \tag{6.5}$$

and in the limit of $\Delta T \to 0$, we obtain a spectrum which corresponds to dR/dT. The effect of temperature on the band structure of a solid can be decomposed into a dilation effect and a phonon population effect. With respect to dilation, we can interpret this change with temperature simply as a change in the lattice constant. In this sense, temperature dilation is closely related to a change induced by hydrostatic stress. The effect of phonon population change is not so easily interpreted. Changes in phonon occupation can result in a broadening of the reflectivity spectrum, a shift in the energy bands, and a change in exciton lifetimes. The role of temperature on the band structure itself has been examined (for example, see [6.12, 13]).

For many systems, the principal effect of temperature modulation is simply to change the size of the energy gaps. In this case, the modulation spectrum does not deviate too far from a simple derivative spectrum, and interpretation is straightforward. Another advantage of temperature modulations is that it can yield a strong signal compared to other techniques. Also, it can be used as a modulation tool where other techniques cannot be applied; for example, it can be used to study metals where electric field modulation cannot be employed. On the negative side, temperature modulation can be difficult to achieve. Typical modulation modes involve heating the sample by an intense light source or passing an electric current through the sample. In either case, the technique is a low frequency one; this presents problems for phase sensitive detection.

An example of a temperature-modulated spectrum for Si [6.14] is presented in Fig. 6.4. We may compare this spectrum with the wavelength modulation spectrum of Fig. 6.3. Overall, they are quite similar, and it is possible to identify common structure in both. However, the line shapes are notably different in the 4–5 eV region. The line shape difference in this

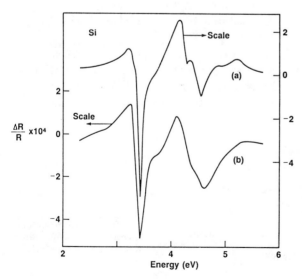

Fig. 6.4. Thermoreflectance spectrum of silicon at (*a*) liquid nitrogen temperature and (*b*) room temperature [6.14]

energy region suggests that the effect of temperature in the 4–5 eV region is not simply to alter the band gaps in a rigid fashion.

Examples of optical spectra obtained for semiconductors can be found in [6.15, 16].

6.1.3 Stress Modulation

Stress modulation can be of two types: hydrostatic or uniaxial. Hydrostatic modulation techniques are infrequently used. Since a hydrostatic stress preserves the symmetry of the crystal of interest, the resulting modulation spectrum resembles those obtained by wavelength modulation or temperature modulation. Hence, little new information is gained in the hydrostatic mode. Uniaxial stress modulation is of greater interest as it can be used selectively to reduce the symmetry. By examining spectra obtained under different stress directions, it is often possible to ascertain the origin and symmetry of critical points in the Brillouin zone. Analyses of stress modulations are usually peformed by means of tensorial algebra. In general, one can express the change in the dielectric tensor in terms of electro-optic and strain tensors. Most of the stress work has been performed on cubic materials; in this case, one can make extensive use of symmetry [6.4].

Several methods have been used to apply modulated stress to crystal samples. Most methods incorporate the use of an electromechanical transducer such as quartz. The modulating frequencies with piezoelectric transducers can be quite high, for example, above 100 kHz. At such frequencies, it may be difficult to avoid spurious signals by the vibrating sample. Special attention must be paid to ensure a very smooth, flat reflecting surface. In most contemporary studies, stress is applied as a static perturbation while a secondary technique, for example, wavelength modulation, is employed. This procedure is frequently necessitated because only small changes are induces in energy bands by the stress.

Figure 6.5 illustrates a typical piezoreflectance spectrum for germanium [6.17] . The general features of the spectrum are in good accord with other techniques such as wavelength modulation or electroreflectance. Examples of stress modulation spectroscopy and related topics may be found in [6.18–21].

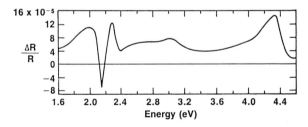

Fig. 6.5. Piezoreflectance spectrum for germanium at room temperature [6.17]

6.1.4 Electric Field Modulation

Because of the highly structured, sharp spectra which electric field modulation produces, it has become one of the most popular modulation techniques. The method employs an alternating electric field either parallel or perpendicular to the reflecting surface of the sample. Several configurations exist for producing the modulating field; some of these include immersing the sample in an electrolytic field or coating the sample with a transparent or semitransparent metallic film which serves as an electrode.

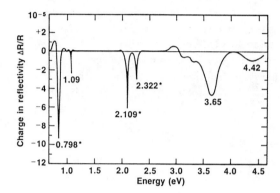

Fig. 6.6. Electroreflectance spectrum for germanium [6.22]. For the three peaks marked with an asterix, multiply the scale by ten

Figure 6.6 illustrates one of the first electroreflectance spectra [6.22]. The sharpness of this spectrum should be contrasted with the piezoreflectance spectrum of Fig. 6.5. Although electric field modulated spectra are sharp, they may be difficult to interpret. The complexity involved in understanding these spectra stems from the application of a nonperiodic perturbation, the electric field, to a periodic system. In particular, an electric field destroys the translational invariance along the direction of the applied field and invalidates Bloch's theorem along that direction. This loss of periodicity is the principal reason for the difficulty of constructing a simplified theory of electric field modulation; however, *Aspnes* [6.23] has demonstrated that under certain conditions using low values of the modulating electric field, the spectrum is drastically simplified. Specifically, the spectra can be related to the third derivative of the unperturbed dielectric function, and as a consequence, the measurements provide a powerful way of resolving closely spaced critical-point structures. Aspnes' analysis may be contrasted with the usual interpretation of electric field modulation. For higher fields, the spectra is not simply related to the zero field optical constants but involves a complicated convolution expression [6.4]. Experimentally, the high electric field range is recognized by a complicated dependence of the line shape on electric field, by oscillations in the spectrum, and by an exponential dependence of the fundamental adsorption edge.

In the low field limit, strong localization of structure in the spectrum occurs, and we can confine our discussion to the immediate vicinity of a critical point. In this limit, the bands may be described by a parabolic dispersion approximation, and the modulated dielectric function is given by

$$\Delta\varepsilon = \text{const.} \times i^{l-3}E^2(\omega - \omega_{cp} + i\Gamma)^{-5/2} \tag{6.6}$$

where l is the order of the critical point, E is the electric field, and Γ is a broadening parameter. The constant factor depends on band parameters and dipole matrix elements but is not a function of the electric field or an explicit function of the energy. Full expressions for one-, two-, and three-dimensional bands have been given by *Aspnes* [6.24]. The chief strength of these expressions is that the energy location of the critical point is given by ω_{cp} and the line width by Γ; the electric field plays a role in determining the amplitudes, but it has no influence in altering the line shape or in shifting the energy of the critical point. Hence, we may determine the critical-point energy and the line width without requiring the value of the electric field (except, of course, to know that the low field limit holds).

Experiments using the low field technique have accurately determined critical-point positions for several semiconductors to an accuracy exceeding that available with wavelength modulation (for example, see [6.25]). The

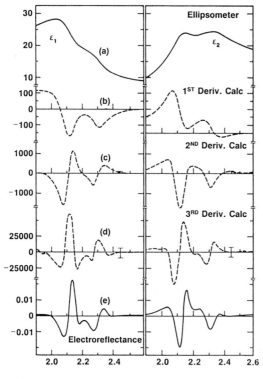

Fig. 6.7. (*a*) Ellipsometric data for the real and imaginary parts of the dielectric function for germanium. (*b–d*) Numerical derivatives of the experimental data; experimental uncertainties are indicated in (*d*). (*e*) Experimental electric field induced $\Delta\varepsilon$ from electroreflectance measurements [6.24]

only real deficiency of this method is one of materials fabrication. In its present form, the technique employs a Schottky barrier configuration which is difficult to achieve for some semiconductors.

Figure 6.7 illustrates the sensitivity and power of low electric field modulation [6.24]. The unmodulated dielectric function for germanium displayed in the figure is a typical solid state spectrum: a broad, slowly undulating curve. The dielectric function in Fig. 6.7 has been measured by ellipsometry techniques. (Ellipsometry methods can be used to measure directly the real and imaginary parts of the dielectric function with polarized light. Contemporary ellipsometric studies for interfaces have been carried out by *Theeten* and *Aspnes* [6.26]). To enhance structure in this curve, we numerically differentiate the dielectric function several times. The calculated third derivative of the dielectric function bears an indisputable resemblance to the low field electroreflectance spectrum. This figure is dramatic; it illustrates both the power of differentiating the spectrum to enhance structure and the utility of low field electroreflectance. We emphasize that in Fig. 6.7 the low field electroreflectance is a more accurate representation of the third derivative than the calculated curve owing to the introduction of noise in any numerical differentiation.

Examples of electric field modulation applied to semiconductors include [6.25–29].

6.1.5 Other Modulation Methods

While the techniques of wavelength modulation, thermoreflectance, piezoreflectance, and electroreflectance have dominated modulation spectroscopies, other methods have also been developed. For example, the application of a strong magnetic field to be a solid can result in dramatic changes in the optical spectrum. Specifically, oscillations resulting from Landau quantization can occur near critical points. Studies of magnetic field induced oscillations have yielded very accurate values of energy gaps, effective masses, and g-factors [6.30, 31]. Modulation of optical spectra with magnetic fields is possible.

The modulation technique of photoreflectance employs two incident photon beams [6.32]. One very intense beam is used to modulate the optical constants; the other beam is swept over photon energy to record the modulated spectrum. A possible interpretation of photoreflectance has been proposed by *Nahory* and *Shay* [6.33]. They have postulated that the modulating beam alters the built-in surface electric field. A modulation of this field is accomplished by neutralization of the surface space charge via free carriers created by an intense light beam. In this interpretation, photoreflectance is simply an electroreflectance technique in which the alternatinig electric field is internal. Photoreflectance does possess a few advantages over electroreflectance; for example, no electrodes need be attached to the sample. However, the technique does not produce as strong a signal as does electroreflectance, and it is not easier to interpret.

Other modulation schemes can be obtained through combination. For example, we can combine stress modulation with electric field modulation to produce a piezoelectroreflectance spectrum. Another possibility is to combine magnetic and electric field to produce a magnetoelectroreflectance spectrum. While these combinations or others may provide us with enriched spectra, the price paid is that the resulting spectra may be difficult to interpret.

6.2 High Energy Reflectivity Measurements

Traditionally, optical work has been performed with low energy photons (1–10 eV) and has served to probe transitions between occupied valence bands and empty conduction bands. The advent of high energy photon sources with synchrotron radiation has opened up another area of study: transitions from core states to conduction band states. Because of the highly localized nature of core states, core levels have essentially no dispersion. Hence, reflectivity measurements can measure conduction band parameters directly; that is, all critical-point structure must reside within the conduction band configuration. Another advantage of core to conduction band transition measurements is that a specific angular momentum component can be associated with the core state. Provided dipole selection rules are obeyed, we can effectively sample the angular momentum character of the conduction bands by core to conduction band transitions.

Before making an analysis of core state to conduction state transitions, we need to consider the possibility of core excitonic effects. Evidence for a core exciton effect comes from a comparison of photoemission data with reflectivity data [6.34, 35]. Photoemission can be used to determine directly the core level energy relative to the valence band maximum energy without the need to consider core excitons. The key to the validity of this assertion is to recognize that final state interactions are identical for photoelectrons arising from either the core or valence band states; the photoelectrons are completely removed from the crystal in both cases. Thus, if we measure the energy of the photoelectron emitted from the core level and the energy of the photoelectron emitted from the valence band maximum, then we can safely take energy differences without bothering to contemplate any core excitonic corrections. Since accurate values for valence band maxima to conduction band minimum exist from a variety of measurements, we can predict the core level to conduction band minimum energy difference (once we are given the "core-valence band maximum" energy). This energy difference can also be determined from a reflectivity measurement. Any discrepancy between the photoemission predicted threshold and the reflectivity measured threshold is

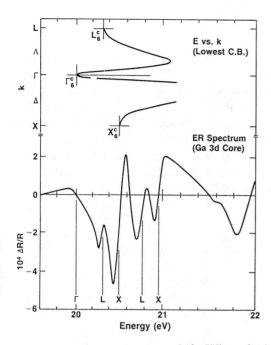

Fig. 6.8. Fine structure in the electroreflectance spectrum for GaAs. Assignment to conduction band minima is indicated [6.36]

indicative of a core exciton shift. When the initial core state is the outermost d-shell on the cation, the size of the core exciton is found to be of the order of 0.1 eV for III-V semiconductors [6.34].

In Fig. 6.8, an electroreflectance spectrum for core to conduction band transitions is displayed for the semiconductor GaAs [6.36]. The implementation of high energy reflectivity measurements has resulted in a better understanding of the conduction band minima ordering in this material. The band ordering of GaAs was thought for a number of years to be $\Gamma_6^c - X_6^c - L_6^c$; however, the study of high energy electroreflectance showed that the correct ordering is $\Gamma_6^c - L_6^c - X_6^c$ [6.36] in agreement with early EPM predictions [6.37]. The ordering of the bands is of crucial importance for explaining the Gunn effect [6.38]. In the past, the Gunn effect had been interpreted in terms of coupling between the two conduction band minima Γ_6^c and X_6^c, but now the coupling is understood to occur between Γ_6^c and L_6^c.

6.3 Photoemission Spectra of Semiconductors

The most powerful expermental tools for probing the electronic structure of solids are to be found in the area of photoelectron spectroscopy. As evidence for such a sweeping statement, one can point to the increasing popularity of photoemission work as contrasted with reflectivity work. The chief reason for the widespread use of photoemission techniques is that, unlike reflectance measurements, photoemission spectra can yield information on the absolute energy placement of an energy band. The distinction between relative and absolute energies is fundamental in band structure studies. For example, given a discrepancy between a calculated and a measured reflectivity spectrum, where does the root of the problem lie? Presented with reflectivity data alone, the conduction band, valence band, or both could be incorrectly placed. However, with photoemission methods, it is possible to examine independently the conduction bands and the valence bands and determine their absolute energy positions. It is even possible, in some cases, to measure directly the dispersion relations of energy bands. A dramatic illustration of photoemission-derived dispersion relations [6.39] is indicated in Fig. 6.9. Here, an experimental band structure extracted from photoemission work is compared to a state-of-the-art pseudopotential calculation for the energy bands of GaAs.

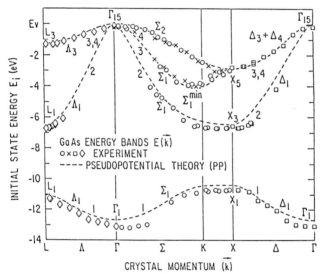

Fig. 6.9. Valence bands for GaAs as determined from angle-resolved photoemission and from pseudopotential theory [6.39]

Another key feature of photoemission is its sensitivity to surface characteristics, either extrinsic or intrinsic in nature. In semiconductors, the penetration depth for a photon at photoemission energy, for example, 10–1000 eV, is at least several dozens of interatomic layers. However, for an electron in the same energy region, the penetration depth, depending on the material, may be as short as one or two interatomic layers. As a consequence, photoelectrons which escape from the crystal carry information related to the crystal surface and to the immediate subsurface region. By carefully tuning the incident radiation, it is possible to alter systematically the escape depth of an electron and to emphasize either bulk or surface spectral features. The surface aspect of photoemission has made this tool preeminent in the experimental study of surface electronic structure. Of course, the surface-sensitive aspect of photoemission can be a liability in the sense that the technique requires ultrahigh vacuum conditions and surfaces free of contamination: reflectivity measurements are more forgiving.

Two principally technical developments have aided photoemission measurements immeasurably. The first is the now almost routine production of ultrahigh vacuum conditions, and the second development, revolutionary in nature, is the implementation of synchrotron radiation as a light source. While the use of synchrotron radiation is not limited in its appliation to photoemission, within the framework of solid state physics, it has had its largest impact here.

The properties of synchrotron radiation are ideally suited for spectroscopic studies. The most crucial asset of synchrotron radiation is the continuous spectrum it provides. The energy range of this spectrum extends from the infrared to the x-ray region. No other light source is so well suited for spectroscopy; for example, discharge lamps are plagued with minimal or no emission in some regions and have highly structured emission in other regions. Another desirable feature of synchrotron radiation is that it is highly collimated in the direction of the electron's flight and linearly polarized in the plane of the orbiting electron. Figure 6.10 illustrates the characteristics of synchrotron radiation. In other respects, the synchrotron provides a well-defined, clean, stable light source. The only possible drawback of synchrotron radiation is its relative inaccessibility. Obviously, a source of synchrotron radiation is not as portable or as economical as, for example, a He lamp.

Photoemission techniques can be classified according to the manner in which the energy and momentum of the incident photon and the ejected

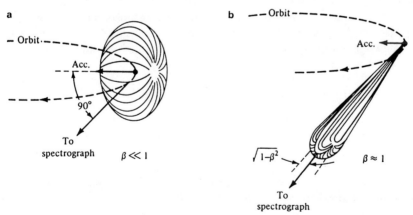

Fig. 6.10. Angular distribution of synchrotron radiation for a nonrelativistic electron (*a*) and for a relativistic electron (*b*). The dipole pattern of the nonrelativistic electrons becomes distorted into a narrow cone as the electron becomes relativistic. The cone is directed along the instantaneous velocity of the relativistic electron [6.46] ($\beta = v/c$)

photoelectron are controlled. We will view the various techniques within the framework of the three-step model of photoemission [6.40]. This model is not the most definitive one for photoemission; however, it is one of the most physical. The first step of this model is the absorption of a photon by a process which corresponds to a bulk excitation. The second step of the model involves the propagation of the excited electron to the surface, and the third step is its escape through the crystalline surface. Owing to the bulk nature of the first step, we have several constraints on the photoemissive process. these constraints are identical to those involved in optical excitations. The initial and final wavevectors are identical so that we have a direct transition. The probability for an excitation to occur beween two bands is dictated by dipole matrix elements, and of course energy must be conserved in the process. The combination of these conditions allows us to write down an expression for the number of photoelectrons ejected with a specific energy for a given incident photon energy:

$$\eta(E_{\mathrm{kin}}, \hbar\omega) = \mathrm{const.} \times \sum_{\mathbf{k},i,f} P_{if}(\mathbf{k})\delta(E_f(\mathbf{k}) - E_i(\mathbf{k}) - \hbar\omega)$$

$$\times \delta(E_f(\mathbf{k}) - E_{\mathrm{kin}} + E_v) \tag{6.7}$$

where $\hbar\omega$ is the photon energy, E_{kin} is the kinetic energy of the photoelectron, E_v is the vacuum level, E_i is the energy of the initial state, and E_f is the energy of the final state. $P_{if}(\mathbf{k})$ is the dipole matrix element between initial and final state. The first delta function in (6.7) ensures energy conservation in the first step corresponding to a bulk exciation; the second delta function imposes energy conservation in the third step corresponding to the electron's escape through the crystalline surface.

Under certain assumptions (6.7) reduces to an extremely useful form. Consider the assumptions of constant matrix elements independent of $\mathbf{k}$ and of flat valence (or conduction) bands or nonconservation of $\mathbf{k}$. The former assumption is usually valid. The latter assumption is usually not; we will give the appropriate disclaimer when it fails to hold. Under these additional approximations, we obtain

$$\eta(E_{\mathrm{kin}}, \hbar\omega) = \mathrm{const.} \times N_i(E_{\mathrm{kin}} - E_v - \hbar\omega)N_f(E_{\mathrm{kin}} - E_v) \tag{6.8}$$

where N_i is the density of states for the initial, occupied states and N_f is the density of states for the final, empty states. Most forms of photoemission sepctroscopy can be understood via (6.8) as detailed in subsequent sections.

6.3.1 X-Ray Photoemission Spectroscopy (XPS) and Ultraviolet Photoemission Spectroscopy (UPS)

The nomenclature for this form of photoemission spectroscopy is somewhat antiquated. Traditionally, XPS has employed an x-ray tube as a radiation source, and UPS has employed an ultraviolet lamp as a radiation source. With the advent of synchrotron radiation, however, the radiation source is no longer a useful criterion for distinguishing between the two methods.

With both XPS and UPS, the mode of operation is to fix the incident photon energy and to measure, as a function of energy, the number of emitted photoelectrons. Hence, the use of synchrotron radiation is not mandatory; it can, however, facilitate the implementation of the two techniques. For example, spectra can be easily obtained with synchrotron radiation at regular frequency intervals. This stepping procedure allows us to pass from spectra emphasizing bulk properties to spectra emphasizing surface properties (or vice versa). With other radiation source, the attainment of uniform photon energy intervals may not be possible.

At high photon energies, photoemission spectra are fairly easy to interpret. From an operational point of view, they appear to replicate the valence band density of states. In a more formal sense, if the photon wavevector is not insignificant compared to a reciprocal lattice vector, which may be the case at large photon energies, then k-conservation still holds, but the transitions involved are not direct. If the transitions are indirect, we effectively average over the final states in (6.7). Moreover, at large photon energies, the final states tend to be plane-wave-like and usually do not contribute to a structured spectrum. In this sense, (6.8) becomes valid. Moreover, we may omit the final density of states from consideration:

$$\eta(E_{\text{kin}}, \hbar\omega) \cong \text{const.} \times N_{\text{i}}(E_{\text{kin}} - E_{\text{v}} - \hbar\omega) \quad . \tag{6.9}$$

By a judicious choice of $\hbar\omega$ and via an analysis of N_{i}, we obtain almost a direct replica of the valence band density of states [6.41, 42].

In general, XPS and UPS produce energy distribution curves (EDC's). The study of these curves is the oldest endeavor of photoemission, and many spectral features of EDC's are well understood. For example, at low photon energies, $\hbar\omega \lesssim 15\,\text{eV}$, EDC's are highly structured. This structure arises from joint density of state effects, that is, both initial and final states play an important role. The highly structured nature of low energy EDC's can provide a stringent test of band structure calculations. Other "understood" features of EDC's involve matrix element effects and penetration depth changes. The matrix element changes are, perhaps, the most interesting. Consider the spectral changes as we progress from low energy to high energy excitations. At low energies, the transitions occur between upper valence bands and lower conduction bands. Strong matrix element effects can occur here. In semiconductors, the initial and final states near the band gap are usually well defined with respect to orbital character, and spectral features may be enhanced or suppressed depending on the size of the dipole matrix element between valence and conduction states. At higher energies, sum rules for the dipole matrix elements demand that the size of the matrix element between initial and final states decreases. As a consequence, with higher energy photons, the spectral features begin to resemble a simple joint density of states.

For representative papers on EDC analysis, see [6.43–45].

6.3.2 Constant Final State and Constant Initial State Spectroscopies

In constant final state (CFS) spectroscopy, the energy analyzer is set to a specific energy E_{kin}, and the incident photon energy $\hbar\omega$ is swept. Under the approximations which led to (6.8), this mode of operation should provide photoemission spectra which are a direct measure of the initial density of states. The scheme is illustrated (after [6.46]) in Fig. 6.11. Since XPS or UPS can also yield a measure of the initial density of states, the strength of CFS spectroscopy lies not in obtaining the initial state density per se but rather in obtaining a measure of surface sensitivity. To illustrate the surface aspect of CFS, recall that the escape depth of a photoelectron is a strong function of its kinetic energy. Hence, once we fix the kinetic energy, we detect electrons emitted from a specific surface region. By choosing different kinetic energy regions and measuring constant final state spectra, we can observe change in the initial state density as we probe closer to or farther from the crystalline surface. Examples of the principles involved in constant final state spectroscopy may be found in [6.47–49].

In constant initial states (CIS) spectroscopy, the photon energy $\hbar\omega$ and the electron kinetic energy E_{kin} are varied simultaneously so that $E_{kin} - \hbar\omega = $ constant. Under the conditions of (6.8) we see that in this mode of operation a direct measure of the final state density is obtained. CIS spectra

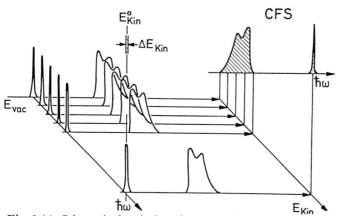

Fig. 6.11. Schematic description of constant final state spectroscopy. The CFS spectra are generated by a series of energy distribution curves at different photon energy $\hbar\omega$. The photoelectron's kinetic energy is held fixed while the photon energy is varied. The resulting CFS spectrum is indicated in the upper right hand corner of the figure [6.46]

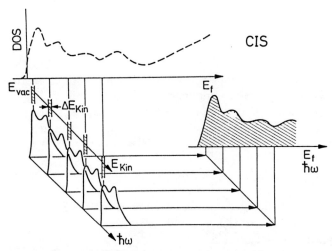

Fig. 6.12. Schematic description of constant initial state (CIS) spectroscopy. The energy interval which accepts electrons from a fixed interval is shifted synchronously with the photon energy $\hbar\omega$. The final state density of states represented by the dashed curve in the upper part of the figure is reproduced in the CIS spectrum as indicated in the right hand part of the figure [6.46]

are particularly useful in that we can probe, in a direct fashion, unoccupied states. The CIS technique is illustrated [6.46] in Fig. 6.12.

We note that, in principle, all the information in a constant initial state spectrum is contained in a family of energy distribution curves measured at closely spaced photon energies. However, in practice, detailed amplitude differences in adjacent EDC's are difficult to interpret.

6.3.3 Angle-Resolved Photoemission Spectroscopy

All the photoemission techniques discussed up to this point are angle-integrated methods, that is, the directions of the incident photon and of the ejected photoelectron are not considered. However, a major area of photo-electron spectroscopy is devoted to angle-resolved measurements. In angle-resolved photoemission, we concentrate on the third step of the three-step photoemission model. Suppose we measure the direction and energy of an ejected photoelectron, that is, we determine the photoelectron wavevector K. Wavevector conservation at the surface breaks down in the perpendicular direction since no periodicity exists in this direction. However, parallel to the surface, the periodicity remains and wavevector conservation still holds. The conservation rule may be written as

$$K_{\|} = k_{\|} + G_{\|} \tag{6.10}$$

where $K_{\|}$ is the parallel component of the external electron wavevector,

$k_\parallel$ is the parallel component of the bulk electron's wavevector, and $G_\parallel$ is the parallel component of a reciprocal lattice vector. We may interpret the need to consider reciprocal lattice vectors as a consequence of the Bloch form of the wavefunctions for bulk states [6.50]. Each electron within the crystal can be pictured as being composed of plane wave contributions of the form $\exp[i(k + G) \cdot r)]$. For each component, we have the possibility of matching the bulk wave to a free electron or photoelectron wave. Thus, the photoelectron can emerge the crystal in a number of possible directions.

If we invoke conservation of energy at the surface, we have

$$E_{\text{kin}} = E_f(k) - E_v \tag{6.11}$$

and we may combine (6.10) and (6.11) to find an expression for $K_\perp$:

$$\frac{\hbar^2 K_\perp^2}{2m} = E_f(k) - E_v - \hbar^2 \frac{(k_\parallel + G_\parallel)^2}{2m} \quad . \tag{6.12}$$

Using (6.10–12) and provided we have certain pieces of information (an accurate band structure, the vacuum level, matrix elements, etc.), we can calculate the directions of photoelectrons generated by a bulk transition. As such, this is fine, but it would be better if we could invert the problem. Given a distribution of energies and directions of photoelectrons for a specific incident photon, we would like to deduce directly an energy band structure. Unfortunately, we cannot proceed along these lines because the perpendicular component of the bulk electron wavevector $k_\perp$ has appeared nowhere in the discussion.

A similar predicament faced us in analyzing reflectivity spectra. If we are given a band structure calculation, then we can produce a calculated reflectivity spectrum. The inverse situation is not so easy; given a reflectivity spectrum, we cannot directly map out the energy bands. While things may appear bleak, they are not desperate; there are a number of special circumstances in which the problem of an indeterminant $k_\perp$ is eliminated or considerably reduced [6.50]. We briefly enumerate some special cases:

(1) Layered compounds. This class of materials includes III-VI semiconductors such as GaSe. For these materials, the dispersion of the energy bands with $k_\perp$ is expected to be small. If the energy bands depend only on $k_\parallel$, then the indeterminancy of $k_\perp$ becomes irrelevant to the problem.

(2) Normal emission. For photoelectrons emitted normal to the crystalline surface, we have $k_\parallel = 0$. This condition considerably simplifies the discussion as we are confined to sampling bulk states as a function of $k_\perp$ along a specific line in k space.

(3) Angle-resolved constant final state spectroscopy. In this mode of operation, E_{kin} and the direction of emission are fixed and $\hbar\omega$ is swept. Thus $k_\parallel$ is fixed and, under suitable conditions, it is possible to sample the band structure as a function of $k_\perp$ just as in the normal emission case.

(4) Two different crystal faces. Another approach to the $k_\perp$ problem has been suggested by *Turtle* and *Calcott* [6.51]. The central feature of their technique is to perform measurements on two crystal faces of the same material. If we can identify spectral features corresponding to the same bulk optical transitions, we have two values for $k_\parallel$, and we may arrive at a unique value for $k_\perp$.

6.3.4 Photoelectron Yield Spectroscopy

In photoelectron yield spectroscopy, we collect all the electrons above the photoemission threshold. From (6.7), we can obtain the yield by integrating $\eta(E_{\text{kin}}; \hbar\omega)$ over all E_{kin}. This, in fact, is not a bad approximation except that it ignores photoelectrons arising from secondary processes, for example, Auger electrons. Secondary processes lead to an accumulation of electrons at low kinetic energy and may dominate the yield function. In its simplest form, we may write the yield as

$$Y(\omega) = \text{const.} \times F(\omega)\mu(\omega) \qquad (6.13)$$

where $F(\omega)$ is a smooth function of ω and $\mu(\omega)$ is the optical absorption coefficient. Since the structure in $Y(\omega)$ arises from $\mu(\omega)$ (over most of the spectrum), Y and μ are simply proportional to each other [6.52].

A more recent technique based on photoelectron yield spectroscopy is partial yield spectroscopy. In partial yield, not all the electrons are collected: only those above a specific energy threshold or those within a specific energy window. The method has a reduced signal level compared to an integrated yield signal, but the energy selection allows one to vary the probe depth. One very profitable use of partial yield spectroscopy has been the study of semiconductor surface states. In this mode, the partial yield spectroscopy technique resembles a constant finial state mode; the electron analyzer is fixed at a specific E_{kin} and $\hbar\omega$ is swept. By a judicious choice of E_{kin}, only secondary electrons are measured. *Eastman* and *Feeouf* [6.49] proceeded in this fashion to examine intrinsic unoccupied surface states for Ge and GaAs. One possible complication with this technique is a sizeable excitonic effect involving an interaction between an electron in a surface state and a hole in a core state.

6.4 Electron Energy Loss Spectroscopy for Semiconductors

Although photons are the major probes for determining the dielectric response function of a solid, electron beams may also serve as probes. The availability of a probe unrelated to photon spectroscopy is valuable for confirming the interpretations using photons. Also, electron probes have a few advantages over photon-based spectroscopy. Electrons can compete with photons in the UV or far UV energy region. For operations in this energy region, photon monochromators are difficult to construct, and the sample response to photon probes can be extremely sensitive to surface preparation. In contrast, electron-based studies are well suited for the UV region and do not suffer these problems. Furthermore, with electron probes we can obtain a direct measure of the imaginary part of dielectric function without resorting to Kramers-Kronig transformations. Reviews on electron energy loss spectroscopy are given in [6.53–55].

6.4.1 Plasmon Excitations in Solids

It is possible for an electron passing through a solid to excite quantized collective longitudinal oscillations of the electron gas, that is, plasmons. The process is best known in simple metals where a Drude analysis works quite well. Plasmon oscillations occur when the dielectric function passes through a zero; at this point, longitudinal oscillations can be created. Given a free-electron gas, $\varepsilon = 1 - 4\pi ne^2/m\omega^2$ (n is the electron density), the plasma frequency is $\omega_\mathrm{p}^2 = 4\pi ne^2/m$. Plasmon excitations are easily observed by transmitting an electron through or by reflecting an electron from a thin film. The energy loss of the electron will exhibit characteristic quantized plasmon losses. It is also possible to excite plasmons in semiconductors. The valence electrons play the role of the free-electron gas and oscillate with respect to the fixed ion cores.

To obtain a quantitative description of the electron energy loss spectrum, we may resort to dielectric response theory [6.53]. If the initial energy of the electron is E_0, the probability it will suffer an energy loss ΔE and be scattered through an angle θ relative to the normally incident primary beam is given by

$$P(\Delta E, \theta) = \left(\frac{e}{\pi \hbar}\right)^2 \frac{mL}{2E_0} \frac{1}{\theta^2 + (\Delta E/2E_0)^2} \mathrm{Im}\left(-\frac{1}{\varepsilon}\right) \qquad (6.14)$$

where L is the thickness of the specimen. Equation (6.14) is valid only for small scattering angles and for $\Delta E \ll E_0$.

With (6.14) and energy loss data, we can obtain a direct measure of $-\mathrm{Im}(1/\varepsilon)$. However, before (6.14) can be implemented, several factors need to be considered. Electrons may suffer additional energy losses at the boundary of the film, that is, surface excitations. One way of eliminating this problem is to examine the angular dependence of the energy loss spectrum. Volume losses decreases in intensity as θ^{-2} whereas surface losses decrease in intensity as θ^{-3}. Another aspect to be considered is that under certain circumstances electrons may suffer energy loss via Cerenkov radiation [6.54, 55]. For example, in zinc-blende and diamond semiconductors, ε_2 can reach values of ~ 20 when $\Delta E \sim 5\,\text{eV}$. If we use an electron with incident energy $E_0 \sim 50\,\text{keV}$, then the condition for Cerenkov radiation is fulfilled, that is, the velocity of the electron ($v_0 = \sqrt{E_0/m} \sim 0.4c$) may exceed the Cerenkov velocity ($v_c = c/\sqrt{\varepsilon} \sim 0.4c$). The Cerenkov problem may be mitigated at higher scattering angles. One other possible problem is the invalidation of (6.14) by multiple loss processes. However, a detailed analysis indicates that only single and two-fold losses are significant; the latter are easily handled [6.53].

6.4.2 Experimental Measurements and Results

Energy loss functions are determined experimentally by the ratio of the number of electrons inelastically scattered to the number of electrons which have passed through the film with no energy loss. The required features of an energy loss spectrometer include an electron beam with a strong, well-collimated current and an analyzer capable of accurately determining the scattered electron's energy and direction.

Energy loss spectra for several III-V semiconductors are presented in Fig. 6.13. The structure in these spectra may be categorized into three distinct energy regions [6.9, 56]. For energy loss ΔE in the region below $10\,\text{eV}$, the structure in $-\text{Im}(1/\varepsilon)$ arises from optical-like interband transitions. The incident electron loses energy by scattering off a valence electron which is promoted into the conduction band. In the $10\text{--}20\,\text{eV}$ region, the value of $-\text{Im}(1/\varepsilon)$ is large. The dominate process in this region is plasmon excitation. In the third energy region above $20\,\text{eV}$, structure in $-\text{Im}(1/\varepsilon)$ is thought to arise from excitations in which the energy lost by the scattered electron is used to promote a core electron from the outermost d-shell of the cation to the lowest conduction band.

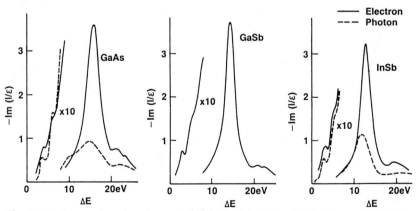

Fig. 6.13. Energy loss function $-\text{Im}(1/\varepsilon)$ for (a) GaAs, (b) GaSb, and (c) InSb. The electron loss results are from [6.56], and the optical measurements are from [6.9]

For low energies, the optical measurements and electron energy loss curves appear to be in good agreement; for higher energies, the magnitude of the optical measurements are factors of two or three times smaller. It has been proposed that the discrepancy in the magnitude is due to a feature of the optical data. It has been demonstrated that surface contaminants can reduce the response of optical measurements in this energy regime whereas they do not significantly affect the electron energy loss spectrum [6.53].

7. High Energy Probes of Semiconductors: X-Rays

For structural studies, the most useful probe of the solid state is the high energy photon. Only short wavelength photons can be used to determine the crystal structure of an ordered material, and it is not possible to give a full description of the electronic structure of a solid without some knowledge of the atomic coordinates. Fortunately, using computer automated x-ray probing devices, it is almost a routine task to obtain accurate crystal structure information. In fact, with new bright sources of x-rays, it may also become possible to obtain surface structural information. Another useful function of x-rays is to probe the valence charge density of a semiconductor. The experimental determination of valence charge densities is difficult but not impossible, and some very good data exist for diamond and zinc-blende semiconductors. Finally, x-rays can be used to monitor temperature effects by studying Debye-Waller factors.

7.1 Crystal Structure Determinations

Three traditional geometries exist for performing x-ray diffraction analyses: the Laue method, the rotating crystal method, and the powder method. The theoretical basis for understanding these traditional methods is simple Bragg theory [7.1]. In each case, the objective is to measure the pattern of diffraction spots obtained when the interlayer spacing, d, satisfies the condition of constructive interference, $2d \sin \theta = n\lambda$ where θ is the angle formed between the incident x-ray and a normal to the crystal and λ is the x-ray wavelength. In the Laue method, the x-ray source is not monochromatic, and the sample is held fixed. Since the x-ray wavelengths have a spread in energy, some interplanar spacings of the crystal may satisfy the diffraction condition. By studying the symmetry of the resulting patterns, it is now fairly routine to determine the crystal axes; such a determination is the primary use of the Laue method. In the rotating crystal method, a monochromatic x-ray source is used, and the crystal is rotated until the Bragg condition is met. Sophisticated versions of this method, with synchronous oscillations of the crystal and film to eliminate the possibility of overlapping reflections, have been very successful in obtaining highly accurate structural information. Finally, the powder method combines a fixed geometry, a monochromatic beam of x-rays and a finely powdered sample, or a polycrystalline sample. By employing a powdered or crystallite specimen, one obtains an averaging over all possible orientations. Crystal structure determinations are made by examining the resultant reflections. The advantage of this method is that it does not require a single crystal. For an elementary review of the traditional methods, the reader is referred to texts such as *Kittel* [7.2] or *Ashcroft* and *Mermin* [7.3]. The work by Buerger [7.4] summarizes modern techniques which use precession camera methods.

7.2 Charge Density Determinations Using X-Rays

Since the crystalline electronic charge density influences the intensity of diffracted x-rays in a well-defined fashion, in many cases x-rays can be used to probe directly the spatial distribution of electrons in condensed matter. In its simplest form, the intensity for a given Bragg reflection is proportional to the corresponding Fourier component of the charge density. By measuring the full intensity distribution, it is possible to obtain the Fourier coefficients of the crystalline charge density.

Even though the use of x-rays to measure charge densities would appear to be a most powerful tool, as indicated earlier, the situation is by no means easy. The changes encountered in the scattering factors in going from the atomic state to the crystalline state are often quite small. Consequently, the accuracy required for measuring these changes must be great. For example, *Batterman* et al. [7.5] find that the x-ray intensities measured for various metals such as copper, iron, and aluminum are within 1 % agreement with the x-ray intensities calculated from free atomic wavefunctions. Hence, just to distinguish between the atomic and crystalline environments, one must have a method with an accuracy considerably better than 1 %. Often the accuracy required exceeds that obtainable from contemporary methods of x-ray analysis.

With respect to the nature of the electronic distribution of charge in the solid state, the 1 % figure mentioned above is somewhat misleading. It does not imply that the cohesion involves minor changes in the outer shell electrons. The changes in intensity distributions come from both valence electrons and core electrons. The core electrons do not play a significant role in cohesion and are not strongly affected in passing from the atomic state to the crystalline state while the valence electrons can be significantly modified in passing from the atom to the solid. However, the core electrons may dominate the x-ray scattering factors and the large valence electron changes may have only a minor effect on the structure factors and can thus be hidden. The problem of extracting valence charge density changes can be less severe in lighter materials where the ratio of valence to core electrons is higher, and where the observed changes in scattering are thus larger.

It is also easier to observe the charge density effects of bonding in covalent materials than in metallic materials. For example, in the case of diamond, some of the measured scattering factors are completely inexplicable
if one imagines the crystalline charge density to consist of a superposition
of atomic densities. The chief example of this effect occurs for the Fourier
component corresponding to the reciprocal lattice vector: $(\frac{2\pi}{a})(2,2,2)$. The
structure factor for this component vanishes for a linear superposition of
atomic densities, and therefore the observed intensity for this component
should also vanish. Yet, the experimental study of *Gottlicher* and *Wolfel*
[7.6] clearly shows a nonvanishing component. This component arises from
extra charge piling up between the atoms and corresponds to the covalent
bond charge. In Fig. 7.1, we illustrate this bond charge for graphite using
experimental [7.7] and theoretical [7.8] plots of the valence electron charge
density.

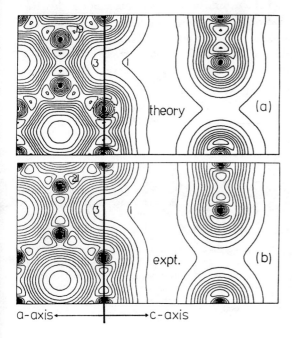

a-axis ←——————→ c-axis

Fig. 7.1. Valence charge densities for graphite. In (*a*) we
present the experimental density of graphite [7.7] and in (*b*)
we present the theoretical density [7.8]. Contours are in units
of 0.05 a.u.

For the experimental findings, some assumptions went into the model-
ing of the charge density. For example, x-rays only measure the intensity of
scattering factor and not the phase. Thus, in some cases it is not clear what
the sign of the charge density Fourier component should be. For most of the
components, this is not a serious problem as the sign for a particular component is assumed not to vary from the sign of the component constructed
by superposing atomic charge densities. To guide one's choice for the signs,
the charge density must meet certain constraints: the charge density must

be normalized, and it must be positive definite everywhere. In order to display the valence charge density, the core contributions are subtracted out by assuming a frozen core configuration. Again, this procedure is usually a good approximation.

In any event, the core regions of such maps are not believed to be very accurate. First, the theory is a "pseudo" density plot with the core density dependent on the pecularities of the pseudopotentials used. Second, the experimental numbers in this region are not reliable owing to difficulties associated with obtaining accurate high Fourier components of the charge. Finally, it is not trivial to correct the experimental plots for thermal vibrations and for inelastic scattering effects.

Nevertheless, the overall agreement between the theoretical and experimental charge density is quite good, and it supports the belief that one-electron approaches can be used to find the theoretical density accurately. One interesting feature of the graphitic charge density is the "double humped" bond charge configuration. This configuration, also observed in diamond, is peculiar to carbon bonding and is not found [7.9] in bonds formed in elemental silicon, germanium, or tin (Fig. 7.2). Some workers have speculated that this unusual bond charge configuration in carbon is indicative of its capacity to form multiple bonds.

Valence charge density (110 plane)

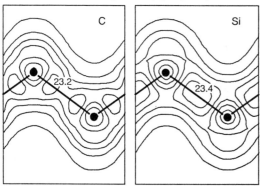

Fig. 7.2. Total valence-charge density plots in the (110) plane for diamond and Si. The charge density is in units of electrons per primitive cell. The contour step is 4. The axes are scaled to facilitate comparison; hence, the length scale is different in these two plots. The black dots denote the atomic positions. Straight lines are drawn to illustrate the atomic chains [7.9]

7.3 Temperature Dependence of X-Ray Reflections

A coherent theory of diffraction effects must account for the observed temperature effects on the scattering factors. Fortunately, it is straight forward to show that the scattering factors must be modified by an exponential temperature factor. In its simplest form, this factor takes the form

$$I(G) = I_0(G)\exp(-16\pi \sin^2 \theta \langle u \rangle^2 / 3\lambda^2) \tag{7.1}$$

where $I_0(G)$ is the intensity of the reflection at $T = 0\,\mathrm{K}$, θ is the scattering angle, λ is the x-ray wavelength and $\langle u \rangle$ is the mean square displacement of the scattering atom excluding the zero point motion which has been incorporated into $I_0(G)$. For most cases, it is sufficient to use (7.1) if the mean displacement follows a linear behavior at high temperatures. For low temperatures, it is difficult to calculate the temperature factors. In principle, the theory should include a knowledge of the phonon eigenfrequencies and the electronic eigenvalues. Thus, very few complete calculations exist [7.10].

For core-related scattering factors, a simple Debye-Waller factor will give credible results, however the "forbidden reflections" associated with bond charges cannot be described by a simple Debye-Waller factor. In Fig. 7.3, to illustrate the situation, we display the experimental results of *Roberto* et al. [7.11] for the behavior of the $(\frac{2\pi}{a})(2,2,2)$ scattering factor in Ge. This scattering factor corresponds to the bond charge component of the charge density in germanium. Also indicated is the predicted behavior of this scattering factor under the assumption of a Debye-Waller term characteristic of the core. The intensity of the scattering factor decreases faster than can be accounted for by the Debye-Waller term. If we associate a simple Debye-Waller factor with this bond charge related scattering factor, then the bond charge would have to oscillate with a larger amplitude than the ion cores. This is not a physically meaningful result.

We can achieve reasonable agreement between theory and experiment by assuming that the bond charge is altered with temperature. This was first suggested by Phillips [7.12]. He proposed that the bond charge scales inversely with the dielectric constant of the semiconductor. From the mea-

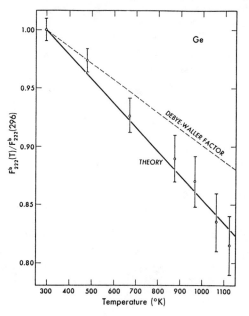

Fig. 7.3. Temperature dependence of the (222) x-ray scattering factor in germanium. The data points are from [7.11]. The solid line shows the temperature behavior as calculated from pseudopotentials with a Debye-Waller factor characteristic of a bonding charge [7.13]. The dotted line indicates the temperature dependence of the Debye-Waller factor for the ion cores

sured temperature behavior of the dielectric constant, we can predict the temperature dependence of the bond charge. This theory gives the correct trend but not the correct magnitude of change. *Chelikowsky* and *Cohen* [7.13] improved upon the theory of Phillips by recognizing that the Debye-Waller factor should be associated with the bond charge. To estimate the temperature depletion of the bond charge, they used the *Brooks-Yu* theory [7.14]. (Similar results would be obtained using Phillips' dielectric theory for the temperature dependence of the bond charge.) The theory of Chelikowsky and Cohen is in good agreement with the experimental results (Fig. 7.3); however, our general knowledge of temperature effects on valence charge densities is far from complete.

8. Diamond and Zinc-Blende Structure Semiconductors

In this chapter, we will concentrate on the tetravalent semiconductors. These materials are, in many ways, archtypical semiconductors. Owing to their elemental nature and their enormous technological value, our theoretical and experimental knowledge of these elements probably exceeds that for any other solid state material. For example, it is often stated that silicon is to solid state physics what the hydrogen atom is to atomic physics. Though clichés are often trivializing in nature, the comparison here is not. The amount of data for silicon is immense; almost every conceivable probe has been applied to silicon with a concurrent analysis of theoretical predictions. Most of the theoretical results given in this chapter are from [8.1].

8.1 Crystal Structure

We begin our survey of these materials by considering the nature of their structure. A ball and stick model of the diamond structure is given in Fig. 8.1. In Table 8.1, we present the relevant lattice constant data [8.2] for both diamond and zinc-blende semiconductors. We can understand the bonding of diamond-structure semiconductors by recourse to the atomic configuration of the tetravalent elements. All elements of this group have a valence configuration of s^2p^2. When bonds are formed, we view this process as the promotion of an s-electron to a p-state to form sp^3 hybrids. This ex-

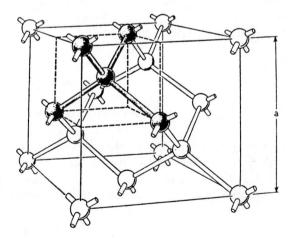

Fig. 8.1.
Diamond crystal structure indicating the tetrahedal coordination

Table 8.1. Lattice constants for diamond and zinc-blende semiconductors from [8.2]

	Crystal	a[Å]		Crystal	a[Å]
Diamond	C	3.567		CuBr	5.691
	Si	5.431		CuCl	5.406
	Ge	5.657		CuI	6.054
	α-Sn	6.491		GaAs	5.654
				GaP	5.451
Zinc-blende	AgI	6.473		GaSb	6.118
	AlAs	5.62		HgS	5.852
	AlP	5.451		HgSe	6.084
	AlSb	6.135		HgTe	6.429
	BAs	4.777		InAs	6.036
	BN	3.615		InP	5.869
	BP	4.538		InSb	6.478
	BeS	4.85		SiC	4.348
	BeSe	5.07		ZnO	4.63
	BeTe	5.54		ZnS	5.409
	CdS	5.818		ZnSe	5.668
	CdSe	6.05		ZnTe	6.089
	CdTe	6.480			

planation accounts for the nature of the bonding since sp^3 hybrid orbitals form tetrahedral bonding patterns which match the symmetry found in the diamond structure. Such hybridization arguments can provide a framework within which the important "metallicity" trend of the tetrahedral elemental compounds can be explained. Consider that carbon in the diamond structure has a rather large band gap and that this gap narrows from carbon to silicon to germanium to tin. For tin the gap vanishes identically, and for lead valence and conduction bands overlap; lead is a metal and does not occur in the diamond structure. We can view this progression as an indication of the energy increasing required to promote an atom from the ground state, $s^2 p^2$ configuration, to the bonding, sp^3, configuration as we descend column IV A of the periodic table.

8.2 The Electronic Structure of Silicon

The band structure of silicon has been calculated by a number of methods. For the most part, these calculations are in good accord. We will concentrate on results obtained from recent empirical pseudopotential work.

In Fig. 8.2, we display the band structure of silicon calculated with two different empirical pseudopotentials. One of the potentials is a simple local potential with three form factors as input; the other is a bit more sophisticated in that it is nonlocal and attempts to capture some of the energy dependence expected for this type of material. Overall, the potentials yield similar band structures. The chief difference resides in their treatment

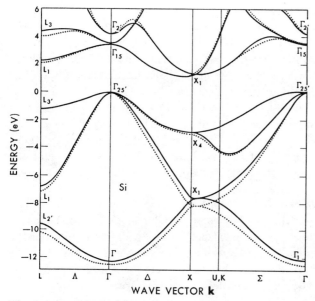

Fig. 8.2. Band structure of silicon. The valence band maximum is taken as the energy zero. Two pseudopotential calculations are illustrated. One is using a simple local potential (dotted line); one is using a nonlocal potential (solid line). The nonlocal potential more accurately reproduces properties of the lowest valence band than the local potential

of the lowest valence band. The nonlocal potential is in better accord with the placement of the lowest band; this is true by construction of the nonlocal term. In Table 8.2, we list the computed eigenvalues from the two different potentials.

The band structure of silicon is different in a fundamental way from other diamond or zinc-blende semiconductors: the ordering of the lowest

Table 8.2. Eigenvalues (in eV) at Γ, X, L high symmetry points for two model pseudopotentials for silicon. Spin-orbit interactions are not included

Point	Level	Local	Energy Dependent Non-local
Γ	Γ_1	−12.53	−12.36
	$\Gamma_{25'}$	0.00	0.00
	Γ_{15}	3.43	3.42
	$\Gamma_{2'}$	4.17	4.10
	Γ_1	8.60	7.69
	$\Gamma_{12'}$	7.82	8.19
X	X_1	−8.27	−7.69
	X_4	−2.99	−2.86
	X_1	1.22	1.17
L	L_2	−10.17	−9.55
	L_1	−7.24	−6.96
	$L_{3'}$	−1.22	−1.23
	L_1	2.15	2.23
	L_3	4.00	4.34

conduction bands of silicon is different from that of germanium or tin. Silicon has the Γ_{15} band lower than the $\Gamma_{2'}$ band. This difference was the source of some controversy in the early days of band calculations. For example, some workers claimed that the first pseudopotential calculations were in strong disagreement with less empirical methods for determining energy bands and with the available experimental data (e.g. see *Kunz* [8.3]). However, optical measurements of silicon-germanium alloys strongly suggested that silicon and germanium were different [8.4]. The issue was decided by the work of *Aspnes* and *Studna* [8.5]. They used low field electroreflectance to resolve transitions from $\Gamma_{25'}$ to $\Gamma_{2'}$ and showed unequivocally that the conduction band ordering is in complete agreement with the pseudopotential predictions.

Another feature of the silicon band structure, related to the lowest conduction band configuration, is the nearly parallel dispersion of the lowest conduction band and the uppermost valence band. Specifically, consider the dispersion along the Λ direction. *Grover* and *Handler* [8.6] proposed on the basis of their electroreflectance data that the critical point at L is essentially two dimensional, i.e., the experimentally measured transverse band mass nearly vanished. The value they obtained for m_t was approximately $0.02\,\mathrm{m}$. The corresponding mass calculated by pseudopotential methods is closer to $0.1\,\mathrm{m}$, but even this value results in a nearly two-dimensional M_0 critical point at the L point. Moreover, the dispersion for the valence and conduction bands is such that the energy difference between these bands is less than $0.01\,\mathrm{eV}$ over half the distance from L to Γ.

This valence-conduction band configuration favors excitonic behavior. It has been traditionally suggested that the rather large discrepancies between the theoretical and experimental optical constants in this energy range arise from such an effect. To illustrate the point, we have displayed the measured [8.7] and calculated imaginary part of the dielectric constant in Fig. 8.3. The measured dielectric function is nearly a factor of two larger near $3.4\,\mathrm{eV}$ than the calculated value for the energy region in question, i.e., the transition energy for the M_0 critical point at L. This discrepancy is also observed [8.7] in the real part of the dielectric function, which is displayed in Fig. 8.4.

We note that corrections to the *Ehrenreich-Cohen* [8.8] formalism which were used to compute the optical constants have been considered. One of the obvious corrections to their formalism is the inclusion of microscopic fields or local fields. Pseudopotential calculations have also been attempted using the formalisms of *Adler* and *Wiser* for the inclusion of local fields [8.9]. Unfortunately, the corrections for local fields do little to improve the dielectric function in this region as indicated in Fig. 8.3. Moreover, the work of *Hanke* and *Sham* [8.10] adds strength to the theory that excitonic effects are responsible for the observed discrepancies.

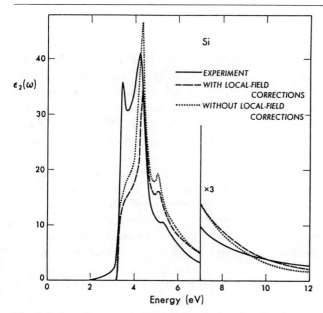

Fig. 8.3. Imaginary part of the dielectric function for silicon from pseudopotential calculations compared to experiment [8.7]. Two calculations are exhibited: with and without local field corrections. Note how local field corrections do not significantly alter the dielectric function near the E_1 structure at about 3 eV. It is thought that excitonic effects are responsible for the rather large discrepancy between theory and experiment in this energy region

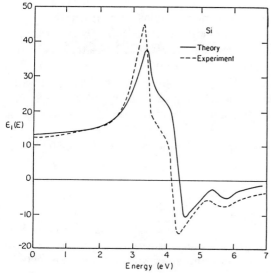

Fig. 8.4. Real part of the dielectric function of silicon. The experimental curve is from [8.7]

In Fig. 8.5, we exhibit the calculated and measured [8.7] reflectivity spectrum for silicon. As for most solid state spectra, this shows little structure, and on first inspection appears to contain little information. As mentioned in our previous discussion, such an assessment would be incorrect. In Fig. 8.6, we display the calculated and measured [8.11] logarithmic derivative of the reflectivity spectrum which yields not the three broad peaks of the undifferentiated spectrum but numerous sharp, spectral features. These features are classified according to a standard nomenclature. The lowest energy structural feature is denoted by E_0 and corresponds to structure from the smallest direct transition. The next higher energy structural feature is denoted by E_1. This feature denotes structure associated with the Λ direction. In the unique case of silicon, the E_0 and the E_1 structural features occur in the same energy region, i.e., the lowest energy direct transitions at L and at Γ have nearly the same energy. In fact, a good deal of work has been peformed to determine precisely where this transition takes place in the Brillouin zone. Piezoelectric experiments [8.12], chemical shifts in Ge-Si alloys [8.13], electroreflectance [8.14], and some wavelength-modulation techniques [8.15] have suggested that the first reflectivity peak arises near the zone center, perhaps along the Δ direction. However, other work [8.6] suggsted that this transition occurs along the Λ direction. Unfortuantely, the pseudopotential work has not resolved this issue since the reflectivity structure in question arises from contributions near Γ and along both the Λ and Δ directions. The dominant transition in the calculations appears to be along the Λ direction, but no firm conclusion can be drawn. What is clear, is that the complexity of this structure does suggest a multiplicity of critical points within this energy region. This conclusion has been drawn by several authors (e.g. [8.16]). The E_2 structure dominates the reflectivity spectrum and occurs at about 4.5 eV. This structure arises from large regions of the Brillouin zone, most notably around the special point $(\frac{2\pi}{a})(\frac{3}{4}, \frac{1}{4}, \frac{1}{4})$. The highest energy structure is denoted by E_1' and occurs near the L point and along the Λ direction. In Table 8.3, we list the prominent reflectivity structure [8.16, 17] for silicon and the origin of this structure in the Brillouin zone.

The valence band density of states for silicon calculated using pseudopotentials is compared with experiment [8.18] in Fig. 8.7. Under certain conditions, it is possible to compare directly the theoretical density of states with photoemission measurements. Specifically, if matrix elements effects are ignored, the density of states can be extracted from XPS or UPS measurements. Thus, the UPS or XPS measurements can provide us with a direct probe of the occupied or ground state properties. We noted earlier that reflectivity spectra have the disadvantage of probing only the relative positions of energy bands and not the absolute position. For the testing of empirical pseudopotential band structures, the photoemission spectra have proven invaluable for the determination of accurate potentials. In particular,

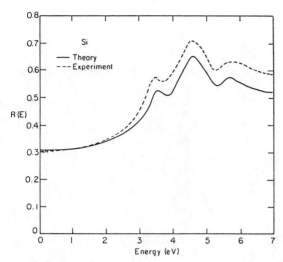

Fig. 8.5. Reflectivity spectrum of silicon. The experimental curve is from [8.7]

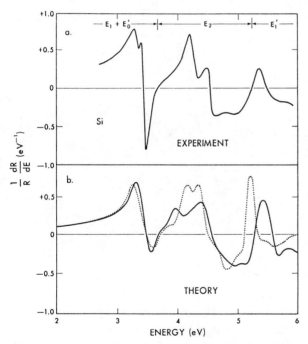

Fig. 8.6. Experimental and theoretical reflectivity derivative spectrum for silicon. The experimental results are from [8.11]. Two theoretical calculations are displayed: one from a local (dotted curve) and one from a nonlocal pseudopotential (solid curve)

Table 8.3. Theoretical and experimental reflectivity structure and identifications including location in the Brillouin zone, energy (in eV), and symmetry of the calculated critical points for silicon

Reflectivity structure		Si Experiment		Associated critical points (cp) location in the Brillouin zone		Symmetry of CP		Critical-point energy	
Theory Local	Nonlocal	5 K[a]	80 K[b]	Local	Nonlocal	Local	Nonlocal	Local	Nonlocal
3.48	3.49	3.40	3.36	$L_{3'}$-L_1	$L_{3'}$-L	M_0	M_0	3.37	3.46
		3.45	3.41	$\Gamma_{25'}$-Γ_{15}	$\Gamma_{25'}$-Γ_{15}	M_0	M_0	3.43	3.42
				Near (0.1,0.02,0.02)	Near (0.1,0.05,0.05)	M_0	M_0	3.46	3.42
3.75	3.70	3.66	(3.88)[c]	Vol. along Δ	Vol. along Δ	...	...	...	...
4.26	4.15	4.30	4.38	Vol. near (0.9,0.1,0.1)	Vol. near (0.9,0.1,0.1)	...	...	...	...
4.53	4.57	4.57	4.57	Large region near (0.5,0.25,0.25) and	Large region near (0.6,0.3,0.3) and	M_2 / M_2	M_2 / M_2	4.53 / 4.49	4.47 / 4.60
5.32	5.58	5.48	...	L_3-$L_{3'}$ / Λ_3-$\Lambda_{3'}$ (0.4,0.4,0.4)	L_3-$L_{3'}$ / Λ_3-$\Lambda_{3'}$ (0.45,0.45,0.45)	M_0 / M_1	M_2 / $\sim M_3$	5.22 / 5.25	5.56 / 5.57

[a] From [8.16] [b] From [8.17] [c] Inferred from $\varepsilon_2(\omega)$ data of [8.17]

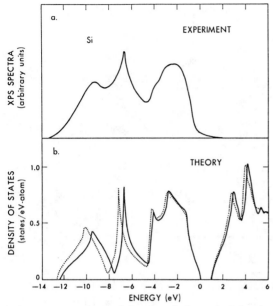

Fig. 8.7. Experimental [8.18] and theoretical density of states for silicon. For the theoretical calculations, the dotted curve is from a local pseudopotential and the solid curve is from a nonlocal pseudopotential. The nonlocal potential is in better agreement with the XPS results, especially for the lowest valence bands

the photoemission measurements have indicated that the local pseudopotentials cannot provide band pictures where both the valence and conduction bands are simultaneously reproduced accurately when compared to experimental band pictures.

For diamond-structure semiconductors, the valence band density of states may be divided into three general regions. Using the top of the valence band as our zero of energy, the region of -13 eV to -8 eV is predominantly of s-like character stemming from the atomic $3s$-states of Si. The region from -8 eV to -4 eV is a transition region with contributions from both s- and p-states. Finally, the region from -5 eV to 0 eV is predominantly p-like. The feature which delineates these spectral regions is a sharp reduction or "dip" in the density of states compared to the average density. The nonuniformity of the density of states arises from hybridization among the atomic orbitals. Thus, any disruption of the crystalline bonding environment will introduce states into the regions of reduced state density. For example, in amorphous materials, where there presumably exist bond angle and bond length deviations from the ideal crystalline state, these regions are strongly affected. The dip around -8 eV fills in, and the upper region of the density of states tends to narrow and shift to higher energies. For surface states or vacancy states where broken bonds are clearly involved, the defect localized states tend to fill in these regions including the fundamental gap.

Table 8.4. Comparison of critical point energies (in eV) for silicon as calculated from model pseudopotentials and as measured by photoemission experiments

Energy level	Theory		Experiment
	Local	Non-local	
$\Gamma_{12'}$	8.60↓	8.19	8.3 ± 0.1[a]
Γ_1	7.82↑	7.69	7.6[a]
$\Gamma_{2'}$	4.17	4.10	4.15 ± 0.05[a]
Γ_1	−12.53	−12.36	−12.4 ± 0.6,[b] −12.5 ± 0.6[c]
X_4	−2.99	−2.86	−2.9,[a] −2.5 ± 0.3[c]
Σ_1^{min}	−4.48	−4.47	−4.4,[a] −4.7 ± 0.3[b,c]
L_3	4.00	4.34	3.9 ± 0.1[a]
$L_{3'}$	−1.22	−1.23	−1.2 ± 0.2[a]
L_1	−7.24	−6.96	−6.4 ± 0.4,[b] −6.8 ± 0.2[c]
$L_{2'}$	−10.17	−9.55	−9.3 ± 0.4[c]

[a] From [8.20]   [b] From [8.19]   [c] From [8.18]

Another nearly universal feature of diamond and zinc-blende semiconductors is the width of the valence band. The valence band width is normally 12–13 eV independent of the constituents. In Table 8.4, we compile photoemission measurements [8.18–20] and compare them to the pseudopotential calculations.

It is also possible to use the pseudopotential calculations to determine band edge parameters. For example, using the pseudopotential wavefunctions it is possible to evaluate the cyclotron mass parameters given by *Dresselhaus* et al. [8.21] and *Kane* [8.22]:

$$F' \cong \frac{2}{m} \sum_n \frac{|\langle \Gamma_{25'} | P_x | \Gamma_{2'}(n) \rangle|^2}{E(\Gamma_{25'}) - E(\Gamma_{2'}(n))} \tag{8.1}$$

$$G' \cong \frac{2}{m} \sum_n \frac{|\langle \Gamma_{25'} | P_x | \Gamma_{15}(n) \rangle|^2}{E(\Gamma_{25'}) - E(\Gamma_{15}(n))} \tag{8.2}$$

$$H' \cong \frac{2}{m} \sum_n \frac{|\langle \Gamma_{25'} | P_x | \Gamma_{12'}(n) \rangle|^2}{E(\Gamma_{25'}) - E(\Gamma_{12'}(n))} \tag{8.3}$$

In Table 8.5, we give the computed and measured [8.23–25] cyclotron mass parameters and conduction band mass parameters associated with the indirect gap. Considering the simplicity of the pseudopotential method and the limited flexibility of adjustments which can be made to the potential, the calculated parameters are more accurate than one might expect. Indeed, the use of wavefunctions derived from pseudopotentials for the computation of dipole matrix elements and mass parameters has long been questioned. However, the insecurity about the correctness of pseudowavefunctions now

Table 8.5. Cyclotron mass parameters and conduction band minimum masses compared to theoretical values for silicon. The magnitude and position of the indirect gap along the Δ direction is also given

	Experiment	Theory	
		Local	Non-local
F'	-5.04[a]	-5.11	-5.07
H'	-4.53[a]	-4.49	-4.23
G'	-0.87[a]	-0.88	-0.89
$m_0/m_{c\perp}$	5.25[b]	5.15	5.31
$m_0/m_{c\|}$	1.09[b]	1.21	1.18
$ak_{min}/2\pi$	0.86[c]	~ 0.85	~ 0.85
E_{ind}	1.15[d]	1.13	1.05

[a] From [8.19] [b] From [8.23] [c] From [8.24] [d] From [8.25]

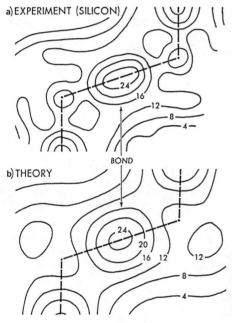

a) EXPERIMENT (SILICON)

BOND

b) THEORY

Fig. 8.8. The valence charge density of silicon (a) from experiment and (b) from theory. The experimental data is based on the work of [8.27]. The contour spacings are in units of electrons per unit cell volume

seems unjustified. This is especially true when one considers the work comparing orthogonalized plane wave calculations of dipole matrix elements with the corresponding pseudopotential calculations [8.26].

Another test of the pseudopotential wavefunctions can come from x-ray work. *Yang* and *Coppens* [8.27] using the x-ray results of several groups were able to synthesize a valence charge density map for silicon. In Fig. 8.8, we present their results compared to the charge density determined from nonlocal pseudopotentials. The central feature of both the measured and calculated density is the existence of a "bond charge" located at the mid-point between neighboring nuclei. This bond charge feature is thought to be crucial for establishing the stability of the diamond structure. *Phillips* [8.28] has discussed the origin of this bond charge using his dielectric theory of semiconductors. This theory is capable of predicting the magnitude of the bond charge and the location of the bond charge maximum in partially covalent materials.

While the pseudopotential charge densities from local potentials yield the correct position and magnitude for the bond charge, they can produce topological errors in its shape. From ab initio studies by *Hamann* [8.29], an all-electron potential will yield a bond elongated along the bonding direction; this alignment is in agreement with experiment. Local pseudopotential calculations produce bond charge densities with the bond axis oriented perpendicular to the bonding direction. In Fig. 8.9, we compare the nonlocal and local pseudopotential results.

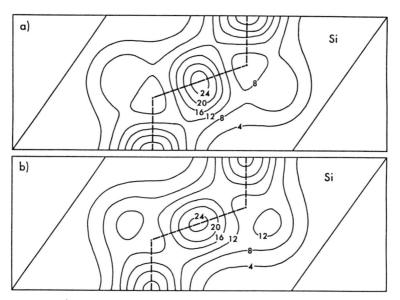

Fig. 8.9. Theoretical valence charge densities from (a) a local and (b) a nonlocal pseudopotential. The contour spacings are in units of electrons per unit cell volume

One method of quantifying the topological differences between the nonlocal and the local pseudopotential results is with a band by band mapping of the charge densities. In Fig. 8.10, we present non-local pseudopotential calculations for Si. In both cases, the upper valence bands have similar appearance. The chief differences in that the total charge densities arise from the lowest valence band. The nonlocal potential allows the *s*-like electrons of the lowest band to see a more attractive potential than does the local potential. Hence, the charge density for the lowest band in the nonlocal case

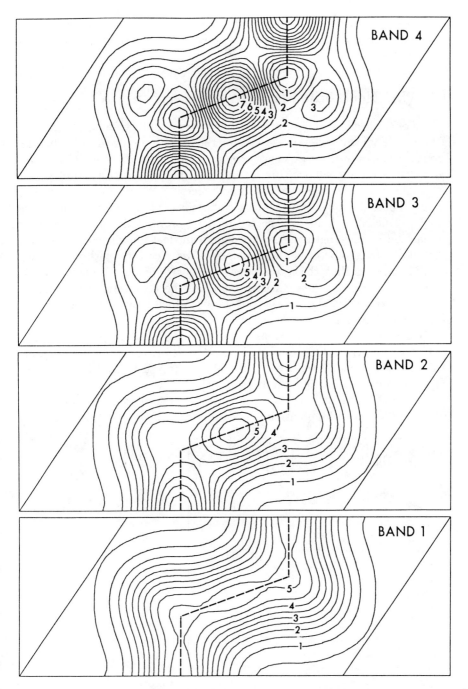

Fig. 8.10. Band by band decomposition of the valence charge density of silicon. The charge density contour spacings are in units of electrons per unit cell volume

is much larger on the nuclear sites than for the local case. This difference, though not large in a global sense, is enough to alter the topology of the bond charge.

8.3 The Electronic Structure of Germanium

The valence electron configuration of germanium and silicon are both s^2p^2; however, significant differences exist for the band structures. The chief differences arise from the core charge configuration. While the nuclear charge increase is exactly balanced by an increase in core electron number, the larger number of core electrons is more effective in screening the nuclear charge. Thus, the valence levels in germanium are less tightly bound compared to silicon, and this is reflected in the more metallic character of the germanium band structure. Another significant feature which distinguishes germanium from silicon is the presence of $3d$ electrons within the core. While it is clear that these d-electrons do not significantly participate in the cohesive process, they can still influence the conduction band configuration. Specifically, the unoccupied bands, which may have considerable $4d$ character, are influenced by an orhtogonality requirment not present for the $3d$ states in silicon. This reasoning is reinforced by empirical evidence which suggests that the presence of d-electrons, i.e. nonlocal pseudopotentials, which incorporate d-orbital corrections, appear crucial in describing the germanium conduction bands [8.30, 31].

In Fig. 8.11, we present the band structure of germanium as determined from empirical pseudopotentials. Unlike the case of silicon, most computa-

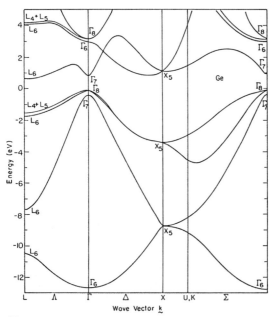

Fig. 8.11. Band structure of germanium. The zero energy reference is at the valence band maximum

tions of the band structure of germanium are in reasonably good agreement although there has been some controversy over the placement of the Γ_{15} conduction-band complex. In particular, some of the early orthogonalized plane wave band structures [8.32] suggested that the Γ_{15} complex is located about 2.5 eV above the valence band maximum. However, the experimental evidence for this transition suggests a higher placement of about 3.2 eV [8.31]; this placement agrees with the pseudopotential results. Specifically, reflectivity structure has been observed at 3.02 eV, 3.20 eV, and 3.50 eV and attributed to transitions involving the spin-orbit split $\Gamma_{25'}-\Gamma_{15}$ complex. The pseudopotential band calculation yields values of 3.01 eV, 3.22 eV, and 3.51 eV for these respective transitions.

The band structure of germanium differs from silicon most significantly in the conduction band arrangement. For example, the Γ_{15} and $\Gamma_{2'}$ levels reverse their ordering. Moreover, while germanium and silicon are both indirect semiconductors, the conduction band minimum in germanium occurs at the L-point as opposed to a point near X in silicon. As noted earlier, the valence band configuration for diamond semiconductors is insensitivie to the constituents: tin, germanium, and silicon have almost identical valence band configurations, but they have quite different conduction band configuratioins. In Table 8.6, we list a compilation of theoretical energy levels at high symmetry points.

Table 8.6. Germanium eigenvalues (in eV) at Γ, X, and L high symmetry points

Γ^v_6	-12.66	X_5	-8.65	L^v_6	-10.39
Γ^v_7	-0.29	X^v_5	-3.29	L^v_6	-7.61
Γ^v_8	0.00	X^c_5	1.16	L^v_6	-1.63
Γ^c_7	0.90			$L^v_4 + L^v_5$	-1.43
Γ^c_6	3.01			L^c_6	0.76
Γ^c_8	3.22			L^c_6	4.16
				$L^c_4 + L^c_5$	4.25

In Fig. 8.12, we display the reflectivity spectrum of germanium as calculated from pseudopotential band theory and as determined by experiment [8.6]. Compared to silicon, germanium exhibits a richer spectrum. The additional structure arises from the larger spin-orbit coupling occurring in germanium. For example, in the E_1 region near 2.2 eV, a distinct doublet structure occurs. This doublet arises from the splitting in the $L_{3'}$ level. In Fig. 8.13, the logarithmic derivative reflectivity spectrum is displayed. Again, both theory and experiment [8.11] are compared in the figure. The derivative spectrum vividly illustrates the rich reflectivity structure available using modulated techniques.

Perhaps the most interesting feature of the germanium reflectivity spectrum is the E_2 peak at 4.5 eV. Initially, the origin of this spectral feature appeared to be located at the X-point and to involve transitions between

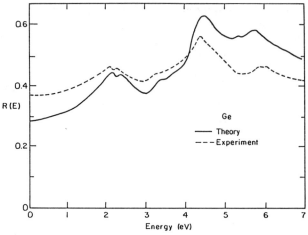

Fig. 8.12. Theoretical and experimental reflectivity spectrum for germanium. The experimental data is from [8.7]

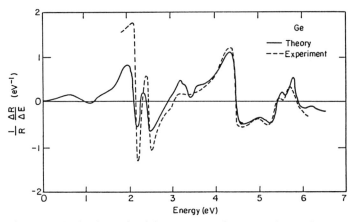

Fig. 8.13. Derivative reflectivity spectrum for germanium. The experimental spectrum is from [8.11]

the uppermost valence band and the lowest conduction band. Although this transition occurs at the correct energy and involves large matrix elements, the phase space associated with this critical point is too small to yield such prominent structure. Thus, it has been suggested that several critical points from various parts of the zone might contribute to this reflectivity feature. This explanation has also proven to be inadequate; *Aspnes* [8.33] using electroreflectance techniques has demonstrated that the E_2 structure arises from a localized region in the Brillouin zone.

The most recent theoretical study of the optical spectrum of germanium appears to be consistent with Aspnes' analysis. The E_2 peak appears to arise from a well-defined, limited region inside the Brillouin zone. This

94

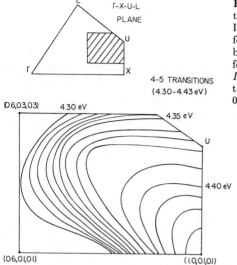

Fig. 8.14. Origin of the E_2 peak in the reflectivity spectrum of germanium. Interband energy contours are illustrated for transitions involving the top valence band and lowest conduction band, i.e., the fourth and fifth bands. The part of the Γ-X-U-L plane displayed is indicated by the shaded region. Contours are drawn in 0.01 eV intervals from 4.30 to 4.43 eV

region is near the special point of *Chadi* and *Cohen* [8.34], i.e., near the point $(\frac{2\pi}{a})(\frac{3}{4}, \frac{1}{4}, \frac{1}{4})$. To illustrate the band configuration near this point, we indicate the interband contours in the Γ-X-U-L plane in Fig. 8.14. We find a very flat, plateau-like region which has large dipole matrix elements. This configuration is compatible with estimates Aspnes has made for band masses associated with the E_2 peak. In Table 8.7, we have listed a compilation of interband masses for Ge from theory and experiment [8.33]. In Table 8.8, we list the reflectivity assignments for Ge and compare them with the results of wavelength modulation measurements [8.11].

As in the case of silicon, good photoemission data exist for germanium. In Table 8.9, we compile positions of various energy levels as determined from measurements [8.19, 20, 32, 33, 35–38] and pseudopotential

Table 8.7. Comparison of the theoretically determined interband masses for germanium and the experimental results from Schottky barrier electroreflectance. No spin-orbit interactions are included. The notation and experimental results are from *Aspnes* [8.33]

Ge	Interband Masses		
Transition	Mass Component (field [110])	Expt. Value (in m_e)	Theor. Value (m_{ij})
E_0	μ_{hh}, $\hat{e}[1\bar{1}0]$	0.0366 ± 0.013	0.022
$E_0 + \Delta_0$	μ_{so}	0.0269	
E_1	μ_T	0.045 ± 0.004	0.050
$E_1 + \Delta_1$	μ_T	0.042 ± 0.005	
E_0'	μ, $\hat{e}[001]$	0.034 ± 0.005	0.047
$E_0' + \Delta_0'$	μ, $\hat{e}[1\bar{1}0]$	0.048 ± 0.009	
$E_0' + \Delta_0' + \Delta_0$	μ, $\hat{e}[001]$	0.062 ± 0.006	
E_2	μ_T	0.139	0.11

95

Table 8.8. Theoretical and experimental reflectivity structure for germanium. Critical point locations in Brillouin zone, energy, and symmetry are given. The experimental values are from *Zucca* and *Shen* [8.11]

Ge Reflectivity structure [eV]		Associated critical points, location in zone		Critical-point energy
Theory	Experiment		Symmetry	[eV]
2.20	2.22	L_6^v-L_6^v (0.5,0.5,0.5)	M_1	2.19
2.40	2.42	$L_{4,5}^v$-L_6^v	M_1	2.39
3.3	3.20	$\Gamma^v{}_{25}$-$\Gamma^c{}_{15}$ complex (0.0,0.0,0.0)	M_0	3.25
4.51	4.5	Region near (0.75,0.25,0.25)	...	...
5.40	5.65	$\Delta^v{}_6$-$\Delta^c{}_6$ (0.5,0.0,0.0)	M_1	5.40
		$\Delta^v{}_7$-$\Delta^c{}_6$		5.35
5.88	5.88	$L_{4,5}^v$-$L_{4,5}^c$ (0.5,0.5,0.5)	M_1	5.88
		L_6^v-L_6^c	M_1	5.60

Table 8.9. Comparison of theoretical and experimental transitions for germanium

Transition	Experiment [eV]		Theory [eV]
Γ_1-$\Gamma_{25'}$	12.6 ± 0.3[a],	12.8 ± 0.4[b]	12.56
L_2-$\Gamma_{25'}$	10.6 ± 0.4[a],	10.5 ± 0.4[b]	10.30
L_1-$\Gamma_{25'}$	7.7 ± 0.2[a],	7.4 ± 0.2[b]	7.52
$\Sigma^{min}{}_1$-$\Gamma_{25'}$	4.5 ± 0.2[a],	4.5 ± 0.3[b]	4.55
$L_{3'}$-$\Gamma_{25'}$	1.4 ± 0.2[c]		1.44
$\Gamma_{25'}$-$\Gamma_{2'}$	0.98[d]		0.99
$\Gamma_{25'}$-Γ_{15}	3.24[e]		3.25
$\Gamma_{25'}$-L_1	0.87[f]		0.85
$\Gamma_{25'}$-X_1	1.2[g]		1.25
$\Gamma_{25'}$-L_3	4.3[c]		4.30

[a] From [8.19]   [b] From [8.35, 36]   [c] From [8.20]   [d] From [8.37]   [e] From [8.33]   [f] From [8.38]   [g] From [8.32]

calculations. Essentially, all the comments on the silicon valence band density of states are applicable to germanium. In Fig. 8.15, we illustrate the photoemission spectrum [8.19] for germanium and compare this spectrum with the calculated valence band density of states. Owing to the omission of matrix-element effects in the valence band density of states, it is not appropriate for us to compare the calculated peak intensities to the photoe-

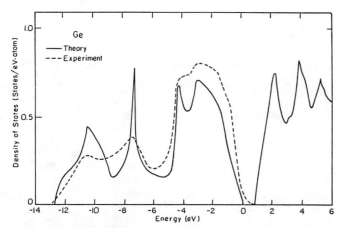

Fig. 8.15. Experimental and theoretical density of states for germanium. The experimental data is from [8.19]. The structure in the experimental data near the top of the valence band, that is, at about -0.5 eV, may arise from surface state contributions

mission intensities. Nevertheless, in Fig. 8.15 there exists enhanced emission near the top of the valence band. In addition, there appears to be a shoulder feature near -0.5 eV present in the photoemission but not present in the calculation. It is quite likely the increased emission and the extra structural feature are induced by surface states. This conjecture receives support from surface calculations for silicon. Thus, while most of the prominent features of photoemission arise from bulk states, surface bands can also contribute. The interpretations of XPS and UPS measurements yield different values for the $L_{3'}$ feature; most likely this difference can be explained by UPS measuring surface contributions in this region while XPS does not pick up such contributions.

The valence charge density of germanium is displayed in Fig. 8.16 and appears quite similar to silicon. While at present we do not have an experimentally determined charge density contour map for Ge, we can examine some specific charge density properties. For example, the temperature de-

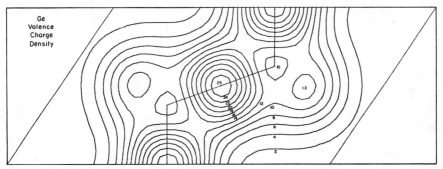

Fig. 8.16. Valence charge density of germanium. Contour values are in units of electrons per unit cell volume

pendence of the $\left(\frac{2\pi}{a}\right)(2, 2, 2)$ reflection has been measured. This reflection is a direct probe of the bonding charge in diamond-structure crystals. Using the techniques described earlier, pseudopotential calculations have been able to reproduce the experimental data illustrated in Fig. 7.3.

8.4 The Electronic Structure of Gray Tin

In many ways, tin is a borderline material. It occurs in two nearly degenerate structural forms: gray tin and white tin. The energy difference between these two structures is so small that the structural transformation occurs near room temperature. Gray tin is the more stable form and corresponds to the diamond structure. In the white tin structure, each tin atom has six close neighbors. Two of the neighbors are slightly further away than the other four. The white tin structure is, therefore, distorted from the ideal diamond structure. One can think of white tin as an intermediate between the covalent diamond structure and the metallic face centered cubic structure [8.39]; that is, it is reasonable to think of tin as a transition element between the tetravalent, covalent element germanium, and the divalent, metallic element lead.

Given the perverse structural properties of tin, it is not surprising that its electronic properties are also unusual. In the gray tin structure, tin is neither ideally semiconducting nor metallic. The band structure of gray tin is presented in Fig. 8.17, and in Table 8.10, we present tabulated eigenvalues at

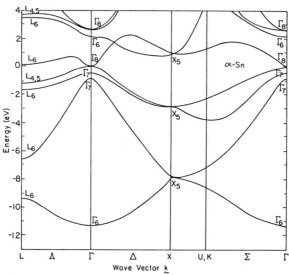

Fig. 8.17. Band structure for gray tin. The energy zero is taken to be the valence band maximum

Table 8.10. α-Sn eigenvalues at Γ, X, and L high symmetry points. Energies are in eV

Γ^c_6	−11.34	X^v_5	−7.88	L^v_6	−9.44
Γ^v_7	−0.80	X^v_5	−2.75	L^v_6	−6.60
Γ^v_7	−0.42	X^c_5	0.90	L^v_6	−1.68
Γ^{v-c}_8	0.00			$L^v_{4,5}$	−1.20
Γ^c_6	2.08			L^c_6	0.14
Γ^c_8	2.66			L^c_6	3.48
				$L^c_{4,5}$	3.77

high symmetry points. The lowest conduction band and the highest valence band precisely touch at the zone center. Thus, the band gap of gray tin is exactly zero. Neither pressure nor temperature changes (except those which convert gray tin to white tin) can alter this unique feature. We can consider gray tin to be an extremely small band gap material or a very poor metal.

Owing to the ease with which tin transforms between the white and gray tin structures, experiments are difficult to perform on gray tin. To date, a reliable modulated reflectivity spectrum does not exist. In Fig. 8.18, we display the calculated reflectivity spectrum of gray tin and compare it to an experimental spectrum [8.40]. While the calculated peak positions of the gray tin structure match up very well with the experimental peak positions, the magnitude of the calculated reflectivity is much higher than experiment. This is especially true at higher energies where the theoretical values are nearly twice as large as the experimental ones. In general, theoretical reflectivity spectra tend to yield larger values for the reflectivity coefficient than are measured by experiment; however, in the case of gray tin the problem is more severe than usual. The problem here probably resides with the experiment, i.e., poor sample quality. Also, we should comment that the theoretical values of the reflectivity spectrum below 0.5 eV are not reliable, as expected for a zero band gap material. In Table 8.11, we indicate re-

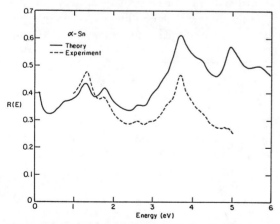

Fig. 8.18. Reflectivity spectrum of gray tin. The experimental data is from [8.40]

Table 8.11. Theoretical and experimental reflectivity structure for α-Sn. Critical point identifications are given including location in the Brillouin zone, energy, and symmetry. Experiment (a) is from [8.40] and (b) from [8.41]

α-Sn Reflectivity structure [eV]			Associated critical points, location in zone		
Theory	Experiment (a)	(b)		Symmetry	Critical-point energy [eV]
1.34	1.365	1.365	L_6^v-$L_{4,5}^v$	M_1	1.34
1.83	1.832	1.845	L_6^v-L_6^c	M_1	1.83
2.31	...	2.28	Γ_8^v-Γ_6^c (0.0,0.0,0.0)	M_0	2.08
2.67	2.62	2.63	Γ_8^v-Γ_8^c	M_0	2.66
2.95	2.85	...	Δ_7^v-Δ_6^c	M_1	2.91
3.40	3.3	3.3	Γ_7^v-Γ_8^c	M_0	3.46
3.78	3.75	3.718	Plateau near (0.75,0.25,0.25)	...	...
4.2	4.0	4.12	Δ_6^v-Δ_7^c (0.6,0.0,0.0)	M_1	4.13
4.31	4.43	4.43	Δ_7^v-Δ_7^c	M_1	4.25
4.91	4.89	4.89	$L_{4,5}^v$-L_6^c	M_1	4.68

flectivity [8.40, 41] assignments for gray tin. These assignments are in good accord with orthogonalized plane wave calculations [8.42]. The calculated density of states is presented in Fig. 8.19 with Table 8.12 indicating the key critical point energies calculated using the EPM and compared to the OPW results [8.42].

In Fig. 8.20, we display the calculated charge density of gray tin. Although it is difficult to quantify bond charges, the bonding charge in gray tin is more diffuse than in germanium consistent with a more metallic material.

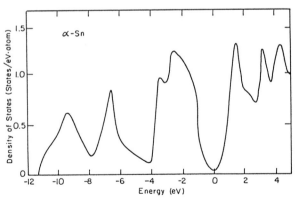

Fig. 8.19. Density of states for gray tin

Table 8.12. Valence band levels for α-Sn. A comparison is made to an orthogonalized plane wave (OPW) calculation [8.42]. All energies are in eV

Transition	Non-local EPM	OPW
Γ_7^v-$\Gamma_8^{c,v}$	0.42	0.32
L_6^c-$\Gamma_8^{c,v}$	0.14	0.14
$L_{4,5}^v$-$\Gamma_8^{c,v}$	1.20	1.43
Σ_1^{min}-$\Gamma_8^{c,v}$	3.32	–
$L_6^v(L_1)$-$\Gamma_8^{c,v}$	6.60	6.17
$L_6^v(L_{2'})$-$\Gamma_8^{c,v}$	9.44	8.92
Γ_6^v-Γ_8^c	11.34	10.49

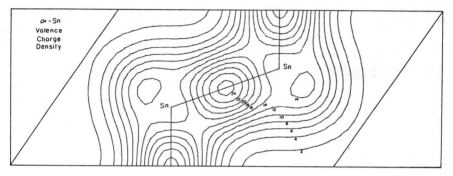

Fig. 8.20. Valence charge density of gray tin. The charge density is in units of electrons per unit cell volume

8.5 Zinc-Blende Structure Semiconductors

A diamond crystal structure can be constructed by displacing two elemental face centered cubic lattices. If we construct a crystal from two different elemental fcc lattices, then we would reproduce the zinc-blende structure. A useful way to compare diamond and zinc-blende materials is to consider the series: Ge, GaAs, and ZnSe. Our interest in the Ge-GaAs-ZnSe series centers on their unique attributes: these compounds are "isocoric", "isoelectric", and "isostructural". The only differences between the three compounds is that the constituents alter in atomic number. Thus, we will single out GaAs and ZnSe for special discussions and briefly summarize results for the other III-V and II-VI semiconductors.

Figuratively speaking, GaAs can be made from Ge by transferring a proton from one Ge atom to another: the atom losing a proton becomes Ga, and the atom gaining a proton becomes As. To construct a ZnSe crystal, we can transfer two protons from one Ge atom to another. In either case, the atomic positions are not altered. A priori it is not obvious how much of a perturbation such a proton transfer is. However, if we consider that

101

the covalent forces must still predominant in III-V crystals, perhaps it is not surprising that these crystals occur quite readily in diamond-like structures. Only when we transfer two or more protons do we get other more ionic crystal structures. Thus, II-VI crystals can be found in either the zinc-blende structure or the wurtzite structure. Even here the zinc-blende crystals tend to be stable compared wurtzite structures. When we consider isocoric constituents, the predominant structure is zinc-blende; when we have consituents with different core configurations, the predominant structure is wurtzite. For a transfer of three protons, the zinc-blende structure becomes much less stable compared to ionic structures such as rocksalt. The close competition between covalent and ionic forces led to much interest in materials like CuCl which has anomalous behavior with respect to bond bending forces [8.28].

8.6 The Electronic Structure of Gallium Arsenide

We can approach the electronic structure of gallium aresenide from the perspective of perturbing the germanium potential. Intuitively, we expect

$$V_S(G) = [V_{Ga}(G) + V_{As}(G)]/2 \cong V_{Ge}(G) \quad . \tag{8.4}$$

That is, the symmetric part of the potential should resemble the form factors of germanium. The antisymmetric form factor,

$$V_A(G) = [V_{Ga}(G) - V_{As}(G)]/2 \tag{8.5}$$

which is a measure of the difference between the gallium and arsenic potentials, should contain the essential information which distinguishes germanium from gallium arsenide. Formally, it is the deviation of $V_A(G)$ from zero which distinguishes zinc-blende from diamond semiconductors. In this sense, we expect a smooth transition from a purly covalent semiconductor [$V_A(G) = 0$], to a highly ionic semiconductor where $V_A(G)$ deviates considerably from zero. Moreover, we might expect that many properties of semiconductors, for example, optical gaps, cohesive energies, dielectric constants, bond charges, etc., might simply scale with an ionicity factor based on $V_A(G)$ or a similar measure. Actually, this is the case, and although $V_A(G)$ is not explicitly used, a more sophisticated measure, based on similar concepts, of ionic versus covalent contributions to crystal binding in diamond and zinc-blende semiconductors has been devised by *Phillips* [8.28].

In Fig. 8.21, we present the calculated band structure for gallium arsenide, and in Table 8.13, we list the energy levels at high symmetry points in the Brillouin zone. We believe the nonlocal pseudopotential approach

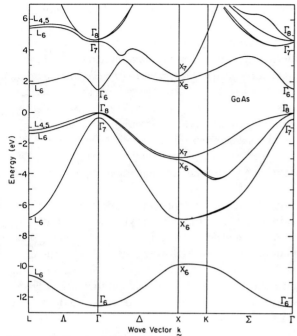

Fig. 8.21. Band structure of gallium arsenide. The valence band maximum is taken to be the zero of energy

Table 8.13. Eigenvalues (in eV) for gallium arsenide at Γ, L, and X high symmetry points

Γ_6^v	-12.55	X_6^v	-9.83	L_6^v	-10.60
Γ_7^v	-0.35	X_6^v	-6.88	L_6^v	-6.83
Γ_8^v	0.00	X_6^v	-2.99	L_6^v	-1.42
Γ_6^c	1.51	X_7^v	-2.89	$L_{4,5}^v$	-1.20
Γ_7^c	4.55	X_6^c	2.03	L_6^c	1.82
Γ_8^c	4.71	X_7^c	2.38	$L_{4,5}^c$	5.52

has yielded one of the most accurate band structures for GaAs to date. In fact, as a result of the extensive experimental studies in this compounds, this band structure may be the most accurate band structure over a large energy range available for any material. By compiling the most recent experimental data, we estimate an error of about 0.1 eV over an energy span of nearly 20 eV. Thus, we have an accuracy of roughly 1 % or better; this is almost an order of magnitude better than other band structures available for GaAs.

As we introduce antisymmetric form factors for the gallium arsenide crystal potential, several significant alterations from a germanium-like band structure may be observed. First, the bottom valence band, which now has atomic s-like character and is localized on the anion, splits off from the rest of the valence band to form what has been termed the "antisymmetric gap". This gap grows with increasing ionicity or charge transfer. Another smaller gap arises from the antisymmetric part of the potential and is located between the first and second conduction bands along the Δ-direction. This smaller gap is important for transport properties of zinc-blende semiconductors and has been observed to have subtle effects on the reflectivity spectrum of the zinc-blendes.

We also note that the band gaps in gallium arsenide tend to be larger than in germanium. In general, as a semiconductor becomes more ionic, the valence band widths narrow and the optical gap grows in size. Part of this effect arises from dehybridization accompanying the change in bonding from covalent to ionic.

Perhaps the most important conclusion from our experience with GaAs is not simply that the pseudopotential approach can yield accurate results. Consider the parametrized nature of the potential. One might expect that the band structure could be adjusted at will. However, if this were the case, most pseudopotential band calculations for GaAs would have placed L_6^c above X_6^c in agreement with the incorrect traditional picture (see correct placement in Fig. 6.8). We do not have very much freedom in adjusting pseudopotential parameters for several reasons. First, of the form factors per atom are used in GaAs, qualitatively only one or two of them are really independent. Moreover, we know from model potentials what the general shape of the potential must be, and in the adjustment process, the form factors are constrained to reproduce roughly the model potentials. Thus, it is simply not possible to reproduce the fundamental optical gaps and arbitrarily place L_6^c and X_6^c.

In Figs. 8.22 and 8.23, we illustrate the computed optical response functions, that is, real and imaginary parts of the dielectric function, for GaAs

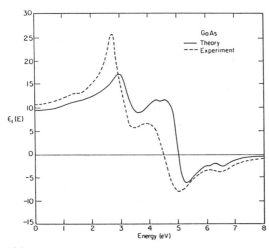

Fig. 8.22. Real part of the dielectric function for gallium arsenide. The experimental data is from [8.7]

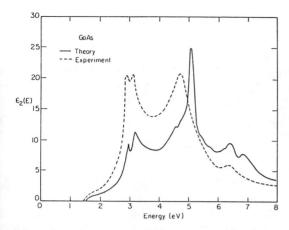

Fig. 8.23. Imaginary part of the dielectric function of gallium arsenide. The experimental data is from [8.7]

and compare them with the experimentally [8.7] determined functions. The information content of the response functions is considerable. It is for this reason that *Phillips* [8.28] based his bonding theories of semiconductors on spectroscopic data rather than following the approach of *Pauling* [8.43] who used thermochemical data to analyze molecular bonding trends.

If we examine the real part of the dielectric function, the general shape is that expected for a harmonic oscillator with a resonant frequency at about 5 eV. We can think of this resonant frequency as a fundamental property of GaAs which represents the average bonding-antibonding energy level separation. Phillips divides up this average bonding-antibonding gap into a part which is ionic and a part which is covalent. Thus, one can extract from the dielectric function relevant parameters for formulating ionicity scales. Such scales are useful for making predictions of a variety of semiconductor properties.

With a knowledge of the real and imaginary parts of the dielectric function, we can derive the reflectivity spectrum [8.7] and reflectivity derivative spectrum [8.17]. In Figs. 8.24 and 8.25, we display these spectra. As for the

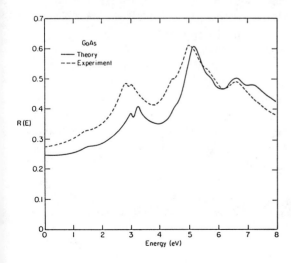

Fig. 8.24. Reflectivity spectrum for gallium arsenide. The experimental data is from [8.7]

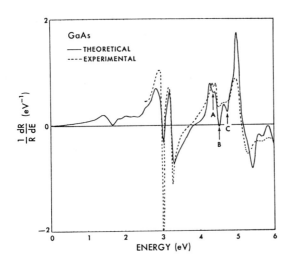

Fig. 8.25. Reflectivity derivative spectrum for gallium arsenide indicating fine structure (A, B, C) as discussed in the text. The experimental data is from [8.11]

diamond structures, we may divide up the zinc-blende structures into five distinct regions. For GaAs, the E_0 region extends from 1 to 2 eV, the E_1 region 2–4 eV, the E_0' region 4–5 eV, the E_2 region 5–6 eV, and the E_1' region 6–7 eV.

The lowest energy region E_0 is dominated by structure originating from the fundamental gap at Γ. Spin-orbit interactions split the upper valence bands of gallium arsenide by about 0.3 eV; for heavier metal constituents, the splittings can be quite large, for example, an eV or more. Thus, the E_0 structure actually has a doublet character.

The E_1 reflectivity peak originates from transitions near the zone boundary at L. Again, spin-orbit interactions can become important in this region by splitting the upper valence bands. We note that older, local pseudopotential calculations gave a different critical point symmetry for this region. The local potential results put an M_0 critical point at L and an M_1 critical point along the Λ direction. The nonlocal results move the M_1 critical point to the zone boundary and eliminate the M_0 point altogether. This later configuration is in better accord with experiment.

The E_0' structure has been somewhat controversial. It can arise from either of two regions: near the zone center or along the Δ direction. If it were to occur at the zone center, we would expect spin-orbit splitting to be important in both the valence and conduction bands. On this basis, recent work by *Aspnes* and *Studna* [8.44] has given support to the zone-center assignment. The traditional argument against this assignment has been the small phase space associated with the Γ point; however, excitonic effects may very well enhance its importance.

As we mentioned in our discussion of Phillips' dielectric theory, the E_2 peak which dominates the absorption spectrum, represents the average bonding-antibonding transitions. This peak arises from transitions from the uppermost valence bands to the lowest conduction bands near the special points $(\frac{2\pi}{a})(\frac{3}{4}, \frac{1}{4}, \frac{1}{4})$ in the Brillouin zone. This assignment is similar to that found in the diamond structure semiconductors. The E_2 peak dominates the spectrum because of the large phase space which contributes to interband transitions in this region and because of large interband dipole matrix elements. At energies above the E_2 peak, reflectivity structure arises from transitions along the Δ direction.

Finally, the E_1' structure arises from transitions from the top of the valence band to the second lowest conduction band at or near the zone boundary at L.

By examining the energy gradients and dipole matrix elements throughout the Brillouin zone, it is possible to determine the origin of structure in the imaginary part of the dielectric function. In such a manner, we have analyzed the contribution to the E_0' reflectivity structure. This structure is complex and has been somewhat controversial. (The structure is marked with the labels A, B and C in Fig. 8.25.) *Rehn* and *Kyser* [8.45] using transverse electroreflectance, observed only a Λ symmetry for this structure. They attributed the structure to the pseudocrossing of the Δ_5 conduction bands. However, *Aspnes* and *Studna* [8.44] have pointed out that this interpretation conflicts with band structure calculations where some Γ symmetry structure is predicted. They further proposed that the Δ symmetry structure arises from a pair of M_1 critical points approximately one-tenth of the way from Γ to X. The most recent pseudopotential calculations agree with this interpretation. The relevant transitions are indicated in Fig. 8.26. The

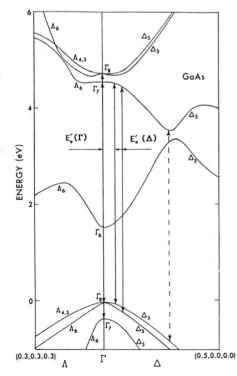

Fig. 8.26. Band structure of GaAs near Γ showing the critical point location for the E_0' structure. The indicated transitions give rise to the structure labeled (A, B, C) in Fig. 8.25

transitions at 4.5 eV (B) and 4.7 eV (C) in Fig. 8.25 result in the corresponding reflectivity structure. Aspnes and Studna also noted the possibility of the pseudocrossing producing some very weak structure at 4.4 eV. This interpretation is supported by the pseudopotential calculations. The 4.4 eV (A) transition corresponds to such a transition.

It should be noted, however, that there also exists a companion M_0 critical point owing to the spin-orbit splitting of the Δ_5 valence band. Since this companion critical point occurs about 0.1 eV higher in energy, it is nearly degenerate with the E_0' structure form Γ and Δ at 4.5 eV. In the calculated derivative spectrum, this structure is masked by the stronger M_1 critical points, and this may be the case in the electroreflectance measurements. In Tables 8.14 and 8.15, we summarize the reflectivity assignments and compare them to OPW results [8.42] and to experimental results [8.17, 44, 46, 47] both from wavelength modulation and Schottky barrier modulation.

In Fig. 8.27, we illustrate the calculated valence band density of states for GaAs, and the results of XPS measurements [8.48]. As for the diamond structure semiconductors, we may divide the density of states into three general regions. The first region is the most tightly bound energy band. Electron states corresponding to this band are strongly localized on the

Table 8.14. Theoretical and experimental reflectivity structure for gallium arsenide. The experimental data is from [8.11]. Critical point location in the Brillouin zone, energy, and symmetry are also given

GaAs Reflectivity structure [eV]		Associated critical points location in zone		Critical-point energy [eV]
Theory	Experiment		Symmetry	
3.03	3.02	$L_{4,5}^{v}$-L_{6}^{c} (0.5,0.5,0.5)	M_1	3.03
3.25	3.25	L_{6}^{v}-L_{6}^{c}	M_1	3.25
4.55	4.44	Δ_{5}^{v}-Δ_{5}^{c}	M_1	4.54
4.70	4.64	Δ_{5}^{v}-Δ_{5}^{c}		4.70
5.13	5.11	Plateau near (0.75,0.25,0.25)	...	5.07
5.59	5.64	X_{7}^{v}-X_{7}^{c} (1.0,0.0,0.0) X_{6}^{v}-X_{7}^{c}	M_0	5.28
5.84	5.91	Δ_{5}^{v}-Δ_{5}^{c} (0.55,0.0,0.0)	M_1	5.76
6.7	6.6[a]	$L_{4,5}^{v}$-$L_{4,5}^{c}$	M_1	6.67
		$L_{4,5}^{v}$-$L_{4,5}^{c}$		6.74

[a] From [8.7]

Table 8.15. Comparison of theoretical and experimental critical point energies (in eV) for gallium arsenide. Also presented are local pseudopotential and orthogonalized plane wave (OPW) calculations

Transition	Experiment		Theory		
	Reflectivity Structure	Critical[d] Point	Non-local EPM	Local[c] EPM	OPW[e]
$E_0\ \Gamma_8^v\text{-}\Gamma_6^c$	1.52[a]	1.52	1.51	1.52	1.34
$E_0+\Delta_0\ \Gamma_7^v\text{-}\Gamma_6^c$	1.86[b]	1.86	1.86	1.87	1.66
$E_1\ L_{4,5}^v\text{-}L_6^c$	3.02[c]	3.04	3.03	2.82	2.62
$E_1+\Delta_1\ L_6^v\text{-}L_6^c$	3.25[c]	3.25	3.25	3.05	2.82
$E_0'(\Gamma)\ \Gamma_8^v\text{-}\Gamma_7^c$	–	4.49	4.54	4.80	4.12
$E_0'+\Delta_0'\ \Gamma_8^v\text{-}\Gamma_8^v$	–	4.66	4.71	4.93	4.30
$E_0'+\Delta_0+\Delta_0'\ \Gamma_7^v\text{-}\Gamma_8^c$	–	5.01	5.05	5.28	4.62
$E_0'(\Delta)\ \Delta_5^v\text{-}\Delta_5^c$	4.44[c]	4.53	4.54	4.38	–
$E_0'+\Delta_0'(\Delta)\ \Delta_5^v\text{-}\Delta_5^c$	4.64[c]	4.71	4.70	4.55	–
Σ	5.11[c]	5.14	5.07	4.88	–
$X_7^v\text{-}X_6^c$	–	4.94	4.92	4.40	4.33
$X_6^v\text{-}X_6^c$	–	5.01	5.01	4.49	4.52
$X_7^v\text{-}X_7^c$	5.64[c]	5.34	5.28	4.67	4.58
$X_6^v\text{-}X_7^c$		5.42	5.38	4.76	4.67

[a] From [8.46]   [b] From [8.47]   [c] From [8.17]   [d] From [8.44]   [e] From [8.42]

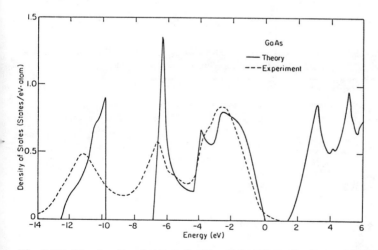

Fig. 8.27. The density of states of gallium arsenide as determined from XPS [8.48] and from pseudopotential theory

anion and are descendants of the atomic As 4s states. The next region of note is a peak arising from the onset of the second valence band. This band shows almost no energy variation along the X-U symmetry direction; in fact, it is very flat over the entire square face of the Brillouin zone. This energy band configuration results in a sharp onset of states above the antisymmetric gap. The character of states associated with the second valence band changes from predominantly cation s-like states at the band edge to predominantly anion p-like states at the band maximum. The third region of interest in the density of states extends from the onset of the third valence band (at about 4 eV below the valence band maximum) to the valence band maximum. This region encompasses the top two valence bands and is predominantly p-like and is associated with anion states. In Table 8.16, we have compiled a listing of experimental data [8.17, 48–50] on the GaAs valence bands and the corresponding predictions form pseudopotential OPW calculations.

We can confirm these qualitative assignments based on the atomic nature of the band states by examining contour maps of the charge densities band by band. In Fig. 8.28, we illustrate such contour maps for GaAs. The first band shows charge strongly localized on the anion with no real bonding character evident. The second band has a most unusual charge density. There is strong covalent bonding evident but little ionic character in the charge density. The chief reason for this charge density configurations is the strong dispersion present in this band. The lowest energy part of the band is characterized by wavefunctions strongly localized on the Ga, but the higher energy part of the band has wavefunctions localized on the As and in the bonding region. The top two valence bands show similar charge densities,

Table 8.16. Selected valence band and conduction band edges for GaAs. Comparison with experiment and several theorectial approaches (energies in eV)

Transition	Photoemission		Theory		OPW[d]
	UPS[a]	XPS[b]	Non-local EPM	local[c] EPM	
L_3^v-Γ_{15}^v	0.8 ± 0.2	1.4 ± 0.3	1.31	0.85	1.06
Σ_1^{min}-Γ_{15}^v	4.1 ± 0.2	4.4 ± 0.2	4.23	3.35	–
X_1^v-Γ_{15}^v	6.9 ± 0.2	7.2 ± 0.2	6.88	6.23	6.43
X_3^v-Γ_{15}^v	10.0 ± 0.2	10.7 ± 0.3	9.87	10.00	10.24
Λ_1^v-Λ_{15}^v	12.9 ± 0.5	13.8 ± 0.4	12.42	12.10	12.44

Transition	Experiment	Non-local EPM
Γ_1^c-X_1^c	0.38	0.52
Γ_{15}^v-X_1^c	1.7	2.16
L_1^c-X_1^c	0.09 ± 0.02	0.20
Γ_{15}^v-X_3^c	2.3	2.51

[a] From [8.49] [b] From [8.48] [c] From [8.17] [d] From [8.42] [e] From [8.50]

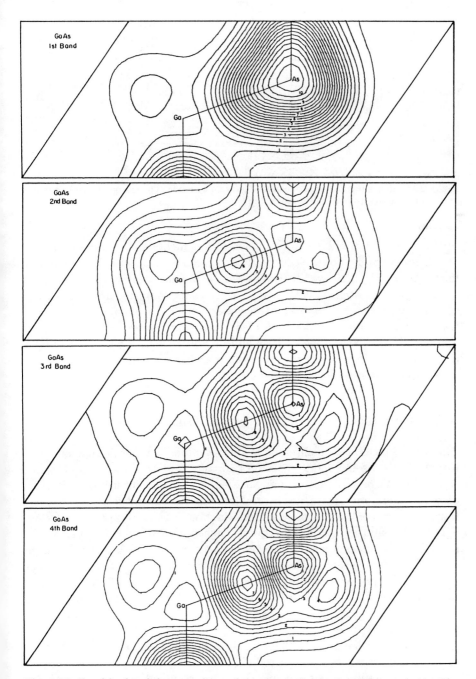

Fig. 8.28. Band by band decomposition of the charge density in gallium arsenide. The charge density contours are in units of electrons per unit cell volume. Note the large asymmetry in the cation/anion charge distribution for this moderately ionic semiconductor

111

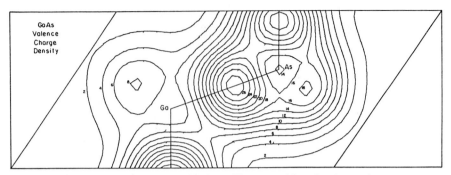

Fig. 8.29. Valence band charge density for gallium arsenide. The charge density contours are in units of electrons per unit cell volume

as expected. The uppermost band has slightly more As character as it is further removed in energy from the Ga-like elements of the second band.

Unfortunately, no experimentally determined charge density plot exists for GaAs. In Fig. 8.29, we illustrate the total valence density for GaAs from a recent pseudopotential calculation. A net charge transfer from the cation to anion is observed; however, it is quite difficult to quantify this charge transfer and to separate the "covalent" bonding charge from the "ionic" bonding charge. Nevertheless, it should be apparent that GaAs is partially ionic, for example from the fact that the charge density maximum along the bonding direction is closer to the anion than the cation.

8.7 The Electronic Structure of Zinc Selenide

The prototypical II-VI compound is zinc selenide. However, unlike our prototypical III-V semiconductor (GaAs) or our prototypical diamond semiconductor (Si or Ge), we do not have as detailed a picture for this class of semiconductors. There are several reasons for this situation. First, extensive experimental information is lacking for ZnSe as compared to GaAs. The larger band gap in ZnSe requires higher photon energies than GaAs for reflectivity measurements. Photon sources at these higher energies have not been routinely available. Also, some of the powerful optical techniques such as Schottky barrier electroreflectance cannot be employed for ZnSe owing to fabrication problems. Second, the Zn 3d-level resides close to the valence band. Traditionally, empirical pseudopotential band calculations do not explicitly include this level in ZnSe.

In Fig. 8.30, we present the band structure of ZnSe, and in Table 8.17, we list the energy levels at selected high symmetry points. Most features of this band structure can be accounted for by extrapolating from Ge to GaAs. Compared to Ge and GaAs, the band gaps in ZnSe, that is, the optical gap and the antisymmetric gap, have increased considerably in size. Moreover, the valence bands have narrowed and show less dispersion.

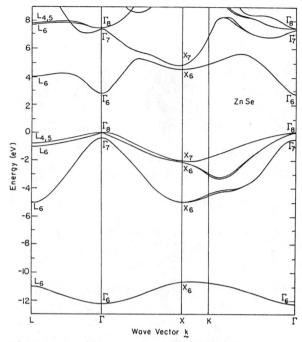

Fig. 8.30. Band structure for zinc selenide. The energy zero is taken to be the top of the valence band. The Zn 3d-level is not explicitly included in the pseudopotential calculation. Experimentally, this level occurs at about 9 eV below the valence band maximum

Table 8.17. Calculated eigenvalues (in eV) for zinc selenide at high symmetry points: Γ, L, and X

Γ_6^v	−12.25	X_6^v	−10.72	L_6^v	−11.08
Γ_7^v	0.45	X_6^v	−4.96	L_6^v	−5.08
Γ_8^v	0.00	X_6^v	−2.17	L_6^v	−1.04
Γ_6^c	2.76	X_7^v	−1.96	$L_{4,5}^v$	0.76
Γ_7^c	7.33	X_6^c	4.54	L_6^c	3.96
Γ_8^c	7.42	X_7^c	5.17	L_6^c	7.68
				$L_{4,5}^c$	7.72

In Fig. 8.31, we display the calculated and measured [8.51, 52] reflectivity spectrum for ZnSe; a derivative spectrum is not available. Owing to the increased ionic component of the bonding in ZnSe, the reflectivity spectrum is shifted to higher energy as compared to Ge or GaAs. It also exhibits much more structure than Ge or GaAs because of the larger separation between bands.

For the most part, the reflectivity spectrum can be analyzed by analogy with GaAs. The E_0 reflectivity structure lies between 2 and 4 eV and corresponds to the minimum energy gap at Γ. The E_1 structure at 4–5 eV arises

113

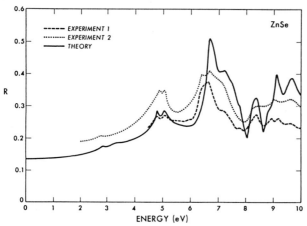

Fig. 8.31. Reflectivity spectrum for zinc selenide. Two experimental measurements are presented: the dashed line is from [8.51] and the dotted line from [8.52]

from transitions near to or at the L point. Structure corresponding to the E_2 peak arises from a localized region near the special point $(\frac{2\pi}{a})(\frac{3}{4}, \frac{1}{4}, \frac{1}{4})$. The E_0' structure at 7–8 eV may be an exception having no analogy in GaAs. It lies above the E_2 structure, thus the origin of structure is reversed in ZnSe as compared to GaAs. However, the origin of the E_0' structure appears to be the same, that is, from near Γ and along the Δ direction. The highest energy reflectivity structure, E_1', occurs at 8–9 eV and corresponds to transitions near the L point.

With the exception of the line shape near the E_2 peak, the pseudopotential results are consistent with experiment. It is possible that the lineshape discrepancy is an artifact of the calculation and is dependent on the sampling scheme used. We note that at energies above our calculated reflectivity, structure may arise from transitions involving the Zn 3d-states. As most pseudopotential calculations do not include these states, we will forgo further discussion of the optical transitions at these energies. In Table 8.18, we have summarized our optical assignments for ZnSe.

It should not be surprising that the density of states of ZnSe may also be interpreted in terms of an extrapolation from the Ge and GaAs band structures. In Fig. 8.32, we compare the calculated density of states for ZnSe with photoemission measurements from both XPS [8.48] and UPS [8.49]. Some of the early pseudopotential band structures, which had potentials based on optical data alone, were in mediocre agreement with the photoemission results. Specifically, local pseudopotentials chosen to reproduce optical gaps tend to overestimate the ionicity of the II-VI semiconductors. As a consequence, the valence bands become quite narrow compared to experiment. Nonlocal pseudopotentials do not suffer from this malady; they can be used to fit optical gaps with no corresponding increase in ionicity.

Table 8.18. Theoretical and experimental [8.51] reflectivity structure for zinc selenide. Critical point identifications including location in the Brillouin zone, energy, and symmetry are presented

ZnSe reflectivity structure [eV]		Associated transitions location in the zone	Symmetry	Critical-point energy [eV]
Theory	Experiment			
4.79	4.75	$L_{4,5}^v$-L_6^c	M_1	4.72
5.06	5.05	L_6^v-L_6^c	M_1	5.00
...	6.00	...	...	...
6.6	6.50	Δ_5^v-Δ_5^c	M_0	6.55
6.71	6.73	Plateau near (0.8,0.2,0.2)	...	
7.22	7.15	Δ_5^v-Δ_5^c (0.6,0.0,0.0)	M_1	7.08
7.47	7.60	Γ_8^v-Γ_8^c	M_0	7.42
7.76	7.80	Γ_7^v-Γ_8^c	M_0	7.87
8.39	8.45	$L_{4,5}^v$-$L_{4,5}^c$, L_6^c	M_0	8.46
		$\Lambda_{4,5}$-$\Lambda_{4,5}$, Λ^c_6 (0.35,0.35,0.35)	M_1	8.48
8.86	8.97	L_6^v-$L_{4,5}$, L_6^c (0.5,0.5,0.5)	M_0	8.74
		Λ_6^v-$\Lambda_{4,5}$, Λ_6^c (0.35,0.35,0.35)	M_1	8.76

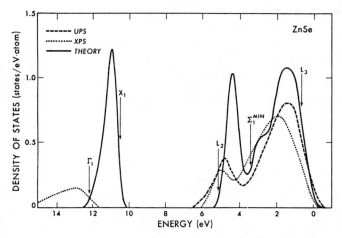

Fig. 8.32. Experimental and theoretical density of states for zinc selenide. The XPS data is after [8.48] and the UPS data from [8.49]. Zinc 3d-state contributions have been subtracted out from the photoemission data. The lowest valence band was not observed in the UPS state

Potentials based on local density theory yield optical gaps which are too small. If one attempts to compensate for this deficiency with a local potential, the optical gap size can only be increased by increasing the ionic character of the semiconductor. Nonlocal potentials which affect only d-orbitals can increase the optical gap by raising the energy of the conduction band but not the valence bands.

Table 8.19. Comparison of theoretical and experimental features in the electronic density of states for zinc selenide. The energies (in eV) are with respect to the valence band maximum

Feature	Experiment		Theory
ZnSe	XPS[a]	UPS[b]	
L_3^v	1.3 ± 0.3	0.7 ± 0.2	1.0
X_5^v	2.1 ± 0.3	—	2.2
Σ_1^{min}	3.4 ± 0.2	3.4 ± 0.3	3.4
L_2^v	5.6 ± 0.3	5.3 ± 0.3	5.1
X_1^v	12.5 ± 0.4	—	10.7
Γ_1^v	15.2 ± 0.6	—	12.3

[a] From [8.48] [b] From [8.49]

In Table 8.19, we summarize the critical point structure of the valence band density of states for ZnSe. Both XPS [8.48] and UPS [8.49] yield similar spectra for ZnSe, except that UPS cannot yield the position of the bottom valence band owing to the rather large emission for the Zn 3d-band and the accompanying obscuring of emission from the bottom band. It is unfortunate that UPS is not able to serve as a check on the lowest band since the best band calculations do not agree with the XPS placement. There are experimental questions about the placement of the lowest band; XPS and UPS often differ in their placement. Most likely, the difference is one of data reduction. It can be nontrivial to subtract the secondary emission from the primary emission. One piece of supporting evidence for

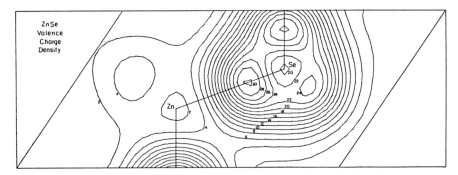

Fig. 8.33. Charge density for ZnSe. The contours are in units of electrons per unit cell volume

the pseudopotential interpretation comes from reflectivity measurements. *Freeouf* [8.52] has identified structure in the reflectivity spectrum of ZnSe which he associates with transitions from the lowest band. If this assignment is correct, then the position of the lowest valence band is in accord with the pseudopotential band structure of ZnSe.

Figure 8.33 shows a plot of the charge density for ZnSe. Again, we note a smooth transition from Ge and GaAs as we progress from a covalent bonding system to a partially ionic system. The charge density disparity between the anion and cation increases and the bond charge shifts even closer to the anion.

8.8 The Electronic Structure of Other III-V and II-VI Semiconductors

Pseudopotentials have been used to determine band structures of many III-V and II-VI semiconductors. Here we will simply compile results for some of these materials rather than provide a detailed analysis for each case. In general, the III-V semiconductors resemble GaAs with small, but not insignificant, differences. Likewise, ZnSe resembles many II-VI semiconductors. Most of the differences between the zinc-blende semiconductors can be ascribed to variations in the competing bonding mechanisms, that is, covalent versus ionic forces. This accounts for the success of Phillips' decomposition of the bonding-antibonding gap into homopolar and ionic parts and the categorization of trends with his ionicity scale.

Let us first consider the III-V compounds with Ga and In cations: GaP, GaSb, InP, InAs, and InSb. The band strcutures for these materials are presented in Figs. 8.34–8.38. The energy levels at high symmetry points are presented in Tables 8.20–8.24. We will concentrate on the band structures of GaP and GaSb; similar discussions will apply to InP and InSb. Because phosphorous is certainly more electronegative than antimony, we expect GaP to be more ionic than GaSb. With this increased ionic character, GaP should have larger optical gaps and more charge transfer than GaSb. Moreover, antimony has wavefunctions which are more diffuse than phosphorous. Intuitively, we expect GaSb to be more metallic and less covalent than GaP. This effect further reduces the optical gaps in GaSb.

Another contrasting effect is the enhancement of relativistic effects in GaSb compared to GaP. Since most of the valence charge is localized on the anion, atomic or core-induced effects associated with the anion, such as spin-orbit interactions, are retained in the solid. Antimony with its higher atomic number has larger spin-orbit interactions than phosphorous. Thus, the valence bands at Γ_{15} are split by 0.76 eV in GaSb, but only by 0.13 eV in GaP.

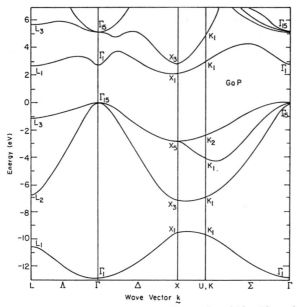

Fig. 8.34. Band structure for gallium phosphide. The valence band maximum is taken as the energy zero. Spin-orbit interactions were not included in this calculation

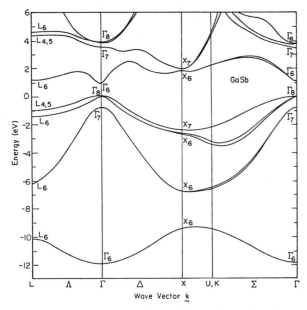

Fig. 8.35. Band structure for gallium antimonide. The energy zero is taken to be the valence band maximum

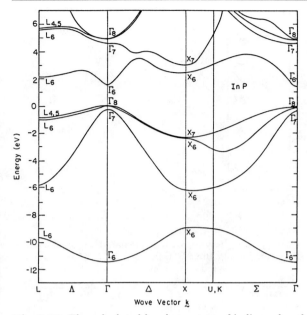

Fig. 8.36. The calculated band structure of indium phosphide. The valence band maximum is the zero of energy

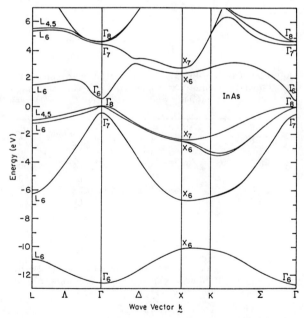

Fig. 8.37. The band structure of indium arsenide. The zero of energy coincides with the valence band maximum

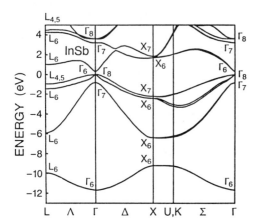

Fig. 8.38. The band structure of indium antimonide. The top of the valence band is the energy zero

Table 8.20. Calculated eigenvalues (in eV) for gallium phosphide at high symmetry points Γ, X, and L

Γ_1^v	-12.99	X_1^v	-9.46	L_1^v	-10.60
Γ_{15}^v	0.00	X_3^v	-7.07	L_2^v	-6.84
Γ_1^c	2.88	X_5^v	-2.73	L_3^v	-1.10
Γ_{15}^c	5.25	X_1^c	2.16	L_1^c	2.79
		X_3^c	2.71	L_3^c	5.74

Table 8.21. Calculated eigenvalues for gallium antimonide (in eV) at the high symmetry points Γ, X, and L

Γ_6^v	-12.00	X_6^v	-9.33	L_6^v	-10.17
Γ_7^v	-0.76	X_6^v	-6.76	L_6^v	-6.25
Γ_8^v	0.00	X_6^v	-2.61	L_6^v	-1.45
Γ_6^c	0.86	X_7^v	-2.37	$L_{4,5}^v$	-1.00
Γ_7^c	3.44	X_6^c	1.72	L_6^c	1.22
Γ_8^c	3.77	X_7^c	1.79	L_6^c	4.43
				$L_{4,5}^c$	4.59

Table 8.22. Calculated eigenvalues for indium phosphide (in eV) at high symmetry points Γ, X, and L

Γ_6^v	-11.42	X_6^v	-8.91	L_6^6	-9.67
Γ_7^v	-0.21	X_6^v	-6.01	L_6^v	-5.84
Γ_8^v	0.00	X_6^v	-2.09	L_6^v	-1.09
Γ_6^c	1.50	X_7^v	-2.06	$L_{4,5}^v$	-0.94
Γ_8^c	4.64	X_6^c	2.44	L_6^c	2.19
Γ_8^c	4.92	X_7^c	2.97	L_6^c	5.58
				$L_{4,5}^v$	5.70

Table 8.23. Calculated eigenvalues for indium arsenide (in eV) at the high symmetry points Γ, X, and L

Γ_6^v	-12.69	X_6^v	-10.20	L_6^v	-10.92
Γ_7^v	-0.43	X_6^v	-6.64	L_6^v	-6.23
Γ_8^v	0.00	X_6^v	-2.47	L_6^v	-1.26
Γ_6^c	0.37	X_7^v	-2.37	$L_{4,5}^v$	-1.00
Γ_7^c	4.39	X_6^c	2.28	L_6^c	1.53
Γ_8^c	4.63	X_7^c	2.66	L_6^c	5.42
				$L_{4,5}^c$	5.55

Γ_6^v	-11.71	X_6^v	-9.20	L_6^v	-9.95
Γ_7^v	-0.82	X_6^v	-6.43	L_6^v	-5.92
Γ_8^v	0.00	X_6^v	-2.45	L_6^v	-1.44
Γ_6^c	0.25	X_7^v	-2.24	$L_{4,5}^v$	-0.96
Γ_7^c	3.16	X_6^c	1.71	L_6^v	1.03
Γ_8^c	3.59	X_7^c	1.83	L_6^c	4.30
				$L_{4,5}^c$	4.53

Table 8.24. Calculated eigenvalues for indium antimonide (in eV) at the high symmetry points Γ, X, and L

The optical reflectivity spectra and logarithmic derivative spectra for the III-V's discussed here are presented in Fig. 8.39–8.48. We also present reflectivity assignments in Tables 8.25–8.29 and experimental data [8.11, 50, 53–57]. Not surprisingly, the trends in reflectivity spectra follow the band structure features. GaP, in contrast to GaSb, is not rich in reflectivity structure owing to the lack of strong spin-orbit interactions. Also, the corresponding reflectivity structure is shifted to higher energy in GaP owing to the larger band gaps.

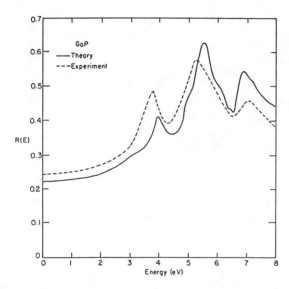

Fig. 8.39. Reflectivity spectrum of gallium phosphide. The experimental data is from [8.7]

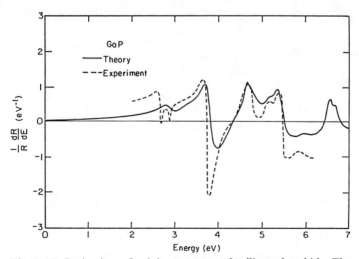

Fig. 8.40. Derivative reflectivity spectrum of gallium phosphide. The experimental data is from [8.53]

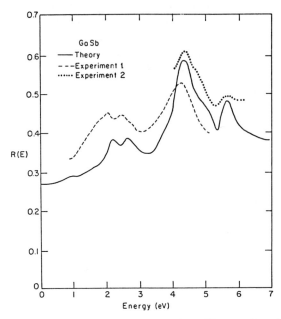

Fig. 8.41. Reflectivity spectrum for gallium antimonide. Two sets of experimental measurements are illustrated. The dashed curve is after [8.54] and the dotted curve is after [8.55]

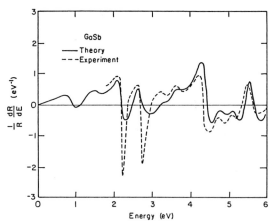

Fig. 8.42. Derivative reflectivity spectrum for gallium antimonide. The experimental data is from [8.11]

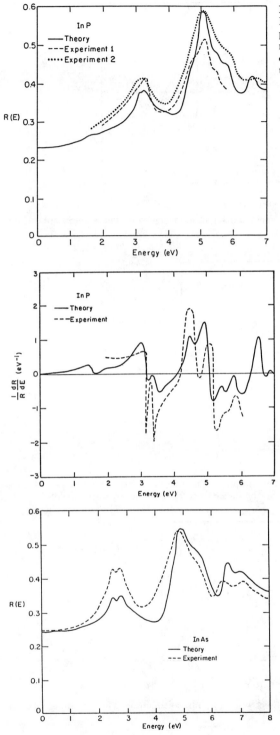

Fig. 8.43.
Reflectivity spectrum for indium phosphide. Two sets of experimental data are presented: the dotted curve is from [8.53] and the dashed curve from [8.56]

Fig. 8.44. Derivative reflectivity spectrum for indium phosphide. The experimental data is from [8.53]

Fig. 8.45.
Reflectivity spectrum of indium arsenide. The experimental data is from [8.11]

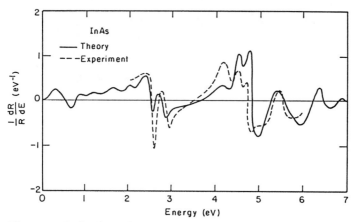

Fig. 8.46. Derivative reflectivity spectrum for indium arsenide. The experimental data is from [8.11]

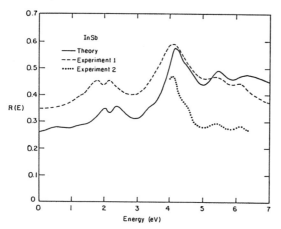

Fig. 8.47. Reflectivity spectrum for indium antimonde. Two experimental sets of data are presented [8.7, 34] illustrated by the dahsed and dotted curves, respectively

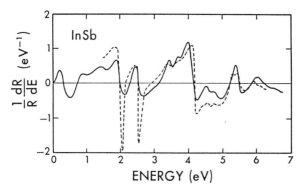

Fig. 8.48. Derivative reflectivity spectrum for indium antimonide. The experimental data (dashed line) is from [8.11]

Table 8.25. Identification of electronic transitions responsible for the prominent theoretical and experimental reflectivity structure in gallium phosphide, including location in the Brillouin zone, energy, and symmetry for the calculated critical points. Experimental data are from [8.53]

GaP Reflectivity structure [eV]		Location in Brillouin zone	Symmetry	Critical-point energy [eV]
Theory	Experiment			
2.95	2.89[a] 2.97	Γ_{15}^v-Γ_1^c (0.0,0.0,0.0)	M_0	2.88
3.89	3.79	L_3^v-L_1^c (0.5,0.5,0.5)	M_1	3.89
4.95	4.80	Δ_5^v-Δ_1^c (0.7,0.0,0.0)	M_1	4.91
5.24	5.19	Γ_{15}^v-Γ_{15}^c (0.0,0.0,0.0)	...	5.24
5.45	5.42	Plateau near (0.6,0.2,0.2)	...	
6.8	6.7[b]	L_3^v-L_3^c (0.5,0.5,0.5)	M_1	6.84

[a] Spin-orbit splitting is not included in the calculation
[b] From [8.50]

Table 8.26. Identification of electronic transition responsible for the prominent theoretical and experimental [8.11] reflectivity structure is gallium antimonide, including location of the Brillouin zone, energy, and symmetry of calculated critical points

GaSb Reflectivity structure [eV]		Location in Brillouin zone	Symmetry	Critical-point energy [eV]
Theory	Experiment			
2.22	2.15	$L_{4,5}^v$-L_6^c (0.5,0.5,0.5)	M_1	2.22
2.86	2.60	L_6^v-L_6^c	M_1	2.67
3.3	3.35	Γ_8^v-Γ_7^c (0.0,0.0,0.0)	M_0	3.44
3.76	3.69	Γ_8^v-Γ_8^c (0.0,0.0,0.0)	M_0	3.77
4.37	4.35	Plateau near (0.7,0.2,0.2)	...	
4.84	4.75	Δ_5^v-Δ_5^c	M_1	4.84
5.13	5.07	Δ_5^v-Δ_5^c	M_1	5.12
5.65	5.65	$L_{4,5}^v$-L_6^c (0.5,0.5,0.5)	M_1	5.43

Table 8.27. Identification of electronic transition for the prominent theoretical and experimental reflectivity structure in indium phosphide, including location in the Brillouin zone, energy, and symmetry of calculated critical points. Experimental work is from [8.53] (except as noted)

InP Reflectivity structure [eV]		Location in Brillouin zone	Symmetry	Critical-point energy [eV]
Theory	Experiment			
1.50	1.42	Γ_8^v-Γ_6^c (0.0,0.0,0.0)	M_0	1.50
3.13	3.24	$L_{4,5}^v$-L_6^c (0.5,0.5,0.5)	M_1	3.13
3.28	3.38	L_6^v-L_6^c		3.28
4.76	4.78	Γ_8^v-Γ_7^c (0.0,0.0,0.0)	M_0	4.64
		Δ_5^v-Δ_5^c (0.2,0.0,0.0)	M_1	4.80
5.05	5.10	Plateau near (0.75,0.25,0.25)	...	5.00
5.44	5.25[a]	Γ_7^v-Γ_8^c (0.0,0.0,0.0)	M_0	5.13
5.73	5.77	Δ_5^v-Δ_5^c (0.7,0.0,0.0)	M_1	5.62
6.55	6.57[a]	$L_{4,5}^v$-L_6^c (0.5,0.5,0.5)	M_1	6.52

[a] From [8.54]

Table 8.28. Identification of electronic transitions responsible for the prominent theoretical and experimental reflectivity structure in indium arsenide, including location in the Brillouin zone, energy, and symmetry of calculated critical points. Experiment is from [8.11] (except as noted)

InAs Reflectivity structure [eV]		Location in Brillouin zone	Symmetry	Critical-point energy [eV]
Theory	Experiment			
2.54	2.61	$L_{4,5}^v$-L_6^c (0.5,0.5,0.5)	M_1	2.53
2.81	2.88	L_6^v-L_6^c	M_1	2.79
4.3	4.39	Γ_8^v-Γ_7^c (0.0,0.0,0.0)	M_0	4.39
4.52	4.58	Γ_8^v-Γ_8^c	M_0	4.63
4.85	4.74	Plateau near (0.75,0.25,0.25)	...	
5.36	5.31	Δ_5^v-Δ_5^c (0.7,0.0,0.0)	M_1	5.24
5.45	5.5	Δ_5^v-Δ_5^c	M_1	5.34
6.49	6.5	$L_{4,5}^v$-L_6^c (0.5,0.5,0.5)	M_1	6.41
6.92	6.8[a]	L_6^v-$L_{4,5}^c$ (0.5,0.5,0.5)	M_1	6.81

[a] From [8.57]

Table 8.29. Theoretical and experimental [8.11] reflectivity structure for indium antimonide including the location in the Brillouin zone, energy, and symmetry of the calculated critical points

InSb Reflectivity structure [eV]		Associated critical points location in	Symmetry	Critical-point energy [eV]
Theory	Experiment	zone		
1.99	1.98	$L_{4,5}^{v}$-L_6^{c} (0.5,0.5,0.5)	M_1	1.99
2.47	2.48	$L_6^{v}L_6^{c}$	M_1	2.47
3.53	3.39	Γ_8^{v}-Γ_7^{c} (0.0,0.0,0.0)	M_0	3.16
3.80	3.78	Γ_8^{v}-Γ_8^{c}	M_0	3.59
		Δ_5^{v}-Δ_5^{c} (0.3,0.0,0.0)	M_1	3.3
			M_0	3.7
4.18	4.23	Plateau near (0.7,0.2,0.2)	...	
4.54	4.56	Δ_5^{v}-Δ_5^{c} (0.5,0.0,0.0)	M_1	4.44
4.74	4.75		M_1	4.69
5.44	5.33	L_4^{v}-L_6^{c} (0.5,0.5,0.5)	M_1	5.26
6.16	5.96	L_6^{v}-$L_{4,5}^{v}$ (0.5,0.5,0.5)	M_1	5.97

The valence band densities of states as determined from pseudopotential band structures and as measured by photoemission are presented in Figs. 8.49–8.53. Identification of key valence band features [8.20, 48–50] are indicated in Tables 8.30–8.34. Two qualitative trends in the valence band densities of states can be ascertained from an overview of the calculations. In general, as the lattice constant increases, the valence band width decreases. One can ascribe this trend to a reduction of hybridization with increasing separation of atomic constituents. The other trend is that more ionic materials have larger antisymmetric gaps than do more covalent materials.

In Figs. 8.54–8.58, we display charge contour maps for the III-V semiconductors. Unfortunately, unlike the case of silicon, we do not have a complete contour map for any of the III-V compounds from x-ray data. Thus, we cannot compare experiment with the charge density extracted from pseudopotential calculations. However, in this case of InSb, *Bilderback* and *Colella* (8.58) have measured quasi-forbidden reflections. These reflections are sensitive test of the asphericity of the valence charge density. Bilderback and Colella used a tetrahedrally distorted spherical-atom model to reproduce accurately the measured structure factors. From their model, it is possible to extract a valence charge density for InSb. In Fig. 8.59, the most recent pseudopotential charge density for InSb is presented and compared to the experimental density within the tetrahedrally distorted atom model.

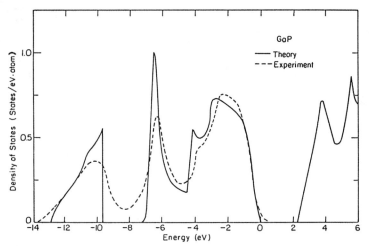

Fig. 8.49. Density of states for gallium phosphide. The experimental data is from XPS [8.48]

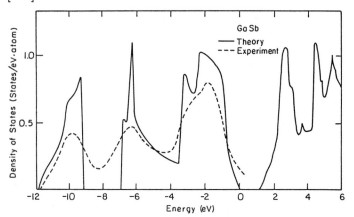

Fig. 8.50. Density of states for gallium antimonide. The experimental data is from XPS [8.48]

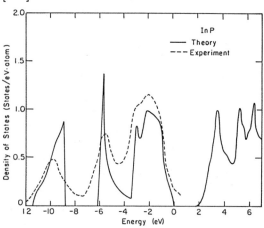

Fig. 8.51. Density of states for indium phosphide. The experimental data is from XPS [8.48]

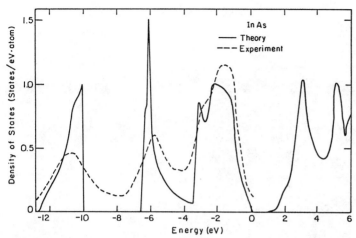

Fig. 8.52. Density of states for indium arsenide. The experimental data is from XPS [8.48]

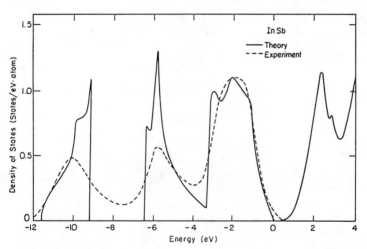

Fig. 8.53. Density of states for indium antimonide. The experimental data is from XPS [8.48]

Also indicated is an older, local pseudopotential charge density. Both potentials place the bond charge maximum in approximately the correct position. However, the more recent nonlocal potential, which contains more accurate valence band information, provides a more accurate magnitude for the bond charge.

Table 8.30. Valence and conduction band features for gallium phosphide as calculated and as measured by experiment. Energies are in eV

Transition	Experiment		Theory
	UPS[a]	XPS[b]	
L_3^v-Γ_{15}^v	0.8 ± 0.2	1.2 ± 0.3	1.1
X_5^v-Γ_{15}^v	–	2.7 ± 0.2	2.7
Σ_1^{min}-Γ_{15}^v	4.1 ± 0.2	4.0 ± 0.3	4.2
X_3^v-Γ_{15}^v	6.9 ± 0.2	6.0 ± 0.3	7.1
X_1^v-Γ_{15}^v	9.7 ± 0.3	0.6 ± 0.3	9.5
Γ_1^v-Γ_{15}^v	11.8 ± 0.5	13.2 ± 0.4	13.0
Γ_{15}^v-X_1^c	2.34[c]		2.16
X_1^c-X_3^c	0.3[c]		0.5
Γ_{15}^c-Γ_{12}^c	10[c]		10.5
Γ_{15}^v-Γ_1^c	2.8[d]		2.8
Γ_{15}^v-Γ_{15}^c	5.0[d]		5.2

[a] From [8.49]   [b] From [8.48]   [c] From [8.50]   [d] From [8.20]

Table 8.31. Theoretical and experimental valence and conduction band features for gallium antimonide. Energies are in eV and are measured from the valence band maximum

Feature GaSb	Experiment	Theory
L_3^v	1.3 ± 0.2[a]	1.2
X_5^v	2.7 ± 0.2[a]	2.5
Σ_1^{min}	3.8 ± 0.2[a]	3.6
X_3^v	6.9 ± 0.3[a]	6.8
X_1^v	9.4 ± 0.2[a]	9.3
Γ_1^v	11.6 ± 0.3[a]	12.0
Γ_{15}^c	3.4[b]	3.6
X_1^c	~1.7[b]	1.7

[a] From [8.48]   [b] From [8.20]

Table 8.32. Theoretical and experimental [8.48] valence band features for indium phosphide. Energies are in eV and are measured from the valence band maximum

Feature InP	Experiment XPS	Theory
L_3^v	1.0 ± 0.3	1.0
X_5^v	2.0 ± 0.2	2.1
Σ_1^{min}	3.2 ± 0.2	3.3
X_3^v	5.9 ± 0.2	6.0
X_1^v	8.9 ± 0.3	8.9
Γ_1^v	11.0 ± 0.4	11.4

Table 8.33. Theoretical and experimental [8.48] valence band features for indium arsenide. Energies are in eV and are measured from the valence band maximum

Feature InAs	Experiment XPS	Theory
L_3^v	0.9 ± 0.3	1.1
X_5^v	2.4 ± 0.3	2.4
Σ_1^{min}	3.3 ± 0.2	3.4
X_3^v	6.3 ± 0.2	6.2
X_1^v	9.8 ± 0.3	10.2
Γ_1^v	12.3 ± 0.4	12.7

Table 8.34. Comparison of theoretical and experimental features in the electronic density of states for indium antimonide. The energies are in eV and are with respect to the top of the valence band

Feature InSb	Experiment		Theory
	XPS[a]	UPS[b]	
L_3^v	1.4 ± 0.3	1.05 ± 0.3	1.0
X_5^v	2.4 ± 0.4	–	2.3
Σ_1^{min}	3.4 ± 0.2	3.65 ± 0.3	3.4
X_3^v	6.4 ± 0.2	6.5 ± 0.3	6.4
X_1^v	9.5 ± 0.2	9.0 ± 0.3	9.2
Γ_1^v	11.7 ± 0.3	11.2 ± 0.5	11.7

[a] From [8.48]   [b] [8.49]

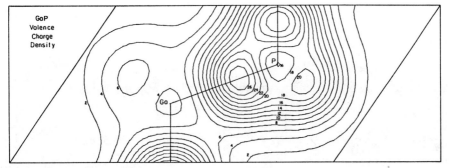

Fig. 8.54. Valence charge density for gallium phosphide. Contours are in units of electrons pe unit cell volume

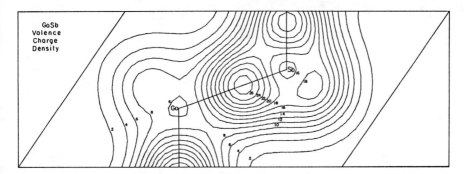

Fig. 8.55. Valence charge density for gallium antimonide. Contours are in units of electrons per unit cell volume

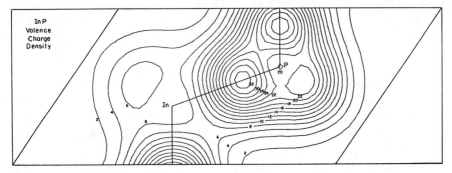

Fig. 8.56. Valence charge density for indium phosphide. Contours are in units of electrons per unit cell volume

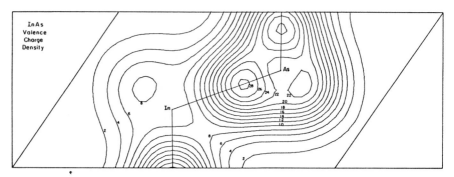

Fig. 8.57. Valence charge density for indium arsenide. Contours are in units of electrons per unit cell volume

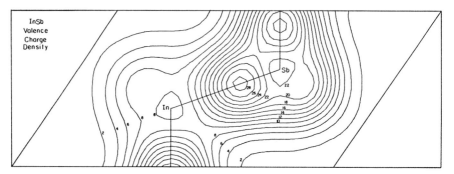

Fig. 8.58. Valence charge density for indium antimonide. Contours are in units of electrons per unit cell volume

With respect to other II-VI semiconductors, we will concentrate on cadmium telluride and mercury telluride. We may approach CdTe from the viewpoint of its position in the series Sn-InSb-CdTe, just as we approached ZnSe in terms of the series Ge-GaAs-ZnSe. The major differences of the Sn-InSb-CdTe series from the Ge-GaAs-ZnSe series are its higher metallicity and spin-orbit interactions. For example, the band gaps are approximately 1 eV smaller and the spin-orbit splittings 0.5 eV larger in the Sn-InSb-CdTe series. Both of these trends are a direct consequence of increasing atomic number and the accompanying weakening of the core potential. It is not so easy to describe the band structure of mercury telluride. HgTe is quite different to other II-VI semiconductors in that it is a negative band gap material. That is the bands Γ_8^v and Γ_6^c are inverted from the usual ordering of II-VI semiconductors. In this sense, mercury telluride is not really a semiconductor but rather a semimetal.

In Figs. 8.60 and 8.61, we present the pseudopotential band structures for CdTe and HgTe respectively. In Table 8.35, we list the calculated energy

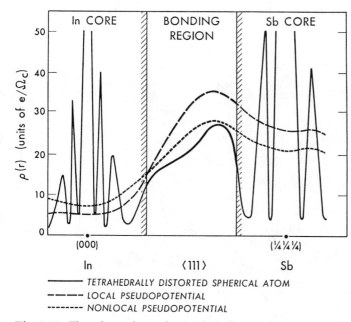

In CORE   BONDING REGION   Sb CORE

(000)   (¼¼¼)

In   ⟨111⟩   Sb

——— TETRAHEDRALLY DISTORTED SPHERICAL ATOM
— — — LOCAL PSEUDOPOTENTIAL
········· NONLOCAL PSEUDOPOTENTIAL

Fig. 8.59. The valence charge density for indium antimonide as calculated from a tetrahedrally distorted spherical-atom model after [8.58]. Also indicated are two pseudopotential calculations: a local potential (long dashed line) and a nonlocal potential (short dashed line). In general, local pseudopotentials fit to optical data tend to overestimate the charge transfer from cation to anion. The pseudopotential charge calculations do not reproduce the nodal structure within the core and should only be compared to the measurements within the bonding region

levels for CdTe at high symmetry points. HgTe can be thought of as having a negative bandgap of $-0.3\,\mathrm{eV}$ if we consider the usual definition of the gap between the top of the valence band Γ_8^v and the lowest conduction band Γ_6^c. This band configuration is similar to that of gray tin. One very useful feature of the band structures of CdTe and HgTe is that the materials can be alloyed to obtain a band gap between the two limiting cases, that is, between HgTe ($-0.3\,\mathrm{eV}$ gap) and CdTe ($1.6\,\mathrm{eV}$ gap).

In Figs. 8.62 and 8.63, we present the reflectivity spectrum for CdTe and HgTe, and in Tables 8.36 and 8.37, we list the origin of the observed reflectivity structure [8.59] within the Brillouin zone. The gross features of the two spectra are very similar; the most noticeable difference occurring near the reflectivity threshold of HgTe. The semimetallic behavior of HgTe

Γ_6^v	-11.07	X_6^v	-9.12	L_6^v	-9.64
Γ_7^v	-0.89	X_6^v	-5.05	L_6^v	-4.73
Γ_8^v	0.00	X_6^v	-1.98	L_6^v	-1.18
Γ_6^c	1.59	X_7^v	-1.60	$L_{4,5}^\mathrm{v}$	-0.65
Γ_7^c	5.36	X_6^c	3.48	L_6^c	2.82
Γ_8^c	5.61	X_7^c	3.95	L_6^c	6.18
				$L_{4,5}^\mathrm{c}$	6.35

Table 8.35. Calculated eigenvalues (in eV) for cadmium telluride at high symmetry points Γ, X, and L

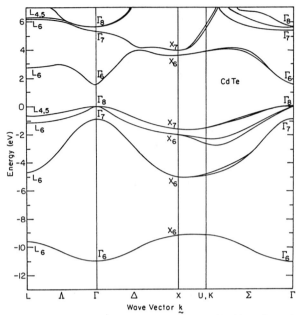

Fig. 8.60. Band structure for cadmium telluride. The valence band maximum is taken as the zero of energy

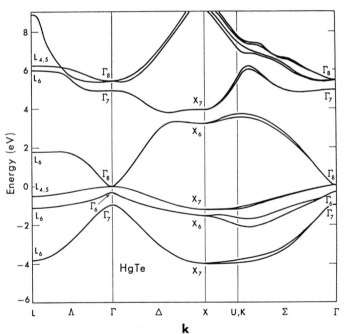

Fig. 8.61. Band structure for mercury telluride. As for gray tin, the band gap vanishes for mercury telluride. The zero of energy is taken at the conjunction of valence and conduction bands

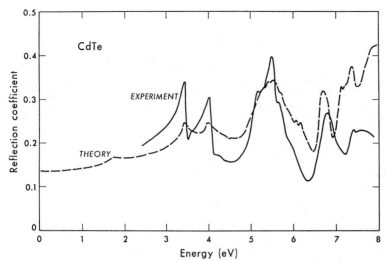

Fig. 8.62. Reflectivity spectrum for cadmium telluride. The experimental data is from [8.59]

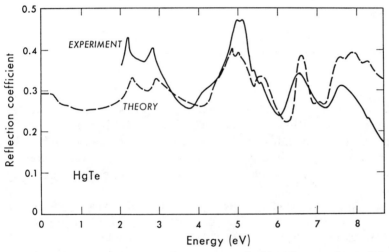

Fig. 8.63. Reflectivity spectrum for mercury telluride. The experimental data is from [8.59]

is evident in this region. However, at higher energies the metallic nature of HgTe is completely suppressed by interband transitions, and HgTe appears as CdTe with the structure shifted to lower energy. One minor discrepancy between theory and experiment for both CdTe and ZnSe is the line shape of the E_2 peak; in experiment there is some structure on the low energy side of the E_2 peak which is not present in the theory.

Table 8.36. Theoretical and experimental [8.59] reflectivity structure for cadmium telluride. Critical-point location in the Brillouin zone, energy, and symmetry are also listed

CdTe Reflectivity structure [eV]		Associated critical points, location in zone	Symmetry	Critical-point energy [eV]
Theory	Experiment			
1.65	1.59	Γ_8^v-Γ_7^c (0.0,0.0,0.0)	M_0	1.59
3.49	3.46	$L_{4,5}^v$-L_6^c (0.5,0.5,0.5)	M_1 l	3.47
4.04	4.03	L_6^v-L_6^c	M_1	4.00
5.16	5.18	Δ_5^v-Δ_5^c (0.5,0.0,0.0)	M_0	5.14
5.50	5.53	Plateau near (0.75,0.25,0.25)	...	
5.68	5.68	Δ_5^v-Δ_5^c (0.75,0.0,0.0)	M_1	5.58
6.00	5.95	Δ_5^v-Δ_5^c	M_1	5.96
6.91	6.82	$L_{4,5}^v$-L_6^c (0.5,0.5,0.5)	M_1	6.83
...	7.44			
7.79	7.6	L_6^v-$L_{4,5}^c$ (0.5,0.5,0.5)	M_1	7.53

In Fig. 8.64, we present a calculated valence band density of states for CdTe and compare it to the photoemission results from UPS [8.49] (a similar comparison is not available for HgTe). The Cd 4d-level is not included in the theory and has been subtracted out from the photoemission data. The agreement between theory and experiment is quite good, especially for the lowest valence band. Some of the salient photoemission data is compiled in Table 8.38.

Figure 8.65 shows the charge density for CdTe; it is very close to that of ZnSe. It is interesting to note that the bond charge for CdTe appears to be a bit more localized than in ZnSe. This difference would seem to be real. Although it is difficult to quantify bonding charge, *Walter* and *Cohen* [8.60] attempted to examine possible correlations of bond charge with Phillips' dielectric theory. Specifically, if the Phillips' ionicity scale is applied to a zinc-blende compound, then one observes a critical ionicity factor which dictates whether a crstal will be stable in the rock-salt six-fold coordinated structure or the zinc-blende (or wurtzite) four-fold coordinated structure. Since *Phillips* [8.28] has suggested that the critical ionicity occurs when the bond charge is small, if we had a measure of the bond charge we could test this theory. The definition of such a charge is to some extent arbitrary; however, if we use some common procedure to define a background density

Table 8.37. Theoretical and experimental [8.59] reflectivity structure for mercury telluride. The critical-point identification is also given in terms of location in the Brillouin zone, energy, and symmetry. For the notation here, the lowest valence band is labeled 1 and the highest valence band 4

HgTe Reflectivity structure [eV]		Associated critical points, location in zone	Sym-metry	Critical point energy [eV]
Theory	Experiment			
0	0	$\Gamma(4-5)$ (0,0,0)	M_0	0
2.32	2.25	$L(4-5)$ (0.5,0.5,0.5)	M_1	2.25
2.92	2.87	$L(3-5)$ (0.5,0.5,0.5)	M_1	2.87
4.03	4.18	Volume near $\Delta(4-5)$ (0.6,0,0)	...	4.03
4.47	...	Volume (4-5) (0.8,0.2,0.2)	...	4.42
...	...	$X(3-5)$ (1,0,0)	M_1	4.71
4.87	4.98	$K(4-5)$ (0.75,0.75,0)	M_2	4.82
5.02	5.10	$\Delta(4-6)$ (0.14,0,0)	...	5.00
		(4-6) (0.14,0.07,0.07)	M_2	5.02
...	5.45	$X(3-6)$ (1,0,0)	M_1	5.43
		$\Gamma(4-7)$ (0,0,0)	...	5.44
5.57	5.62	$\Delta(3-6)$ (0.2,0,0)	M_1	5.52
		(3-6) (0.15,0.07,0.07)	...	5.57
6.63	6.53	Volume (4-6) (0.6,0.5,0.3)	...	6.53
7.07	...	Volume (3-6) (0.6,0.5,0.3)	...	7.02
7.57		Volume (4-7) (0.6,0.4,0.1)		7.47
7.88	7.6	Volume (3-7) (0.6,0.3,0.1)	...	7.75
8.32	8.3	Volume (3-7) (0.6,0.3,0.1)	...	8.2

Table 8.38. Comparison of theoretical and experimental features of the valence band of cadmium telluride. The energies are in eV and are with respect to the top of the valence band

Feature CdTe	Experiment XPS[a]	UPS[b]	Theory
L_3^v	0.9 ± 0.3	0.7 ± 0.2	0.9
X_5^v	1.8 ± 0.2	—	1.7
Σ_1^{min}	2.7 ± 0.3	2.8 ± 0.2	2.7
X_3^v	5.1 ± 0.2	4.7 ± 0.2	5.2
X_1^v	—	8.7 ± 0.3	9.1
Γ_1^v	—	—	11.1

[a] From [8.48] [b] From [8.49]

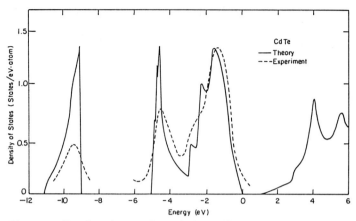

Fig. 8.64. Density of states for cadmium telluride. The experimental data is from UPS [8.49]. The Cd 4d-states have not been included in the pseudopotential calculations and contributions from the 4d-states have been subtracted from the experimental data

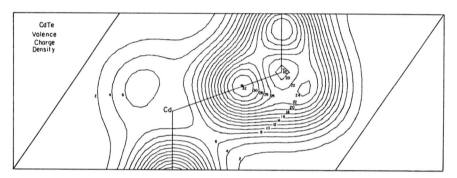

Fig. 8.65. Valence charge density for cadmium telluride. Contours are in units of electrons per unit cell volume

and subtract it to obtain the bond charge Z_b, then any trends we obtain with the crystal ionicity are unlikely to be greatly affected by our definitions. If we choose a background charge density ϱ_0 which is the value ϱ at the lowest level contour completely surrounding the bond charge maximum, then we may define the bond charge from an integral over the volume Ω_0 contained within this lowest contour, that is

$$Z_b = \int_{\Omega_0} (\varrho - \varrho_0) d\tau \quad . \tag{8.6}$$

The bond charge given by this definition of Z_b is plotted against Phillips' crystal ionicity in Fig. 8.66. The magnitude of the bond charge apparently goes to zero near $f_i = 0.8$. This is very close to the critical ionicity ob-

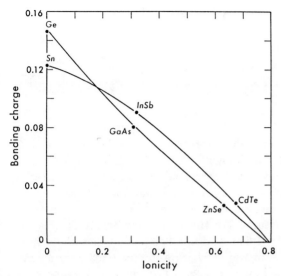

Fig. 8.66. Bond charge as a function of ionicity for two isoelectric series of zinc-blende semiconductors. The ionicity scale is from [8.28]. The bond charge as determined from pseudopotential calculations appears to vanish at the critical ionicity value of 0.785 as predicted by Phillips' dielectric theory. The critical ionicity parameter separates four-fold and six-fold coordinate binary compound semiconductors

tained by Phillips, $f_c = 0.785$, which divides zinc-blende/wurtzite from the rock-salt structures. This very dramatic result suggests that the stability of tetrahedral partially ionic crystals is determined primarily by electrostatic forces connected with bond charges.

9. Wurtzite Structure Semiconductors

The wurtzite structure II-VI semiconductors are closely related to the II-VI zinc-blendes. In analogy with the diamond and zinc-blende structures, the wurtzite structure can be constructed by considering two interpenetrating lattices. However, in this case they are hexagonal close packed lattices. The nearest neighbors and next nearest neighbors are the same in the ideal wurtzite and zinc-blende structures. For the ideal wurtzite case, the lattice parameters are $c/a = 2\sqrt{6}/3 = 1.633$, and $u = 3/8$ [9.1]. When the nearest neighbor distance is the same in the wurtzite and zinc-blende structures, the lattice constants are related by $a_z = \sqrt{2}a_w$. For wurtzite, there are four atoms per unit cell in contrast to two for zinc-blende. Since the volume per atom is the same, a given volume of reciprocal space for wurtzite contains approximately twice as many reciprocal lattice points. The lattice constants for several wurtzite structure semiconductors are given in Table 9.1.

Some common wurtzite semiconductors are BeO, ZnO, ZnS, ZnSe, CdS, and CdSe. The last four of these compounds can also be crystallized in the zinc-blende structure. The most studied materials in this group are ZnO, ZnS, CdS, and CdSe, and we will focus on EPM calculations for these materials.

The first EPM application to the wurtzite structure was the calculation of the electronic properties of ZnS [9.2]. This material is a particularly instructive one to study since there is considerable information available for both the zinc-blende and wurtzite modifications. The next applications were to CdS and CdSe [9.3, 4]. The calculations were done in a similar manner to the early applications of the EPM to the diamond and zinc-blende semiconductors [9.5].

The pseudopotential for wurtzite can be written in a similar form to that of zinc-blende

$$V(\boldsymbol{r}) = \sum_{\boldsymbol{G}} [S_S(\boldsymbol{G})V_S(\boldsymbol{G}) + iS_A(\boldsymbol{G})V_A(\boldsymbol{G})]e^{i\boldsymbol{G}\cdot\boldsymbol{r}} \tag{9.1}$$

where the symmetric and antisymmetric form factors $V_S(\boldsymbol{G})$ and $V_A(\boldsymbol{G})$ are given by half the sum and difference respectively of the form factors for the two types of atoms in the unit cell. The symmetric and antisymmetric structure factors can be written as

$$S_S(\boldsymbol{G}) = \frac{1}{n}\sum_{j} \exp(-i\boldsymbol{G}\cdot\boldsymbol{\delta}_j) \tag{9.2}$$

Table 9.1. Lattice constants (Å) for wurtzite-structure semiconductors

	a	c
AlN	3.111	4.978
AgI	4.580	7.494
BP	3.562	5.900
BeO	2.698	4.380
CdS	4.135	6.749
CdSe	4.299	7.010
CdTe	4.57	7.47
CuBr	4.06	6.66
CuCl	3.61	6.42
CuI	4.31	7.09
GaN	3.190	5.189
InN	3.533	5.693
MgTe	4.54	7.38
SiC	3.076	5.048
ZnO	3.250	5.207
ZnS	3.814	6.257
ZnSe	3.996	6.626
ZnTe	4.27	6.99

$$S_A(G) = -\frac{i}{n}\sum_j P_j \exp(-iG \cdot \delta_j) \qquad (9.3)$$

where n is the number of atoms per unit cell (four for wurtzite), δ_j is the basis vector of the jth atom in the unit cell, and the index j runs over all atoms in the cell. The operator P_j is $+1$ if j denotes one type of atom and -1 for the other type. This is essentially the same definition given earlier which is designed to limit the magnitude of the structure factor to be ≤ 1 and to allow the use of zinc-blende form factors for wurtzite without a change in normalization. The small density difference between zinc-blende and wurtzite is ignored.

If the center of the unit cell is chosen so that the position of each atom of the first type moves to the position of an atom of the second type upon spatial inversion, then the structure factors are real. This can be achieved for both zinc-blende and wurtzite.

The magnitudes of the structure factors are given in Table 9.2. It is interesting to note the similarity bewteen the zinc-blende and wurtzite structure factors for reciprocal lattice vectors of similar magnitudes (e.g. $G^2 = 3, 8, 11, 12$ in units of $(2\pi/a)^2$). We also note that the u parameter of wurtzite enters the pseudopotential Hamiltonian only through the structure factor.

To obtain explicit expressions for the wurtzite structure factors, we choose standard primitive translation vectors and place atoms of one type at

$$r_1 = [\tfrac{1}{6}, \tfrac{1}{6}, \tfrac{1}{2}(\tfrac{1}{2} + u)] \qquad (9.4)$$

Table 9.2. Reciprocal lattice vectors G and structure factors $S(G)$ for wurtzite and zinc-blende, and form factors V^S and V^A in Ry. Columns 4 and 5 contain the structure factor; in wurtzite for the case $u = 3/8$. The structure factors which do depend on the parameter u are shown as two-place decimal fractions

G (Wurtzite)	G^2	$|S^S(G)|$	$|S^A(G)|$	ZnS V^S	V^A	CdS V^S	V^A	CdSe V^S	V^A
000	0	1	0						
001	$\frac{3}{4}$	0	0						
100	$2\frac{2}{3}$	$\frac{1}{2}$	0	-0.24		-0.26		-0.25	
002	3	0.71	0.71	-0.22	0.23	-0.24	0.23	-0.23	0.19
101	$3\frac{3}{12}$	0.33	0.80	-0.19	0.19	-0.20	0.18	-0.20	0.15
102	$5\frac{2}{3}$	0.35	0.35	-0.06	0.10	-0.03	0.08	-0.07	0.09
003	$6\frac{3}{4}$	0	0						
210	8	1	0	$+0.03$		$+0.03$		$+0.01$	
211	$8\frac{3}{4}$	0	0						
103	$9\frac{5}{12}$	0.80	0.33	$+0.06$	0.03	$+0.04$	0.05	$+0.03$	0.05
200	$10\frac{2}{3}$	$\frac{1}{2}$	0	$+0.07$		$+0.04$		$+0.04$	
212	11	0.71	0.71	$+0.07$	0.02	$+0.04$	0.05	$+0.04$	0.05
201	$11\frac{5}{12}$	0.33	0.80	$+0.07$	0.02	$+0.04$	0.05	$+0.04$	0.05
004	12	0.00	1.00		0.02		0.05		0.05
202	$13\frac{2}{3}$	0.35	0.35	$+0.04$	0.01	$+0.02$	0.03	$+0.02$	0.03
104	$14\frac{2}{3}$	0.00	0.50		0.01		0.02		0.02
213	$14\frac{3}{4}$	0	0						
(Zinc-blende)									
000	0	1	0						
111	3	$\frac{\sqrt{2}}{2}$	$\frac{\sqrt{2}}{2}$	-0.22	0.23	-0.24	0.23	-0.23	0.19
200	4	0	1		0.15		0.13		0.12
220	8	1	0	$+0.03$		$+0.03$		$+0.01$	
311	11	$\frac{\sqrt{2}}{2}$	$\frac{\sqrt{2}}{2}$	$+0.07$	0.02	$+0.04$	0.05	$+0.04$	0.05
222	12	0	1		0.02		0.05		0.05
400	16	1	0	0		0		0	

and

$$-\boldsymbol{r}_2 = [-\tfrac{1}{6}, -\tfrac{1}{6}, -\tfrac{1}{2}(\tfrac{1}{2} - u)] \quad . \tag{9.5}$$

Atoms of the second type are located at $+\boldsymbol{r}_2$ and $-\boldsymbol{r}_1$. The basis vectors used above are those representing primitive translation vectors of the real space lattice. For the reciprocal lattice $[l, m, n]$ represents a reciprocal lattice vector relative to the set of primitive reciprocal lattice translations. The symmetric and antisymmetric structure factors are then given by

$$S_S = \cos\left[2\pi\left(\frac{l}{6} + \frac{m}{6} + \frac{n}{4}\right)\right]\cos(2\pi n u/2) \tag{9.6}$$

$$S_A = \cos\left[2\pi\left(\frac{l}{6} + \frac{m}{6} + \frac{n}{4}\right)\right]\sin(2\pi n u/2) \quad . \tag{9.7}$$

The coefficients l and m are treated equally in this choice of crystal axes. Other conventions are also commonly used.

The symmetry classification of *Rashba* [9.6] is chosen here. Other different classifications are often used for the Δ and/or U axes. The major point of confusion is the interchange of Γ_6 and Γ_5 between the various conventions. The selection rules are given in Table 9.3, and naming of points, lines, and planes in the Brillouin zone is shown in Fig. 9.1.

Table 9.3. Selection rules for wurtzite. Allowed dipole transitions are listed. For $E \parallel c$, only transitions between states of the same symmetry are allowed

$E \perp c$	$E \parallel c$
$\Delta_1, \Delta_2, \Delta_5 \rightleftharpoons \Delta_6$	$X_i \rightleftharpoons X_i$
$\Delta_3, \Delta_4, \Delta_6 \rightleftharpoons \Delta_5$	
$U_1, U_4 \rightleftharpoons U_2, U_3$	
$P_1, P_2, P_3 \rightleftharpoons P_3$	

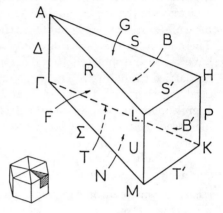

Fig. 9.1. The hexagonal Brillouin zone ▶

The calculations involve computations of the energy eigenvalues and wavefunctions. To check on the band structure, a calculation of the imaginary part of the complex frequency-dependent dielectric function was made. This required a computation of the eigenvalues and eigenvectors on a mesh of k-points in 1/24 of the Brillouin zone. Because of the hexagonal symmetry, an isotropic dielectric function calculation similar to that carried out for the cubic crystal is not appropriate. Two calculations are necessary corresponding to the situations where the electric field is parallel and perpendicular to the c-axis. For a polarization of the electric vector parallel to the c-axis (taken to be in the z-direction) we have

$$\varepsilon_2^{\parallel}(\omega) = \frac{e^2 \hbar}{\pi m^2 \omega^2} \sum_{ij} \int_{\mathrm{BZ}} \delta(\omega_{ij}(\mathbf{k}) - \omega) |\langle u_{i\mathbf{k}}| \frac{d}{dz} |u_{j\mathbf{k}}\rangle|^2 d^3 k \qquad (9.8)$$

where the notation is similar to that given earlier (see 4.10). For the perpendicular polarization, either d/dx or d/dy can be used in the matrix element.

The details involved in extracting the fundamental gaps and spin-orbit splittings are given in the original references. Two parameters of interest are the crystal-field splitting of the valence band $\Gamma_1^v \to \Gamma_6^v$ denoted by α

and the spin-orbit parameter denoted by δ. The splitting in energy of the fundamental gap without spin-orbit coupling $\Gamma_6^v \to \Gamma_1^c$ is $E_a + \delta/3$ where E_a is the value of the gap with spin-orbit coupling $\Gamma_9^v \to \Gamma_7^c$. This neglects the small interaction of the top of the valence band with other bands via spin-orbit coupling.

9.1 The Electronic Structure of Hexagonal Zinc Sulfide

The EPM calculation for ZnS was the first attempt to use pseudopotential form factors derived for one structure to calculate the electronic propeties of a material having a different crystal structure. The form factors for cubic ZnS (zinc-blende) were determined using the schemes described earlier. These form factors, which are only defined at fcc reciprocal lattice vectors, have to be interpolated to yield form factors appropriate to the hexagonal lattice (Table 9.2). The structure factors for wurtzite (9.4, 5) are then used together with the appropriately scaled form factors to construct the Hamiltonian matrix. The number of plane waves used as a basis must be increased relative to zinc-blende because of the higher density of reciprocal lattice points in this case .

The bulk of the experimental information comes from reflectivity measurements taken over a wide range of energy. For wurtzite, polarized light measurements can be compared with calculations of $\varepsilon_2^{\parallel}$ and $\varepsilon_2^{\perp}$ taken over a wide range of energy. For wurtzite, polarized measurements yield more information then measurements made with "mixed polarization". In addition, Kramers-Kronig analyses of the reflectivity which give a direct determination of ε_1 and ε_2 are helpful, but these functions are not generally experimentally available. At the time when these calculations were done, photoemission techniques had not been developed sufficiently to be central in determining band states. In recent work, angular-resolved photoemission has become a vital tool. The application of this technique to wurtzite materials will be discussed later. In the first examples discussed here, we will focus on reflectivity data analysis to test the validity of the EPM calculation.

There is no standard nomenclature for the reflectivity peaks that also assigns the transitions to a specific region of the Brillouin zone. We choose the nomenclature of *Cardona* and *Harbeke* [9.7] and summarize the results of the reflectivity analysis in Table 9.4. This table gives the somewhat limited data available at the time of the calculation; however, it should be pointed out that there has not been a drastic change in the experimental situation since that time.

Since the form factors for the wurtzite ZnS case were determined by interpolating zinc-blende form factors, we note that it is the optical spectrum of zinc-blende which generates the band structure of the wurtzite materal. The form factors are given in Table 9.2.

Table 9.4. Position in energy (eV) of peaks in reflectivity. For the E_1 peaks, we give low-temperature values; other values are room-temperature values and are not expected to shift by mor than 0.1 eV upon going to low temperature

	ZnS cubic	ZnS $E \perp c$	ZnS $E \parallel c$	CdS $E \perp c$	CdS $E \parallel c$	CdSe $E \perp c$	CdSe $E \parallel c$
$E_1 A$				5.0[c]		4.3[c]	
$E_1 B$	5.9[a]	5.75[a]	5.75[a]	5.6	5.7	4.9	5.0
E_0'				6.2[b]	6.3[b]		6.1[b]
F_1		6.6[b]		7.1		6.8	
E_2	7.0/7.4	7.0/7.5[b]	7.0/7.5	8.0[d]	8.0[d]	7.5	7.5
E_1'	9.8	9.6	9.7	9.2	9.3	8.4	8.6
F_3[b]				9.8	9.8	9.2	9.3

[a] The E_1 peak of ZnS is not split into part A and part B. This peak is named E_0' in [9.7] of the main text.
[b] Shoulder.
[c] Average of spin-orbit split peaks.
[d] this peak has a weak should 0.4 eV higher.

The band structure $E(\boldsymbol{k})$ for wurtzite is given in Fig. 9.2 along some symmetry lines in the Brillouin zone. This material is a direct gap semiconductor with valence band maximum and conduction band minimum both at the zone center Γ.

The comparison of cubic (Fig. 9.3) and hexagonal ZnS is useful for understanding the electronic structure and more generally as a method to analyze electronic structure of complex materials using results for simpler modifications. The studies of *Birman* [9.8] used tight-binding wavefunctions

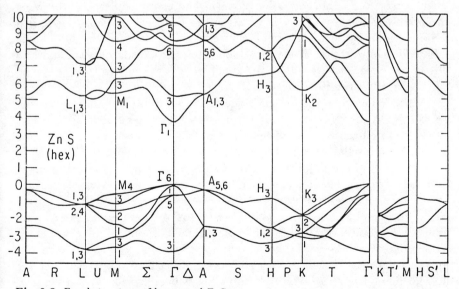

Fig. 9.2. Band structure of hexagonal ZnS

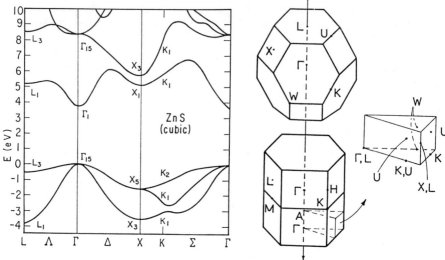

Fig. 9.3. Band structure of cubic ZnS

Fig. 9.4. Comparison of zones: (top) aligned zones of zinc-blende and wurtzite: (bottom) position in the hexagonal zone of special points of the cubic zne

to illustrate the correspondence between states along the Λ symmetry line in zinc-blende and wurtzite states along the Δ symmetry line in going from Γ to A and back to Γ. If the two zones are aligned so that the cubic Δ axis lies along the hexagonal Λ axis (Fig. 9.4), then the hexagonal planes of the two direct lattices are parallel. One finds the following result: Γ_1, L_1, and L_3 (cubic) correspond to Γ_1, Γ_3, and Γ_5 (hexagonal); Γ_{15} (cubic) corresponds to Γ_6 plus Γ_1 (hexagonal). The energy differences between the corresponding levels is very small in the EPM calculations. There is a striking similarity between the Λ direction in zinc-blende and the "unfolded" Δ direction in wurtzite. These correspondences are a result of symmetry and do not arise from the fact that the zinc-blende form factors were scaled to be used in the wurtzite structure.

The similarity in the optical structure of wurtzite and zinc-blende extends beyond the structure arising from states near the Δ axis of wurtzite. Table 9.5 summarizes some of the principal transitions and Fig. 9.5 contains $\varepsilon_2(\omega)$ for both polarizations. Using the band structure (Fig. 9.2, Table 9.5) and the $\varepsilon_2(\omega)$ of Fig. 9.5, it is possible to assign the various optical peaks to interband transitions. It is also useful to compare the spectrum of wurtzite with its zinc-blende counterpart.

The fundamental gap is $(\Gamma_6 \Gamma_1) \to \Gamma_1$ for wurtzite and $\Gamma_{15} \to \Gamma_1$ for zinc-blende. Spin-orbit effects are not included; these would cause some small changes in the gap. The first major peak in ε_2 for zinc-blende is a Λ transition near L, which gives rise to an M_1 critical point. Another M_0 critical point lies at L. The corresponding wurtzite peak for perpendicu-

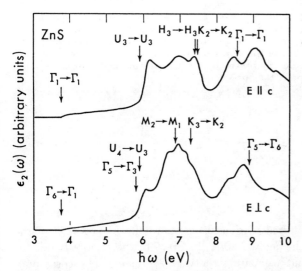

Fig. 9.5. Computed $\varepsilon_2(\omega)$ in arbitrary units as a function of ω in eV for hexagonal ZnS

Table 9.5. Identification of optical structure of hexagonal ZnS. Column 1 lists the important regions of the zone, and column 2 lists the important transitions in these regions. Column 3 lists the energy, and column 4 lists the square of the magnitude of the dipole matrix element in relative units of the transition in column 2. The squares of the matrix elements are summed over initial and/or final states in the case of degeneracy. Column 5 lists the energy of structure in the calculated $\varepsilon_2(\omega)$ caused by the region listed in column 1. Shifts of $\sim 0.2\,\text{eV}$ or more may be expected because of the coarse mesh used to calculate ε_2. The last column names the reflectivity structure caused by the regions and transitions listed

Region	Trans.	[eV]	ME	ε_2	Ident.
M_0 cp at	$\Gamma_6 \to \Gamma_1$	3.8	1.4$\perp$	3.8	Gap
M_0 cp at	$\Gamma_1 \to \Gamma_1$	3.8	1.4$\parallel$	3.8	Gap
M_1 cp near	$\Gamma_5 \to \Gamma_3$	5.8	1.8$\perp$	6.0	E_1
M_1 cp near	$U_4 \to U_3$	5.9	0.7$\perp$	6.0	E_1
M_1 cp near	$U_3 \to U_3$	5.9	1.0$\parallel$	6.1	E_1
Region around	$M_2 \to M_1$	6.9	1.5$\perp$	6.7&6.9	E_1 & E_2
Region around	$K_3 \to K_3$	7.3	0.8$\perp$	7.2	E_2
Large region including	$H_3 \to H_3$	7.4	2.3$\parallel$	7.0&7.4	E_3
Region around	$K_2 \to K_2$	7.5	1.4$\parallel$	7.4	E_2
Large region including	$\Gamma_5 \to \Gamma_6$	8.9	2.6$\perp$	8.7	E_1'
Very large region	$\Gamma_1 \to \Gamma_1$	8.6	2.1$\parallel$	8.5&9.0	E_1'

lar polarization comes from transitions along Λ near Γ centered about the $\Gamma_5 \to \Gamma_3$ transition. There is an M_0 critical point at Γ and an M_1 halfway between Γ and A. This result is consistent with the correspondence discussed earlier. Transitions $U_4 \to U_3$ also contribute to this peak; there are M_0 and M_1 critical points listed in Table 9.5 that contribute around 5.9 eV. For parallel polarization, the peak comes from a larger region near the U axis but excluding the region near M. The transition is $U_3 \to U_3$.

It is instructive to compare the energy bands in zinc-blende along the Λ axis with corresponding levels in wurtzite. With the zones aligned, the L

147

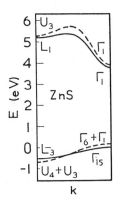

Fig. 9.6. Comparison of the energy levels along the Λ axis in zinc-blende with the levels along a corresponding line in wurtzite. the line in wurtzite begins at Γ and ends on the U axis $2/3$ of the way from M to L. The bands of wurtzite are indicated by broken lines. The two valence bands of wurtzite are practically degenerate

point in zinc-blende is mapped to Γ and also onto the U axis 0.67 of the way from M to L in the hexagonal zone. In Fig. 9.6, the energy bands for ZnS in the zinc-blende and wurtzite structures are given. The correspondences observed in the band structure lead to the similarity in the optical spectra. For cases where interband transitions in the wurtzite are expected to be strong but would destroy the above similarity, it is found that these transitions are reduced by weak optical matrix elements.

The second major peak in the zinc-blende materials is generally considered to come from transitions in a region in the Brillouin zone near X and K. In wurtzite this peak has a shoulder at 6.6 eV for pependicular polarization which originates from transitions on the F face of the zone beginning at the U axis and extending almost halfway toward the Δ axis. There are critical points at M which is on the edge of this region. The strongest transition is $M_2 \rightarrow M_1$. Another contribution to the second peak comes from $K_3 \rightarrow K_2$. For parallel polarization, the region near H contributes.

Up to 8 eV the structure in ε_2 arises from transitions terminating on the first or second conduction band. Higher conduction bands contribute above 8 eV, and the dip in the spectrum around 8 eV separates these contributions. The prominent transitions are listed in Table 9.5. More details relating interband transitions to structure in $\varepsilon_2(\omega)$ for wurtzite are given in the original references.

When the EPM was first applied to wurtzite materials, the techniques associated with determining valence electron charge densities had not yet been developed. The first application of these techniques to wurtzite appeared in 1973. This study compared the valence electronic charge density for ZnS in the wurtzite and zinc-blende structures [9.9]. The EPM was used to obtain charge densities for individual bands, and the special k-point scheme for wurtzite was developed to compare results with the standard calculations of the charge density. The wurtzite and zinc-blende crystal structures are given in Fig. 9.7 to illustrate the similarities and the planes used for displaying the charge density.

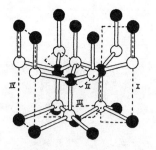
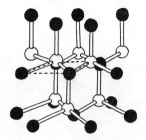

WURZITE   ZINC BLENDE

Fig. 9.7. (a) Wurtzite and (b) zinc-blende crystal structurs. The wurtzite structure is aligned with the c axis along the z direction, and zinc-blende is oriented with the $(1,1,1)$ direction pointing along the z direction

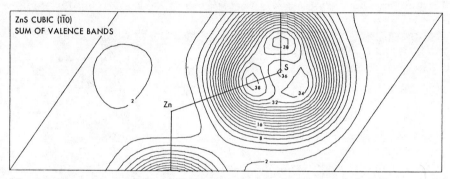

ZnS CUBIC (1$\bar{1}$0)
SUM OF VALENCE BANDS

Fig. 9.8. Total charge density for ZnS in the zinc-blende structure $(1,\bar{1},0)$ plane

The total valence charge density for cubic ZnS is given in Fig. 9.8 in the $(1\bar{1}0)$ plane. This plane is illustrated by the broken lines in Fig. 9.7b. The amount of charge around the S atom within a radius of 75 % of the nearest neighbor distance is approximately 7.3 e and only 2 % of the charge is in the core region. The charge density for both the zinc-blende and wurtzite cases is given in units of electronic charge per primitive cell. Since band by band charge densities have been given for zinc-blende materials earlier in this volume, we do not repeat them here.

For wurtzite, there are eight valence bands. The charge density contour maps for bands 1 and 2 are almost identical, hence band 2 is not shown here. Figures 9.9–12 give the individual charge density maps for bands 1 and 3 to 8. Figure 9.12b depicts the charge density of the first conduction band assuming it were occupied. The plane referred to in these plots is shown as plane I in Fig. 9.7a.

The plots of the electron density for the individual bands reveal the bonding and angular momentum nature of these bands. Bands 1 and 2 are s-like around the S ion while the rest of the bands are of predominantly p-character. Bands 6 and 8 are almost pure p_{xy}-like and p_z-like respectively

149

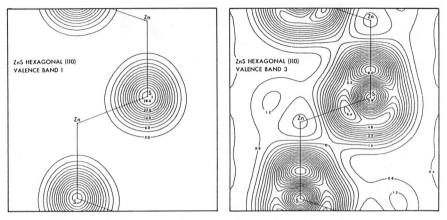

Fig. 9.9. ZnS wurtzite charge density bands 1 and 3, (1,1,0) plane

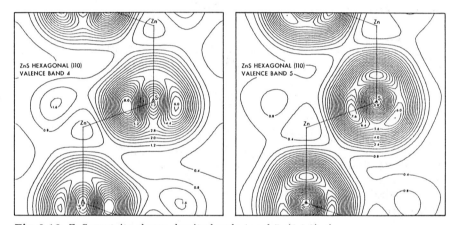

Fig. 9.10. ZnS wurtzite charge density bands 4 and 5, (1,1,0) plane

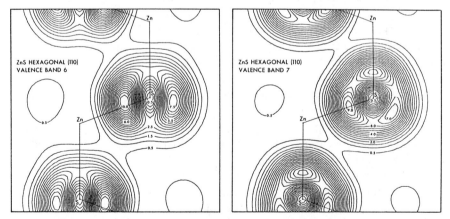

Fig. 9.11. ZnS wurtzite charge density bands 6 and 7, (1,1,0) plane

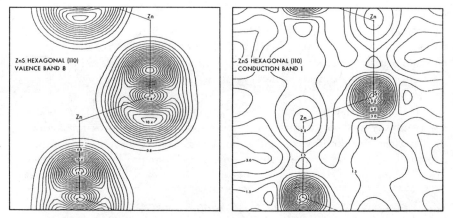

Fig. 9.12. ZnS wurtzite charge density bands 8 and 9, (1,1,0) plane

while band 9 is free-electron-like except for some charge concentration on the S atoms.

Figure 9.13 contains a plot of the total charge density in plane I (Fig. 9.7a). The topology of the chains of bonds in this plane are not found in zinc-blende whereas the zigzag pattern of the zinc-blende structure is found

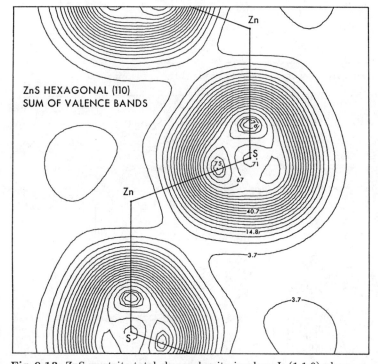

Fig. 9.13. ZnS wurtzite total charge density in plane I, (1,1,0) plane

151

in the (101) plane which is labeled as plane II in Fig. 9.7a. The total charge density in this plane is given in Fig. 9.14. Figures 9.15 and 9.16 contain the total charge density in planes III and IV (Fig. 9.7a). The results plotted in the four wurtzite planes enable one to gain a three-dimensional perspective of the total charge density. The crystalline pseudopotential for ZnS is given in Fig. 9.17.

It is instructive to compare Figs. 9.13 and 9.14 which illustrate an asymmetry in the electron distribution. Although the ionic cores are arranged in a perfect tetrahedral configuration, the charge density does not follow precisely. The bond in the z direction differs from the bonds in the other

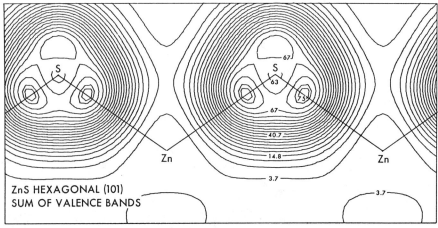

Fig. 9.14. ZnS wurtzite total charge density in plane II, (1,0,1) plane

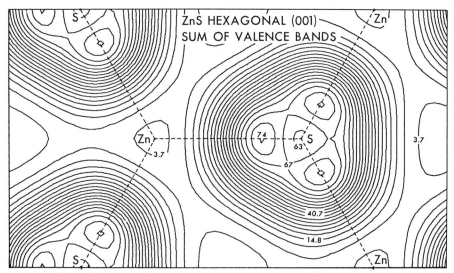

Fig. 9.15. ZnS wurtzite total charge density in plane III, (0,0,1) plane; the S atoms lie in this plane

152

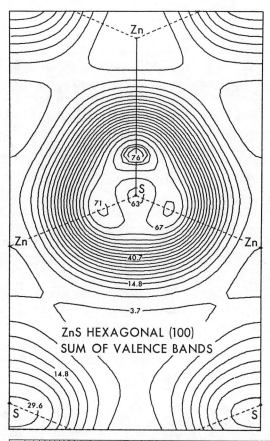

Fig. 9.16. ZnS wurtzite total charge density in plane IV, (1,0,0) plane; the S and Zn atoms in the center of the figure lie in this plane

ZnS HEXAGONAL (100)
SUM OF VALENCE BANDS

Fig. 9.17. Crystalline pseudopotential for ZnS in wurtzite structure in plane I, (1,1,0) plane

ZnS POTENTIAL HEXAGONAL (110)

tetrahedral directions. The charge is large along z and centered on the bond whereas the covalent charges in the other three directions are pushed slightly out of the bond. This asymmetry results from the structural difference between wurtzite and zinc-blende beyond the second nearest neighbors. For zinc-blende, the four tetrahedral bonds exist in identical geometrical configurations. In the wurtzite case, along z, the atoms are placed symmetrically in planes perpendicular to the z direction leading to an effective interaction along the bond. The other three bonds interact with an asymmetrical distribution resulting in an electrostatic force pushing the charge slightly out of the bond.

The asymmetrical charge effect can be demonstrated for an ideal wurtzite crystal with a model of effective charges. The asymmetry produces an electrostatic polarization. Using the calculated charge density from the energy band calculation, the dipole moment p perprimitive cell can be estimated. The calculated value is $p \sim 10^{-19}$ esu cm which is around 50 times smaller than that of a common ferroelectric material like BaTiO$_3$. The net polarization is likely to contribute to the nonideal c/a ratio found for wurtzite materials.

Hence, comparisons of the zinc-blende and wurtzite charge densities yield useful information about the bonding and electronic propeties of these materials. The charge densities presented here were computed with wavefunctions calculated at many points in the Brillouin zone. The effort involved can be greatly reduced by using the special point scheme of *Chadi* and *Cohen* [9.10]. Computations based on only two special points yield total charge densities in good agreement with those discussed here. The special points are

$$k_1 = (\sqrt{3}/4, \sqrt{3}/8, 1/4) \tag{9.9}$$

$$k_2 = (\sqrt{3}/8, -\sqrt{3}/8, 1/4) \ . \tag{9.10}$$

9.2 The Electronic Structure of Hexagonal CdS and CdSe

The EPM calculations of the electronic structure of CdS and CdSe were done at about the same time as the original ZnS calculations [9.3]. Optical data were used to obtain form factors for CdS and CdSe.

The resulting band structures are given in Fig. 9.18 and 9.19. They are similar to the band structure for ZnS (Fig. 9.2). The calculated ε_2 for CdSe is shown in Fig. 9.20 and Table 9.6 contains the identification of the optical structure in terms of interband transitions. Near the fundamental gap the band structures lare in satisfactory agreement with experiment. Spin-orbit splitting is larger for the Cd compounds than for ZnS, and the effects are seen in experimental spectra.

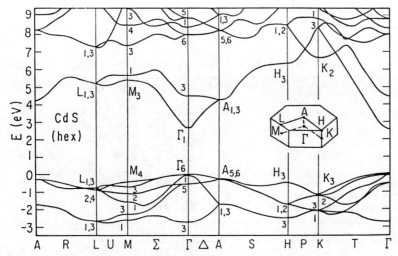

Fig. 9.18. Band structure of hexagonal CdS

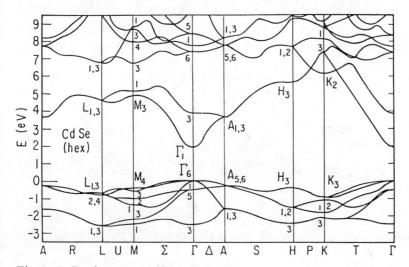

Fig. 9.19. Band structure of hexagonal CdSe

Although spin-orbit interactions and the differences in the Zn and Cd pseudopotentials results in qualitative differences in the electronic structure of the Cd compounds compared to ZnS, the overall electronic structure is similar. Hence, we rely on ZnS to serve as a prototype for wurtzite structure materials and refer to the original reference [9.3] for a detailed discussion of the optical spectra.

Recently, angle-resolved photoemission studies have been performed for CdS by *Stoffel* and *Margaritondo* [9.11]. These researchers conclude that

Table 9.6. As in Table 9.5 (for CdS and CdSe)

Region	Trans.	CdSe			CdS		
		[eV]	ME	ε_2	[eV]	ME	Ident.
M_0 cp at	$\Gamma_6 \rightarrow \Gamma_1$	2.0	1.0⊥	2.0	2.6	1.1⊥	Gap
M_0 cp at	$\Gamma_1 \rightarrow \Gamma_1$	2.0	1.0∥	2.0	2.6	1.1∥	Gap
M_1 cp at	$\Gamma_5 \rightarrow \Gamma_3$	4.3	1.4⊥		5.0	1.5⊥	$E_1 A$
M_1 cp at	$U_4 \rightarrow U_3$	5.0	0.7⊥	5.2	5.7	0.8⊥	$E_1 B$
M_1 cp at	$U_3 \rightarrow U_3$	5.0	0.9∥	5.2	5.6	0.9∥	$E_1 B$
M_2 cp at	$H_3 \rightarrow H_3$	6.0	3.5∥	6.1	6.7	3.8∥	E_0'
M_2 cp at	$M_2 \rightarrow M_1$	6.2	1.4⊥	6.2	6.8	1.4⊥	E_1
Region around	$K_3 \rightarrow K_2$	7.1	0.7⊥		7.8	0.8⊥	E_2
Region around	$K_2 \rightarrow K_2$	7.2	1.4∥		8.0	1.5∥	E_2
Large region including	$\Gamma_5 \rightarrow \Gamma_6$	7.9	2.4⊥	7.8	8.5	2.5⊥	E_1'
Very large region	$\Gamma_1 \rightarrow \Gamma_1$	7.7	2.1∥	7.9	8.4	2.2∥	E_1'

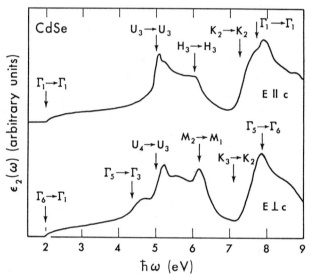

Fig. 9.20. Computed $\varepsilon_2(\omega)$ in arbitrary units as a function of ω in eV for hexagonal CdSe

the EPM band structure calculation is in qualitative agreement with experiment but underestimates the band dispersion. In particular, the upper valence band width is found to be greater in experiment than the predicted value. Similar effects were found previously for II-VI zinc-blende compounds for which a local pseudopotential was used. The additional complexity of the presence of a shallow d-band in Cd, which is excluded in these calculations, should be considered in a more modern calculation. Despite the shortcomings noted, it is impressive that the recent data is in reasonable agreement with the predicted electronic structure computed 15 years earlier.

9.3 The Electronic Structure of Hexagonal ZnO

An interesting example of a more modern wurtzite band calculation is the application of nonlocal pseudopotentials to study ZnO [9.12]. The motivation for this calculation is two-fold. In addition to providing an analysis of the electronic structure of ZnO, another major objective of this work was to provide a usable pseudopotential for oxygen. Oxides are among the most abundant materials, hence calculations for these materials are highly desirable. However, useful pseudopotentials for O are difficult to obtain because of the noncancellation of the valence p-states. The problems associated with the absence of p-states in the core for first row elements were discussed earlier in this volume. The approach used in the ZnO calculation to overcome this problem was to employ a simple local potential for Zn and a nonlocal or angular-momentum (l)-dependent potential for O. The nonlocal potential allows the s- and p-states of O to experience different attractive potentials. An earlier local EPM calculation [9.13] was judged to be in only fair agreement with experiment.

The construction of the O pseudopotential involves the determination of an O^{6+} potential to yield measured spectroscopic term values of O^{5+} which consists of one electron plus the O^{6+} core. This core pseudopotential is then screened and the atomic energy eigenvalues and wavefunctions of this pseudoatom are compared with the results of all electron atomic calculations for oxygen. The pseudopotential is then altered until the valence eigenvalues and wavefunctions outside the core region are reproduced.

The pseudopotential for O^{6+} was chosen to be of the following form

$$V_l(r) = -\frac{2Z}{r}\tanh(r) + A_l \exp\left(-\frac{r^2}{R_l^2}\right) \tag{9.11}$$

where A_l and R_l are adjustable parameters fit to atomic calculations. The values used were: $A_0 = -4.0\,\mathrm{Ry}$, $A_1 = -6.5\,\mathrm{Ry}$, and $R_0^2 = R_1^2 = R^2 = 2.0$ a.u. This model potential therefore depends on three adjustable parameters. It also has the correct asymptotic behavior at large r, that is, $V_l(r \to \infty) = -(2Z/r)$ in atomic units ($e^2 = 2, \hbar = 1, m = \frac{1}{2}$); and converges rapidly in wavevector space. This latter feature is particularly important for calculations using plane wave basis sets. Although the weak nature of the potential will result in a chage density which will not be accurate near the core, the converging Fourier series makes band structure and other associated calculations tractable.

The local part of the potential ws taken to be $V_{l=0}(r)$ and the nonlocal part emplyed a projection operator $P_{l=1}$ to project out the $l = 1$ component of the wavefunction. The form of the nonlocal potential is $(V_{l=1} - V_{l=0})P_1$. Using the decomposition described here, the matrix elements between plane wave states $|K\rangle$ and $|K'\rangle$ can be fit with analytic expressions of the form

$$V_{\mathrm{L}}(|\boldsymbol{q}|) = \langle \boldsymbol{K} | V_{l=0}(r) | \boldsymbol{K}' \rangle = \frac{a_1}{q^2}\{1 + \exp[a_2(q - a_3)]\}^{-1} \qquad (9.12)$$

$$V_{\mathrm{NL}}(\boldsymbol{K}, \boldsymbol{K}') = \frac{3\pi^2}{\sqrt{KK'}}\frac{A_1 - A_0}{\Omega_a}R^2 \cos(\theta_{\boldsymbol{K}\boldsymbol{K}'})$$
$$\times \exp\left[\frac{-R^2}{4}(K^2 + K'^2)\right] I_{3/2}\left(\frac{1}{2}R^2 K K'\right) \qquad (9.13)$$

where $|\boldsymbol{q}| = |\boldsymbol{K} - \boldsymbol{K}'|$, $I_{3/2}$ is a modified Bessel function, $\theta_{\boldsymbol{K}\boldsymbol{K}'}$ is the angle between $\boldsymbol{K}$ and $\boldsymbol{K}'$, Ω_a is the atomic volume, and the a_i are listed in Table 9.7. For Zn, the matrix elements were also fit numerically using a local potential

$$V_{\mathrm{Zn}}(q) = \frac{a_1}{q^2}(1 - a_2 g^2) \exp(-a_3 q^2) \qquad (9.14)$$

where the a_i for Zn are also given in Table 9.7.

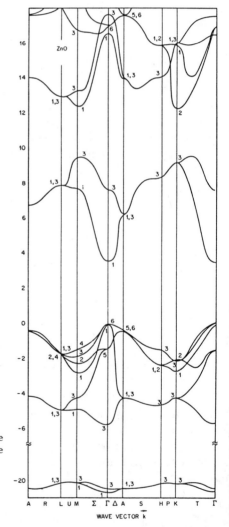

Table 9.7. Ionic pseudopotential parameters for O^{6+} and Zn^{+2}. The units are such that if q is in a.u., then $V(q)$ is in Ry. The potentials are normalized to an atomic volume, $\Omega_a = 80.4$ a.u.

	Zn^{2+}	O^{6+}
a_1	-0.63	-1.92
a_2	0.17	1.80
a_3	0.10	2.00

Fig. 9.21. Band structure for ZnO. The energies are in eV with the zero taken at the valence band maximum

The self-consistent calculation was performed using a density functional expression for exchange and correlation. A plot of the band structure is given in Fig. 9.21. The calculated band gap of 3.5 eV is in good agreement with the measured value of 3.3 eV. The calculated density of states and reflectivity spectra (Fig. 9.22) are also consistent with experiment [9.14, 15] although the magnitude of the reflectivity at higher energies is too low in the theoretical spectrum. The calculated pseudocharge density is given in Fig. 9.23.

Some features of this calculation should be emphasized. Unlike the EPM calculations discussed earlier, the ZnO study used potentials which involved no adjustable parameters fit to ZnO experimental data. Both the Zn and O potentials were derived from properties related to the atoms

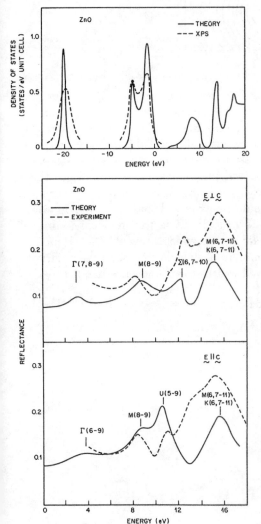

Fig. 9.22. Calculated electronic density of states and reflectivity spectrum for ZnO. The density of states calculation is compared to the x-ray photoelectron spectroscopy results of [9.14]. The theoretical reflectivity spectrum is compared to the measured reflectivity in [9.15]. Prominent structure is labeled by its origin in the Brillouin zone

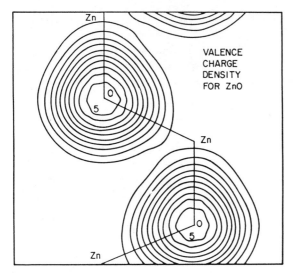

VALENCE
CHARGE
DENSITY
FOR ZnO

Fig. 9.23. Valence pseudocharge density of ZnO. The charge density normalized to one electron per unit cell. The contour are in units of 0.5 e per unit cell

themselves. Hence, this calculation is closer to a first-principles approach than to a standard EPM approach. The effects of the nonlocal nature of the pseudopotential are also worth discussing further. One of the major discrepancies between theory and experiment for CdS was the width of the upper valence bands. As discussed earlier, the calculated values were too narrow compared to angle-resolved photoemission results. Since these bands are associated primarily with the p-states on the anion, and since O is more attractive than S, it would be expected that these bands would be narrower for ZnO than for ZnS or CdS. It is the nonlocal nature of the potential used for the ZnO calculation which prevents this. Hence, it is expected that nonlocal pseudopotential calculations for other wurtzite semiconductors might give improved widths for the valence band states.

10. Chalcopyrite Structure Semiconductors

The chalcopyrite structure semiconductors composed of elements from columns II, IV, and V of the periodic table represent a natural extension of the III-V zinc-blende compounds. These ternary compounds have very interesting linear and nonlinear optical properties. There is considerably more structure in the experimental reflectivity and modulated reflectivity for these materials than the corresponding III-V compounds. Typical materials in this group are $ZnGeP_2$ and $CdSnAs_2$; these are the chalcopyrite analogs of GaP and InAs respectively.

The chemical formula for these materials is $A^{II}B^{IV}C^V_2$ which is a ternary analog of the $B^{III}C^V$ zinc-blende semiconductors in which alternate cation sites are occupied by atoms of the group II and group IV elements surrounded in tetrahedral coordination by group V anions. The chalcopyrite real-space unit cell can be viewed as two zinc-blende unit cells stacked and compressed along the c axis. The two cations of the ternary are in alternating positions along the c-axis replacing the cations of the corresponding III-V compound. There is also a slight displacement of the anions from their original zinc-blende positions. Figure 10.1 illustrates the structure for $ZnGeP_2$ which is the material we will use as prototype for the chalcopyrites. Table 10.1 contains the lattice constants for a representative group.

The pseudopotential Hamiltonian has the usual form, and $V(\boldsymbol{r})$ can be expanded in the reciprocal lattice with form factors $V(\boldsymbol{G})$ given by

$$V(\boldsymbol{G}) = \frac{1}{8} \sum_{a} \exp(i\boldsymbol{G} \cdot \boldsymbol{\tau}_a) V_a(\boldsymbol{G}) \tag{10.1}$$

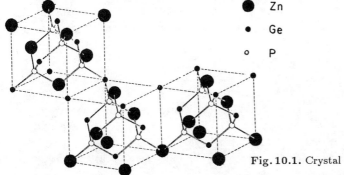

- ● Zn
- · Ge
- ○ P

Fig. 10.1. Crystal structure of $ZnGeP_2$

161

Table 10.1. Lattice constants (Å) for some semiconductors in the chalcopyrite structure

	a	c
CdGeAs$_2$	5.943	11.217
CdGeP$_2$	5.741	10.775
CdSiAs$_2$	5.884	10.882
CdSiP$_2$	5.678	10.431
CdSnAs$_2$	6.094	11.918
CdSnP$_2$	5.900	11.518
ZnGeAs$_2$	5.672	11.153
ZnGeP$_2$	5.465	10.771
ZnSiAs$_2$	5.61	10.88
ZnSiP$_2$	5.400	10.441
ZnSnAs$_2$	5.852	11.704

where τ_a is a basis vector for each atom in the primitive cell, and $V_a(G)$ is the atomic pseudopotential form factor for atom a. The structure factor $\exp(iG \cdot \tau_a)$ also appears in (10.1).

Using the above picture, our prototype material ZnGeP$_2$ crystallizes in the body-centered-tetragonal structure with eight atoms per primitive cell. This basis vectors for (10.1) are given by

$$\text{Zn:} \quad \tau_1^{Zn} = (0,0,0), \quad \tau_2^{Zn} = (0, \tfrac{1}{2}a, \tfrac{1}{4}c)$$

$$\text{Ge:} \quad \tau_1^{Ge} = (0, 0, \tfrac{1}{2}c), \quad \tau_2^{Ge} = (0, \tfrac{1}{2}a, \tfrac{3}{4}c)$$

$$\text{P:} \quad \tau_1^{P} = (au, \tfrac{1}{2}a, \tfrac{1}{8}c), \quad \tau_2^{P} = (a\overline{u}, \tfrac{3}{4}a, \tfrac{1}{8}c),$$

$$\tau_3^{P} = (\tfrac{3}{4}a, au, \tfrac{7}{8}c), \quad \tau_4^{P} = (\tfrac{1}{4}a, a\overline{u}, \tfrac{7}{8}c),$$

where $a = 5.46\,\text{Å}$, $c = 10.71\,\text{Å}$, and $u = 0.2582$ at room temperature. The primitive cell has a volume $\tfrac{1}{2}a^2c$, and for the ideal structure contains four zinc-blende primitive cells of volume $\tfrac{1}{4}a^3$. Because of the alternating cation positions, two types of chains are formed: Zn-P-Ge-P-Zn chains along $(1, \pm 1, 0)$ and Zn-P-Zn-P-Ge-P-Ge-P-Zn along the $(0, \pm 1, 1)$ and $(\pm 1, 0, 1)$ directions. The unit cell doubling relative to zinc-blende is caused by the Zn-P-Zn and Ge-P-Ge linkages along the z direction. There is also a slight compression along the z-axis measured by the parameter $\varepsilon = 2 - c/a$. for ZnGeP$_2$, the P anion, which is tetrahedrally bonded to two Zn and two Ge atoms, is slightly displaced towards the smaller Ge cations. This displacement closer to group IV cations is found in all the other chalcopyrites in this series except for the ZnSn compounds. The displacement is characterized by the parameter $\sigma = 4u - 1$.

The EPM band structure and reflectivity for ZnGeP$_2$ ws calculated by *Varea de Alvarez* and *Cohen* [10.1]. In 1974 detailed studies were reported comparing the theoretical results for the electronic structure with reflectivity and modulated reflectivity [10.2] and with x-ray photoemission spectra for ZnGeP$_2$ and CdSnAs$_2$ [10.3]. A description of the theoretical calculation for

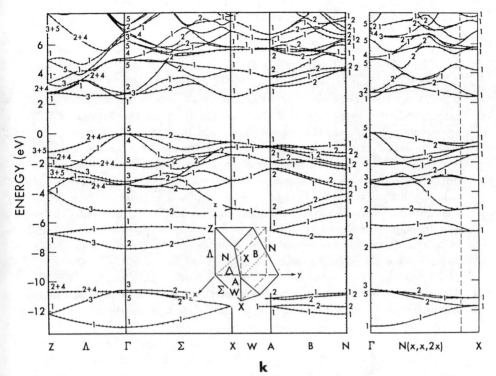

Fig. 10.2. Band structure of ZnGeP$_2$ along principal symmetry directions, irreducible part of the Brillouin zone and practical Brillouin zone (*dotted lines*) showing the notation for symmetry points used in this work

ZnGeP$_2$ will be given here as will some comparisons with measured data. For detailed comparisons, the reader is referred to the original papers.

The Brillouin zone for the chalcopyrite structure can be obtained by folding down the first Brillouin zone of zinc-blende. The Brillouin zone and resulting band structure is shown in Fig. 10.2. The G vectors used in the folding down process to construct the chalcopyrite Brillouin zone from zinc-blende are $\boldsymbol{\Gamma} = (0,0,9)$ $\boldsymbol{W_x} = (1,0,1)$, $\boldsymbol{W_y} = (0,1,1)$ and $\boldsymbol{X_z} = (0,0,2)$. The set of $\boldsymbol{G}$ vectors for chalcopyrite can be grouped into four sets related to the zinc-blende G's by: $\boldsymbol{G_1} = \boldsymbol{G}_{\mathrm{zb}} + \boldsymbol{\Gamma}$; $\boldsymbol{G_2} = \boldsymbol{G}_{\mathrm{zb}} + \boldsymbol{W_x}$; $\boldsymbol{G_3} = \boldsymbol{G}_{\mathrm{zb}} + \boldsymbol{W_y}$, and $\boldsymbol{G_4} = \boldsymbol{G}_{\mathrm{zb}} + \boldsymbol{X_z}$.

The form factors of the potential given in (10.1) can be grouped into symmetric and antisymmetric combinations

$$V_{\mathrm{S}}(\boldsymbol{G}) = \tfrac{1}{4}[V_{\mathrm{Zn}}(\boldsymbol{G}) + V_{\mathrm{Ge}}(\boldsymbol{G}) + 2V_{\mathrm{P}}(\boldsymbol{G})] \tag{10.2}$$

$$V_{\mathrm{A}}(\boldsymbol{G}) = \tfrac{1}{4}[V_{\mathrm{Zn}}(\boldsymbol{G}) + V_{\mathrm{Ge}}(\boldsymbol{G}) - 2V_{\mathrm{P}}(\boldsymbol{G})] \tag{10.3}$$

$$V_{\mathrm{A}}^{\mathrm{C}}(\boldsymbol{G}) = \tfrac{1}{2}[V_{\mathrm{Zn}}(\boldsymbol{G}) - V_{\mathrm{Ge}}(\boldsymbol{G})] \tag{10.4}$$

where $V_A^C(G)$ is the antisymmetric form factor associated with the cation potentials. The associated structure factors are given in the original references. The form factors were taken from other EPM calculations and not fit to ZnGeP₂ data. Form factors for the zinc-blende analogue GaP were used directly; that is, $V_S(G) = V_S^{GaP}(G)$ and $V_A(G) = V_A^{GaP}(G)$. For $V_A^C(G)$ the potentials for $V_{Zn}(G)$ and $V_{Ge}(G)$ were extracted from EPM calculations for Ge and for II-VI compounds. Some extrapolations of $V(q)$ are necessary to obtain the appropriate chalcopyrite form factors.

The band structure and $\varepsilon_2(\omega)$ calculations were done by expanding the wavefunctions in plane waves and diagonalizing the resultant secular equation. The energies and wavefunctions were evaluated in the 1/16 irreducible part of the Brillouin zone. For convenience, a practical Brillouin zone (PBZ) was introduced for the $\varepsilon_2(\omega)$ calculation. The PBZ corresponds to the region in k-space enclosed by planes $k_z = 0$, $k_z = 2\pi/c$, $k_x = k_y$, $k_y = 0$, and $k_z = \pi/a$. It can be shown that this region is completely equivalent to the usual irreducible Brillouin zone. Both zones are shown in Fig. 10.2.

Spin-orbit corrections were calculated at a few points in the Brillouin zone. Using atomic structure calculations, the ratio of the cation and anion spin-orbit splittings were fixed. The remaining spin-orbit parameter was fit to diamond-structure Ge at the Γ point.

The band structure of ZnGeP₂ can be obtained to a first approximation by folding the band structure for GaP into the smaller chalcopyrite Brillouin zone. In the folding process, each chalcopyrite wavevector corresponds to four zinc-blende wavevectors. The most important deviations from the folded zinc-blende band structure appear at points where two bands of the

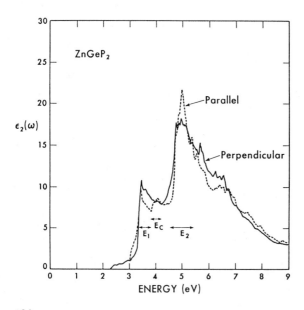

Fig. 10.3. Theoretical $\varepsilon_2(\omega)$ for ZnGeP₂ for light polarized parallel and perpendicular to the c axis of the crystal

same symmetry cross. Since GaP has an indirect band gap $\Gamma_{15} - X_1$ and the X_1 state of GaP maps to Γ in ZnGeP$_2$, it is expected that the lowest interband transition in ZnGeP$_2$ should be a direct gap at Γ with weak oscillator strength. Transitions near Γ contribute to the onset of $\varepsilon_2(\omega)$ shown in Fig. 10.3 and to the E_0 region of the reflectivity given in Fig. 10.4. The experimental reflectivity is also shown in Fig. 10.4, (and its temperature dependence in Fig. 10.5). The corresponding identification in terms of interband transitions appears in Table 10.2. To facilitate the resolution of the

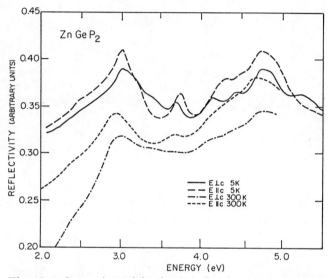

Fig. 10.4. Comparison of the theoretical and experimental $R(\omega)$ for ZnGeP$_2$ in the parallel and perpendicular polarizations

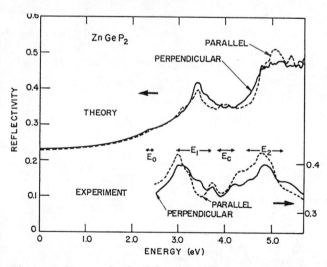

Fig. 10.5. Measured reflectivity of ZnGeP$_2$ at 5 and 300 K

165

Table 10.2. Theoretical and experimental reflectivity structure and their identifications, including the location in the Brillouin zone and energy of the calculated critical points for ZnGeP$_2$

Theoretical Peak position [eV]	Experimental Peak position [eV]				Reflectivity structure		Location in zone	cp energy [eV]
	(a)	(b)	(c)	(d)	Polarization (a)	Peak		
		2.08[e]				A'	Γ_4–Γ_3	
		2.145[e]		2.05		B'	Γ_5–Γ_3	
	2.14	2.21[e]		2.11	∥, ⊥	C'		
					⊥	B''		
	2.29	2.3[e]			=	C''	Γ_5–Γ_2	
2.31	2.31	2.46	2.39	2.34	∥, ⊥	A	$\Gamma_{\bar{2}}$–$\Gamma_{\bar{1}}$	2.31[f]
2.27	2.51	2.53	2.46	2.40	⊥	$\{\,B$	$\Gamma_{\bar{1}}$–$\Gamma_{\bar{1}}$	2.27[f]
	2.63							
2.43	2.67	2.59	2.52	2.48	=	C	$\Gamma_{\bar{2}}$–$\Gamma_{\bar{1}}$	2.43[f]
3.04					=		X_1–X_1(15, 16–17, 18)	3.04 $\left\{\begin{array}{l}3.50^{f}\\3.03^{f}\end{array}\right.$
3.41	3.02	3.02	2.97	2.87 (2.92)	∥, ⊥	$E_1(1)$	N_1–N_1(16–17) (0.2, 0.2, 0.4)	3.42[f]

Theoretical Peak position [eV]	Experimental Peak position [eV]				Reflectivity structure		Location in zone	cp energy [eV]
	(a)	(b)	(c)	(d)	Polarization (a)	Peak		
3.37					⊥		X_1–X_1(13, 14–17, 18)	3.36 $\left\{ \begin{array}{l} 3.35^f \\ 3.37^f \end{array} \right.$
3.41	3.08	3.15	3.09	3.05	⊥, ∥	$E_1(2)$	N_2–N_1(15–17) (0.2, 0.2, 0.4)	3.50^f
3.6	3.2	3.22	3.13	3.32	⊥(∥)	$E_1(3)$	N_2–N_1(16, 17) (0.3, 0.3, 0.38)	3.6
3.9	3.41	3.48	3.41	3.64	⊥	$E_1(4)$	Σ_2–Σ_1(16, 18) (0.25, 0.25, 0)	3.95
4.0	3.74 (3.72)	3.75	3.71	3.83	∥(⊥)	E_c	X_1–X_1(11, 12, 17, 18)	3.9
4.6	4.17				⊥		Λ(13–17) (0, 0, 0.6) Σ(14–17) (0.25, 0.25, 0)	4.6
4.76	4.3				∥		Δ(15–17) (0.34, 0, 0)	4.76
4.77	4.46				⊥	E_2	Γ–Γ(13–18)	4.77
5.05	4.73				∥		(14–17) (0.16, 0.5, 0)	5.05
4.96	4.79				⊥		X(16–20) and along Σ	4.96
5.21	4.92	(4.93)			∥(⊥)		Δ(15–18) (0.5, 0, 0)	5.21

a This work at 5 K
b Thermoreflectance work of Shileika at 120 K [10.4, 5]
c Electroreflectance work of Shileika at 300 K [10.5]
d Electroreflectance work of Shay at 300 K [10.6]
e Wavelength-modulated absorption work of Shileika at 77 K [10.5]
f Spin-orbit Hamiltonian included

fine structure in $R(\omega)$, a modulated spectrum, $(1/R)dR/d\omega$, was also used [10.2] to identify the interband transitions.

The E_1 region for ZnGeP$_2$ is rich in structure. For GaP this region contains two spin-orbit split peaks E_1 and $E_1 + \Delta_1$, whereas for ZnGeP$_2$ there are five resolvable structures which are also seen in other chalcopyrite semiconductors. A critical-point analysis of this region of the spectrum assigns the lower energy structure to the N plane along the $2\pi(x/a, x/a, 2x/c)$ direction. This is equivalent to the Λ transitions in GaP when the quasi-cubic model is used. A strong critical point is found near $x = 0.2$. The higher energy part of the structure originates from transitions in the N plane with a critical point close to $(0.3, 0.3, 0.38)$ (bands 16–17) and another near Σ close to $(0.25, 0.25, 0)$ (bands 16–18). These two critical points have the same origin in the quasi-cubic model.

The structure in the E_c region is assigned to transitions at the X point. This structure is difficult to interpret because the $X_1 - X_1$ transition responsible for the structure is associated with an M_0 singularity at lower energy. The analogue of this structure in zinc-blende is $L_3 - L_1$.

For the prominent E_2 peak, at least five structures are found. Referring to the zinc-blende analogue, most of the contribution at the E_2 peak comes from direct transitions along Δ and Σ. When mapping these symmetry lines or directions into the chalcopyrite zone, the Δ line is folded into the Δ, Λ, and $(1 - x, 0, 1)$ directions of the chalcopyrite Brillouin zone. The zinc-blende Σ line folds into the Σ, $(x, 0, 2x)$, and $(1 - x, 0, 2x - 1)$ directions in chalcopyrite. An analysis of this peak in terms of interband transitions is given in Table 10.2 along with experimental data [10.2, 4–6]. In the reflectivity spectrum, the strength of the E_2 peak of ZnGeP$_2$ is reduced compared to GaP. This reduction seems to be a general property of the chalcopyrite semiconductors. As in the case of the zinc-blende materials, the calculated E_2 peak is larger than experiment. This feature may be caused by many-body effects (electron-hole or exciton correlations). Two other discrepancies between theory and experiment are found for ZnGeP$_2$ which are not found in the zinc-blende calculation. The calculated E_2 peak is narrower than the measured peak, and it is shifted to higher energies by about 0.3 eV. There is a one-to-one correspondence in the structure between theory and experiment when the 0.3 eV shift is accounted for. This suggests that if small changes in the form factors were made, much better agreement between the calculated and measured spectra could be obtained. Since no experimental data on ZnGeP$_2$ was used in obtaining the form factors, the overall agreement found is impressive despite the small shift needed to align the E_2 peak.

Another theoretical-experimental study which served both as a test of the band structures and as a probe of the bonding properties of the chalcopyrites involved the use of measured x-ray photoemission spectra (XPS), the calculated density of states, $N(E)$, and the calculated charge density profiles. The materials studied were $ZnGeP_2$ and $CdSnAs_2$ [10.3]. A comparison of the measured XPS spectrum $I(E)$ with the computed $N(E)$ for $ZnGeP_2$ yielded good agreement (Fig. 10.6). In addition, sturcture in $I(E)$ was correlated explicitly Zn-P and Ge-P bonds through contour plots of electron charge densities integrated over selected energy intervals $\varrho_{\Delta E}(\mathbf{r})$.

The approach involved the computation of the charge $\varrho_{\Delta E}(\mathbf{r})$ within an energy region ΔE rather than the more standard approach of evaluating

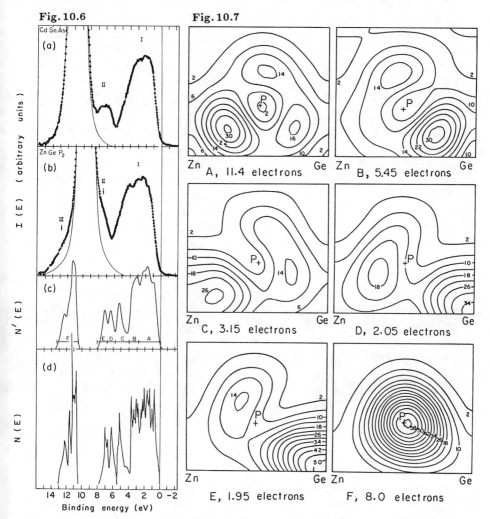

Fig. 10.6   **Fig. 10.7**

Fig. 10.6. (a) XPS spectrum for $CdSnAs_2$; (b) spectrum for $ZnGeP_2$; (c) broadened theoretical density of states for $ZnGeP_2$; (d) calculated valence-band density of states for $ZnGeP_2$

Fig. 10.7. Calculated electronic charge-density contour plots for $ZnGeP_2$ corresponding to density-of-states peaks A, B, C, D, E, and F (Fig. 10.6). The plots are normalized to the number of electrons contained in each peak. This value is given for each plot

the charge density $\varrho(\boldsymbol{r})$ for a particular band n. The energy regions were chosen to correspond to specific energy intervals for which $N(E)$ contains interesting structure such as a sharp peak. For ZnGeP$_2$, six important regions, A to F, were identified, as shown in Fig. 10.6c. Figure 10.7 contains plots of $\varrho_{\Delta E}(\boldsymbol{r})$ for each region calculated in the $x = y$ plane which contains the Zn, Ge, and P ions.

It is instructive to analyse the chalcopyrite $N(E)$ structure in analogy with zinc-blende where three prominent peaks in $N(E)$ are found. Peak I is near the top of the valence band, separated from a second narrower peak (II) by a small valley, followed by a gap which separates this structure from the lowest energy peak III. Charge density calculations for each energy region reveal that electrons in peak I correspond to bonding sites, that peak II contains states which are mostly s-like around the cation with some pile up of charge in the bonding region, and that peak III corresponds to electron states which are s-like around the anion.

Because of the added complexity of the chalcopyrite structure compared to zinc-blende, the $N(E)$ spectrum is expected to be more complex. This is, in fact, the case, as shown in Fig. 10.6 which contains the XPS spectra for CdSnAs$_2$ and ZnGeP$_2$, a broadened theoretical $N'(E)$ for ZnGeP$_2$, and the $N(E)$ without Gaussian broadening. The reason for calculating $N'(E)$ is to facilitate comparisons between experiment and theory. As stated before, these comparisons indicate good overall agreement. However, detailed structure in the measured and calculated chalcopyrite curves differ in approximately the same way as their zinc-blende counterparts when a local EPM approach is used. For example, for zinc-blende, peak I is usually too narrow in local EPM calculations, and nonlocal EPM approaches are necessary to give the correct width for this peak. However, the bonding properties of the electrons in each peak should not change in character when using a nonlocal EPM. The detailed contour lines can vary as discussed earlier for Si, but the existence of bond charges or charge transfer is easy to discern.

We begin the analysis of the peaks in terms of $\varrho_{\Delta E}(\boldsymbol{r})$ with the highest energy structure. The "highest energy" corresponds to the region of $N(E)$ near the top of the valence band or the "lowest-binding-energy" region. This is peak I in zinc-blende, and it is now split into two regions A and B in the chalcopyrite case. Figure 10.7 illustrates the charge densities for these regions $\varrho_A(\boldsymbol{r})$ and $\varrho_B(\boldsymbol{r})$. The A region corresponds to Zn-P bonding while region B is associated with the Ge-P bonds. The number of electrons in each region is 11.4 for A and 5.45 for B. Since the Ge-P bond lies lower in energy, it has stronger covalent bonding character; this is consistent with arguments based on the strengths of the pseudopotentials involved. The splitting of peak I by the energy difference of the two bonds is seen in the XPS spectrum. Despite the difference in overall width between the measured and calculated spectra because of the local EPM approximations, both show four distinct peaks within peak I.

Peak II splits into three peaks C, D, and E in ZnGeP$_2$. The C region (3.15 electrons) contains electron states which concentrate charge on Zn with some charge in the Ge-P bond, while regions D (2.05 electrons) and E (1.95 electrons) yield charge accumulation on Ge. As in the case of the A and B peaks, this ordering in energy is expected because of the stronger attraction of the Ge pseudopotential compared to Zn. Peak II in the XPS spectra is partially hidden by the peaks arisinig from the d-bands. This is unfortunate because the peak II region is part of $N(E)$ most affected by the differences in the cation potentials.

Peak III is discernable in the ZnGeP$_2$ XPS spectrum but not for CdSnAs$_2$. This region is labeled F in $N'(E)$, and it contains eight electrons which are mostly s-like around the anion site. The concentration of electrons around P shown in Fig. 10.7 for this peak is similar to that found in the analogous zinc-blende compounds.

Although the above analysis has used results for ZnGeP$_2$, the results of this study comparing $N(E)$ and $\varrho_{\Delta E}(\boldsymbol{r})$ is expected to be fairly general for chalcopyrite semiconductors based on elements in this region of the periodic table. The changes in bonding properties of the $N(E)$ peaks for the prototype ZnGeP$_2$ compared to its zinc-blende analog GaP are found to be understandable in terms of the changes in structure and the potentials of the elements involved. The approach in which features in $I(E)$ are related to characteristic charge distributions is useful for complex materials since it allows experiments dealing with spectral studies to be related to those based on structural analysis.

11. IV-VI Semiconductors

The IV-VI semiconductors are among the most interesting materials in solid state physics. Many are found in the rock-salt structure, and structural transitions are common. The most widely studied compounds in this group are PbTe, PbSe, PbS, SnTe, and GeTe. Their lattice constants are given in Table 11.1. These materials have small gaps which are usually less than 0.5 eV, hence they are good candidates for devices like infrared lasers and detectors. Despite their simple crystal structure, some of these compounds exhibit ferroelectric, paraelectric, and superconducting behavior. In addition, the temperature dependence of the energy gaps, the energy positions of impurity levels, the high doping levels found, the static dielectric constants, and the electronic structure of some of the alloys of these compounds appear to be anomalous compared to the "conventional behavior" of the diamond and zinc-blende semiconductors.

Table 11.1. Lattice constants (Å) for IV-VI semiconductors

GeTe	5.996
PbS	5.936
PbSe	6.124
PbTe	6.454
SnSe	6.020
SnTe	6.313

We will focus on PbTe and SnTe as prototypes for the group and use the properties of these compounds to illustrate common features. In addition to electronic, optical, and bonding properties which will be discussed in a manner similar to previous discussion for other classes of semiconductors, some of the anomalous properties will be investigated, and some theoretical attempts to explain them will be described.

The electronic structure of the lead salts (PbTe, PbSe, and PbS) are similar, hence PbTe will be representative of this group. For SnTe, there is an inversion of the conduction and valence bands near the L point of the Brillouin zone relative to PbTe. This inversion results in distinct topological changes in this region of k-space relative to the lead salts. It is believed that GeTe is similar to SnTe, but many consider this an open question at this time.

11.1 Electronic Band Structure

There have been many electronic band structure calculations for these materials, particularly for PbTe. These include OPW [11.1], APW [11.2–4], KKR [11.5], and pseudopotential [11.6–9] calculations. Although there is general agreement among the calculations on the energy levels and their spacings, the results do differ in detail. Hence at this point, the finer features of the band structures for this group of compounds are not as well-determined as for the diamond and zinc-blende semiconductors. Many of the existing band structure calculations have relied on some empirical input, and the new approaches such as ab initio pseudopotentials have not yet been actively applied to this area.

Because of the heavy elements composing these compounds, it is necessary to include relativistic corrections to the Schrödinger equation. For the EPM, this simply amounts to the inclusion of a spin-orbit term since other corrections are assumed to be accounted for when choosing the appropriate pseudopotential form factors. Both local [11.8] and nonlocal [11.9] pseudopotential calculations have been made for these compounds. We discuss here the form of the spin-orbit part of the Hamiltonian appropriate for local pseudopotential calculations. The changes for nonlocal potentials are given in the literature [11.9].

For the rock-salt structure, a choice of origin halfway between the two atoms in the unit cell yields a basis vector to the atoms of $\pm(1, 1, 1)a/4$. As in the zinc-blende case, the pseudopotential form factors can be grouped into symmetric and antisymmetric combinations, $V^S(G)$ and $V^A(G)$. Because of the form of the structure, we have

$$2V^S(G) = V_1(G) + V_2(G) \quad \text{for } G^2 \text{ even} \tag{11.1}$$

$$2V^A(G) = V_1(G) - V_2(G) \quad \text{for } G^2 \text{ odd} \tag{11.2}$$

where $V_1(G)$ and $V_2(G)$ correspond to form factors for the individual atoms.

The spin-orbit contributions can be included using a scheme proposed by *Weisz* [11.10] for white tin and later extended to compounds by *Bloom* and *Bergstresser* [11.11]. For the homopolar case, the pseudopotential Hamiltonian matrix element in the plane wave representation becomes

$$H_{k's',ks} = \frac{p^2}{2m}\delta_{kk'}\delta_{ss'} + S(k - k')$$
$$\times [V(|k' - k|)\delta_{ss'} - i\lambda_1(k' \times k) \cdot \sigma_{s's}] \tag{11.3}$$

where S is the structure factor, V is the pseudopotential, s is the spin index, and σ represents the Pauli matrices. The last term in (11.3) is the spin-orbit contribution, and λ_1 is treated as a spin-orbit parameter.

To extend (11.3) to the case of compounds, it is convenient to decompose λ_1 into symmetric λ^S and antisymmetric λ^A parts in the same manner as was done for the pseudopotential form factors. Equation (11.3) then becomes

$$
\begin{aligned}
H_{k's',ks} = {} & \frac{p^2}{2m}\delta_{kk'}\delta_{ss'} \\
& + S^S(k-k')[V^S(|k'-k|)\delta_{ss'} - i\lambda^S(k'\times k)\cdot\sigma_{s's}] \\
& + iS^A(k-k')[V^A(|k-k'|)\delta_{ss'} - i\lambda^A(k'\times k)\cdot\sigma_{s's}] \quad (11.4)
\end{aligned}
$$

where S^S and S^A are the symmetric and antisymmetric structure factors. The parameters λ^S and λ^A are estimated from atomic splittings using a method due to *Herman* [11.12]. As an example, estimates for the valence splittings at Γ for SnTe, GeTe, and PbTe are 0.98, 0.77, and 1.82 eV respectively.

Figure 11.1 displays a recent EPM band structure calculation for PbTe. This figure also contains the density of states for this compound. The minimum gap for PbTe appears at L between L_6^+ (valence) and L_6^- (conduction). A similar band structure is found for PbSe; however, the band structures without spin-orbit splitting and hence the "parent" band states differ for

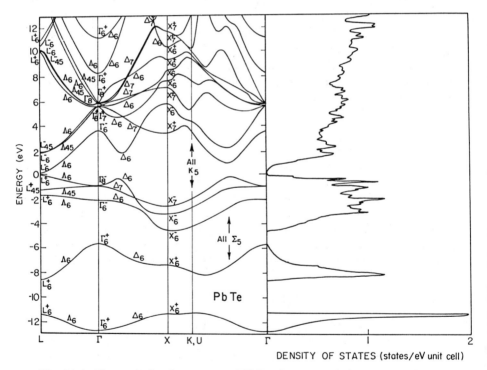

Fig. 11.1. Electronic band structure of PbTe along some high symmetry lines in the Brillouin zone. The calculated density of states is also given

174

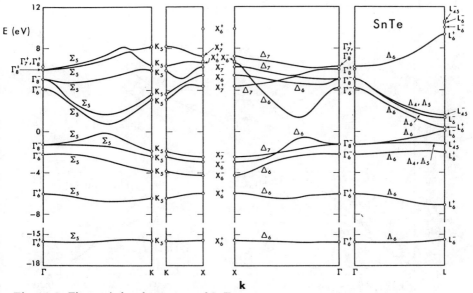

Fig. 11.2. Electronic band structure of SnTe

these compounds [11.9]. In fact, band structure calculations for PbTe differ in their assignment of "parent" states (11.7, 13). Secondary valence band maxima and minima occur along Σ and Δ.

Although the band structure of SnTe (Fig. 11.2) is similar to that of PbTe, several differences are evident, especially near the minimum band gap. The top of the valence band at L is L_6^- while the minimum conduction band state at L is L_6^+. Since L_6^+ is s-like around the group IV element and p-like around the group VI [11.13], this difference is important. It is relevant in interpreting Knight-shift data and the temperature dependence of band states. The L_6^- (valence)-L_6^+ (conduction) ordering is considered to be the correct one for SnTe.

Another interesting difference between the band structures of PbTe and SnTe near L involves the dispersion of the bands perpendicular to the Γ-L symmetry line in the hexagonal face of the Brillouin zone at L. It was shown by *Tung* and *Cohen* [11.14, 15] that the minimum gap for SnTe is not at L but near L as shown in Fig. 11.3. The Tung-Cohen model results from overlapping parabolic valence and conduction bands with gaps forming at the intersections. This model has also been proposed for GeTe and for other semiconductors, and it is sometimes referred to as a "camel's-back" or "hump" dispersion curve.

Because of the differences in the band structures for PbTe and SnTe near the minimum gap, alloys of these compounds are particularly interesting. The reversal of the states at L and the movement of the maxima and minima from the L point can be examined using an EPM alloy model

175

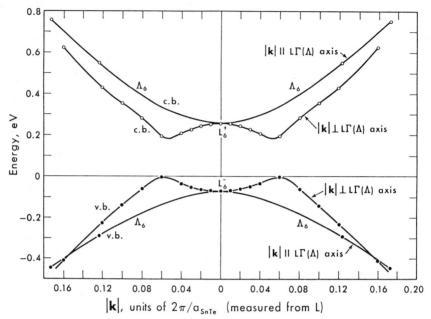

Fig. 11.3. SnTe energy bands near L in directions parallel and perpendicular to the Λ axis at L. The dots refer to the calculated points for the valence band (v.b.), and the open circles represent calculated points for the conduction band (c.b.)

[11.16]. The simplest approach to use in calculating the alloy band structure is to use linear scaling of the pseudopotential form factors and lattice constants, e.g.

$$a_{Sn_xPb_{1-x}Te} = xa_{SnTe} + (1-x)a_{PbTe} \quad . \tag{11.5}$$

The resulting band structure for the alloys are given in Fig. 11.4. The bands are shown for the direction parallel to Λ and perpendicular to Λ at the L point for alloy concentrations corresponding to $x = 0, 0.25, 0.5, 0.75, 1.0$. As shown in Fig. 11.4, the L_6^+ and L_6^- reversal occurs between $x = 0.25$ and 0.5. The Tung-Cohen hump-like structure begins for x between 0.5 and 0.75. This dispersion gives rise to a complex Fermi surface [11.16] for the hole states in the SnTe rich alloys.

To study states away from the fundamental gap, photoemission results using x-ray and uv sources have been compared with the calculated band structures [11.9]. These studies should be considered to be preliminary. Detailed comparisons with results of angular resolve photoemission measurements have not yet been performed for this series of compounds.

Several optical studies have been made, and comparisons between calculated and measured reflectivities and modulated reflectivities have been presented [11.8, 16]. Results for PbTe and PbSe are given in Figs. 11.5–7.

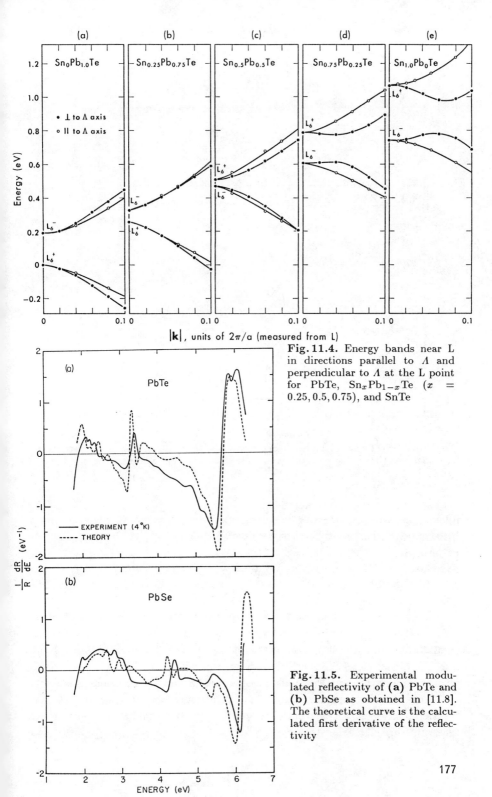

Fig. 11.4. Energy bands near L in directions parallel to Λ and perpendicular to Λ at the L point for PbTe, $Sn_x Pb_{1-x} Te$ ($x = 0.25, 0.5, 0.75$), and SnTe

Fig. 11.5. Experimental modulated reflectivity of (a) PbTe and (b) PbSe as obtained in [11.8]. The theoretical curve is the calculated first derivative of the reflectivity

177

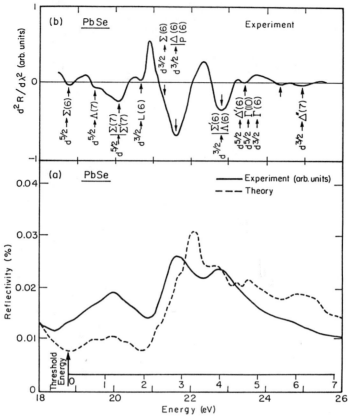

Fig. 11.6. Reflectivity (**a**) and second derivative spectrum for measured reflectivity (**b**) for PbSe. The theoretical reflectivity curve is indicated by the broken line

The band-to-band transition assignments of the structure in the experimental second derivative reflectivity spectrum is given in Table 11.2. The low energy part of the calculated reflectivity spectrum is lower in magnitude than the measured spectrum for both compounds. Similar behavior was found for diamond and zinc-blende spectra. It is believed that electron-hole effects are responsible for this feature in the diamond and zinc-blende cases. Perhaps a similar explanation is appropriate for the IV-VI semiconductors.

Charge density studies [11.13, 18] have been carried out to examine the bonding, properties, and symmetries of specific band states such as L_6^+ and L_6^-. The results for PbTe and PbSe are given in Fig. 11.8 for the total valence charge density and in Fig. 11.9 for the charge density contours associated with the valence band maximum and conduction band minimum at L. The fractional charges inside touching spheres around anions and cations are given in Table 11.3.

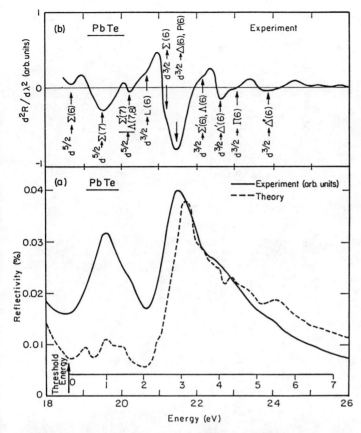

Fig. 11.7. Reflectivity (a) and second derivative spectrum for measured reflectivity (b) for PbTe. The theoretical reflectivity curve is indicated by the broken line

The total valence charge density is consistent with an ionic model in which two electrons are transferred from the cation to the anion. As shown in Fig. 11.8, the charge around the cation sites is mainly s-like while the anion sites attract valence charge of s- and p-character. There is less charge transfer from the cation to the anion in PbTe than in PbSe. Relative values are given in Table 11.3. This table contains the fractional charges in percent corresponding to each of the five filled valence bands and the total charge density around each element. The sphere radii chosen to compute the charge were taken to be $r_{\text{cation}} = 1.29\,\text{Å}$, $r_{\text{anion}} = 1.94\,\text{Å}$ for PbTe and $r_{\text{cation}} = 1.22\,\text{Å}$, $r_{\text{anion}} = 1.83\,\text{Å}$ for PbSe. These values agree to within $10\,\%$ with the ionic radii for Pb^{++}, Se^-, and Te^-. It is assumed that all the charge is concentrated within the spheres around each atom. This approximation allows the values to be normalized to $100\,\%$ in Table 11.3. The calculated effective charge is approximate for each compound, but it allows a comparison between them. The values (in units of electric charge) are 2.1

179

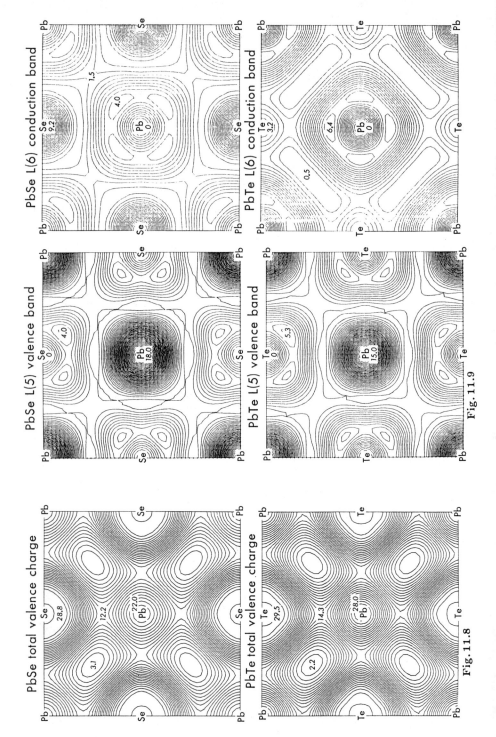

Fig. 11.8

Fig. 11.9

180

Table 11.2. Assignment of minima in the experimental second derivative of the reflectivity to individual core-conduction band transitions. The energy zeros are taken at the respective reflectivity thresholds at $\Sigma(6)$ corresponding to 18.65 eV for PbTe and 18.8 eV for PbSe. Σ'_1, Δ' and Δ'' stand for regions in K-space around Σ and Δ respectively. P is the critical point with the coordinates (0.625, 0.46, 0) which also gives rise to the highest peak in ϵ_2

PbSe

Transition	Theory	Experiment
$d^{5/2} \to \Sigma(6)$	0	0
$d^{5/2} \to \Lambda(7)$	0.70	0.68
$d^{5/2} \to \begin{cases}\Sigma(7)\\ \Sigma'(7)\end{cases}$	1.20	1.24
$d^{3/2} \to L(6)$	1.75	1.85
$d^{3/2} \to \Sigma(6)$	2.55	2.60
$d^{3/2} \to \begin{cases}\Delta(6)\\ P(6)\end{cases}$	3.05 / 3.45	2.82
$d^{3/2} \to \begin{cases}\Sigma'(6)\\ \Lambda(6)\end{cases}$	3.95 ± 0.1	4.02
$d^{5/2} \to \Delta'(6)$	4.55	
$d^{5/2} \to \Gamma(10)$ $d^{3/2} \to \Gamma(6)$	4.85	4.57
$d^{3/2} \to \Delta''(7)$	6.45 ± 0.2	6.33 ± 0.1

PbTe

Transition	Theory	Experiment
$d^{5/2} \to \Sigma(6)$	0	0
$d^{5/2} \to \begin{cases}\Sigma(7)\\ \Sigma'(7)\end{cases}$	0.70 / 1.20	0.92
$d^{5/2} \to \Lambda(7, 8)$	1.55	1.58
$d^{3/2} \to L(6)$	1.97	1.99
$d^{3/2} \to \Sigma(6)$	2.55	2.58
$d^{3/2} \to \begin{cases}\Delta(6)\\ P(6)\end{cases}$	3.15	2.85
$d^{3/2} \to \begin{cases}\Sigma'(6)\\ \Lambda(6)\end{cases}$	3.65	3.46
$d^{3/2} \to \Delta'(6)$	4.05	3.98
$d^{3/2} \to \Gamma(6)$	4.50	4.36
$d^{3/2} \to \Delta''(6)$	5.65	5.30 ± 0.2

and 7.9 for Pb and Se in PbSe and 2.5 and 7.5 for Pb and Te in PbTe. Hence, the approximate charge transfers are 1.9 and 1.5.

Charge density plots for the band extrema of PbSe and PbTe (shown in Fig. 11.9) clearly illustrate the angular momentum character of these states with respect to the cation and anion. The top of the valence bands at L has L_6^+ symmetry for both compounds. The L_6^+ state originates from an L_1^+ orbital in the absence of spin-orbit interactions. A group-theoretical analysis predicts that this state should have s-like and d-like symmetry around the cation and p-like symmetry about the anion. The contours in Fig. 11.9 displaying these results are consistent with Table 11.3. For the conduction band minimum, the L_6^- state in these compounds originates from the L_2^- orbital of PbSe and the L_3^- orbital of PbTe. Both are p-like around the cation and s- and d-like around the anion. They differ in detail as shown in Fig. 11.9 and this leads to changes in their electronic structure. It is believed that the differences in the effective masses and temperature coefficients of this band for the two compounds arise from the differences in the charge distribution properties of the two parent states.

Fig. 11.8. Total valence electronic charge density for PbSe and PbTe

Fig. 11.9. (a) Electronic charge-density contours for PbSe and PbTe for the valence state L(5). (b) Charge density contours for PbSe and PbTe for the conduction state L(6)

Table 11.3. Calculated fractional charges (in percent) inside touching spheres around anions and cations in terms of $l = 0, 1, 2$ atomic angular functions. The values are given for each valence band individually and for the total valence charge. Also indicated are values for the states $L_6^+[L(5)]$ and $L_6^-[L(6)]$ forming the smallest gap at the point L of the Brillouin zone

Band	PbSe						PbTe					
	Pb			Se			Pb			Te		
	s	p	d	s	p	d	s	p	d	s	p	d
1	1	1	0	97	1	0	3	1	0	95	1	0
2	55	0	0	18	24	3	70	0	0	13	13	4
3	0	12	0	0	85	3	0	16	0	0	81	3
4	5	8	1	1	80	5	4	10	2	0	79	5
5	21	2	2	0	70	5	12	2	3	0	80	3
Total	16	4	1	23	52	4	18	6	1	22	50	3
		21			79			25			75	
Total for a simple ionic model	20	0	0	20	60	0	20	0	0	20	60	0
$L(5)$	45	0	1	0	54	0	29	0	2	0	69	0
$L(6)$	0	43	0	28	0	29	0	58	0	9	0	33

11.2 Applications of the Electronic Band Structure

As stated earlier, the physical properties of the IV-VI compounds are unusual and interesting. The EPM can be used to compute some of the band structure characteristics to explain some of the observations. In the previous section, the band structure, density of states, dielectric function, and charge density were computed to explore measured properties such as the minimum band gap, reflectivity, modulated reflectivity, photoemission, bonding and Knight shift (using valence and maximum symmetry). Here we examine the pressure and temperature dependencies of the minimum gap and the electron-phonon coupling. The influence of the latter on the superconducting behavior is also briefly discussed. Another fertile area of study is the structural transitions in compounds like GeTe. This, however, is a more appropriate area of study for the ab initio pseudopotential method since schemes for the study of structural properties have not been developed significantly for the EPM.

Because of their use in infrared light generation and detection, the band gap variations with temperature and pressure of the IV-VI compounds represent an important property to study. Using temperature, it is possible to tune the band gaps and in turn the frequency for generation and detection of infrared radiation. Pressure and temperature effects are second order corrections to the band structure. These effects can be estimated by computing the changes of the individual energy bands with changes in pressure and temperature. For hystrostatic pressure P at constant temperature T, the variation of band energy E_n is

$$\left.\frac{\partial E_n}{\partial P}\right|_T = \left.\frac{1}{\Omega}\frac{\partial \Omega}{\partial P}\right|_T \Omega\left.\frac{\partial E_n}{\partial \Omega}\right|_T \tag{11.6}$$

where Ω is the unit cell volume. The compressibility K can be obtained from experiment

$$K = \left.\frac{1}{\Omega}\frac{\partial \Omega}{\partial P}\right|_T \tag{11.7}$$

and the deformation potential term

$$\left.\Omega\frac{\partial E_n}{\partial \Omega}\right|_T \tag{11.8}$$

can be computed directly from the band structure [11.19]. The results [11.19] are in reasonable agreement for the band gap in PbTe, but some descrepancies exist for PbSe.

The dependence of the minimum gap on temperature is more interesting than its pressure variation. In particular, whereas most semiconductor band gaps decrease with increasing temperature, the minimum gap in PbTe has the opposite correlation, i.e. a positive coefficient. This has important consequences for the tuning of this gap. It was pointed out earlier [11.20, 21] that the use of a temperature-dependent structure factor would give the correct sign for the effect. Band calculations [11.19–21] were made to estimate the magnitude of this coefficient.

Following the approach for the pressure coefficient described above, the temperature coefficient can be expressed assuming constant pressure

$$\left.\frac{\partial E_n}{\partial T}\right|_P = \left.\frac{1}{\Omega}\frac{\partial \Omega}{\partial T}\right|_P \Omega\left.\frac{\partial E_n}{\partial \Omega}\right|_{T,P} + \left.\frac{\partial E_n}{\partial T}\right|_{\Omega,P} \quad . \tag{11.9}$$

The contribution in E_n originates from two contributions. One contribution arises from anharmonic changes given by the product of the thermal expansion coefficient

$$\alpha = \left.\frac{1}{3\Omega}\frac{\partial \Omega}{\partial T}\right|_P \quad ,$$

and a deformation potential

$$\left.3\Omega\frac{\partial E_n}{\partial \Omega}\right|_{LT} \quad .$$

The other contribution

$$\left.\frac{\partial E_n}{\partial T}\right|_{\Omega}$$

can be viewed as an electron-phonon interaction term. An estimate of the anharmonic or expansion contribution can be made using the measured values of the thermal expansion coefficient α and a computation of

$$\left.\frac{\partial E_n}{\partial T}\right|_{\Omega}$$

The latter term is also calculated for the pressure coefficient as described earlier. For most semiconductors, the two contributions (expansion and electron-phonon) are comparable.

Calculation of the electron-phonon contribution is more complex [11.22]. There are two main contributions, one proposed by *Fan* [11.23] and another by *Antonchik* [11.24] and by *Brooks* and *Yu* [11.25]. Fan proposed a temperature-dependent self-energy correction involving the scattering of an electron in band n at wavevector $\boldsymbol{k}$ by the emission (absorption) and reabsorption (reemission) of a phonon of frequency ω and wavevector $\boldsymbol{q}$. This electron-phonon term in second order gives the following form for the shift in the band energy

$$\Delta E_n(\boldsymbol{k}) = \sum_{n'q} \frac{|M_q|^2}{E_n(\boldsymbol{k}) - E_{n'}(\boldsymbol{k}+\boldsymbol{q}) \pm \hbar\omega} \tag{11.10}$$

where M_q is the electron-phonon matrix element. Fan considered only intraband ($n = n'$) and intravalley contributions. Intervalley contributions were added later, and interband terms are also expected to contribute.

Antonchik, Brooks, and Yu formulated a different approach. This scheme replaced the zero temperature structure factor $S_a(\boldsymbol{G})$, for an atom a, by a temperature-dependent structure factor

$$S_a(\boldsymbol{G}, T) = \exp(i\boldsymbol{G} \cdot \boldsymbol{\tau}_a) \exp[-W_a(|\boldsymbol{G}|, T)]$$

$$W_a(|\boldsymbol{G}|, T) = \tfrac{1}{6}|\boldsymbol{G}|^2 \langle u_a^2 \rangle \quad , \tag{11.11}$$

where $\exp[-W_a(|\boldsymbol{G}|, T)]$ is the square root of the usual Debye-Waller factor, which is in turn related to the total mean square displacement $\langle u_a^2 \rangle$, of atom a. Operationally, this approach involves the replacement of the zero temperature structure factor by the measured temperature-dependent $S_a(\boldsymbol{G}, T)$ via the Debye-Waller factors.

There are other approaches [11.26] to calculating temperature-dependent energy shifts, but it is generally agreed that a calculation of the above two contributions is a correct scheme for evaluating the temperature dependence of band states. Following this prescription, it was found (11.19–21) that the latter Antonchik-Brooks-Yu term was dominant, and the Fan terms were neglected for the IV-VI compounds. Recent calculations [11.27] for diamond and zinc-blende semiconductors suggest that both terms are essential for these materials. It is possible that a more detailed analysis of the IV-VI compounds will show that the Fan contributions are more important than concluded previously. It has been proposed [11.19] that these terms may account for discrepancies found in the PbTe and PbSe calculations.

It is interesting to interpret the temperature and pressure dependence of individual states in terms of their charge distributions. This behavior can be shown by direct calculation and by physical arguments related to the orbital symmetries of the bands. Band states respond to pressure and temperature in a specific way depending on the angular momentum character of the state. In general, s-like states rise in energy faster then p- or d-like states in response to pressure. The reverse is generally true for the temperature variation of a band state. This can be easily shown for the constant volume Antonchik-Brooks-Yu contribution.

A direct way of demonstrating these effects is by examining the pressure and temperature coefficients for individual states and gaps. It is found that the above "rules of thumb" can be trusted much of the time. Examples which illustrate the use of these rules are the minimum direct gap at Γ for the zinc-blende semiconductors and the minimum direct gap at L for PbTe. For the zinc-blendes, the top of the valence band is p-like while the minimum conduction band state at Γ is s-like. Hence, the Debye-Waller temperature coefficient will be larger for the valence band maximum than the conduction band minimum. Since both move up in energy with increasing temperature, the gap decreases when the temperature is raised. For PbTe (and PbSe), the motion of the Pb atom is assumed to dominate the temperature dependence, and since L_6^+ (valence) is s-like while L_6^- (conduction) is p-like, the gap increases with temperature. The Fan terms should be included, and sometimes these yield cancellations of the above effects.

The experimental coefficient for PbTe is 4.3×10^{-4} eV/K between 150 and 450 K. Above 450 K, the measured gap becomes independent of temperature. It is believed that the second valence band maximum at Σ becomes the top of the valence band at elevated temperatures and that its temperature coefficient is approximately the same as the L_6^- state. Hence, their relative change with temperature is very small. The EPM results do not confirm this proposal since the state at Σ appears to be different in character to L_6^-. Hence, the saturation of the temperature coefficient at high temperatures is not understood, but EPM calculations [11.19] have provided significant information about these states.

Some calculations [11.19] of the Fan terms have been made, but these are complicated. Intravalley and intervalley contributions must be included.

Intravalley terms are expected to decrease the gaps with rising temperature, but intervalley contributions may be of either sign. Further studies are necessary before this problem can be considered to be understood in the same depth as in the diamond and zinc-blende cases [11.27].

Intervalley scattering of electrons by phonons is also of interest for the superconductivity properties of IV-VI compounds. It was suggested [11.28] that this mechanism could pair electrons and cause superconductivity in degenerate semiconductors at temperatures of the order of tenths of a Kelvin. Both GeTe and SnTe were shown to have the desired band structure features and both are superconducting. In addition, the superconducting transition temperature is a strong function of the carrier density as predicted by the theory.

A central feature of the intervalley mechanism is its ability to pair electrons by means of large wavevectors phonons. The coupling constants or deformation potentials for this process must be large enough to cause sufficient electron pair attraction to overcome the repulsive Coulomb interaction. These coupling constants can be computed from the pseudopotential form factors.

More generally, deformation potentials are needed to estimate band shifts under pressure and various observations related to Raman scattering in semiconductors. The EPM provides a relatively striaghtforward scheme based on the rigid-ion model [11.29] which can be used to compute the electron-phonon coupling constants. This approach has been used [11.30], and the results are in excellent agreement with experiment.

The calculations begin by expanding the crystal potential for a small displacement δR_l^a and associating the change in the potential with the electron-phonon part of the Hamiltonian, i.e.

$$\sum_{la} [V_a(r - R_l^a - \delta R_l^a) - V(r - R_l^a)] = \sum_{la} \delta R_l^a \cdot \nabla V_a(r - R_l^a)$$
$$= H_{el\text{-}ph} \tag{11.12}$$

where R_l^a is a lattice vector to atom a in cell l and $V_a(r)$ is the atomic pseudopotential. The displacement can be expanded in phonon coordinates,

$$\delta R_l^a = \sum_{q\alpha} A_{q\alpha} \hat{\varepsilon}_{q\alpha}^a \exp(iq \cdot R_l^a)(a_{q\alpha} + a_{-q\alpha}^\dagger) \tag{11.13}$$

where $\hat{\varepsilon}_{q\alpha}^a$ is a polarization vector, $a_{q\alpha}$ and $a_{-q\alpha}^\dagger$ are phonon annihiliation and creation operators, and $A_{q\alpha} = (\hbar/2M_\alpha N\omega_{q\alpha})^{1/2}$ is the phonon amplitude for wavevector q, frequency $\omega_{q\alpha}$, and polarization index α; M_α and N are the ion mass and the number of unit cells. The electron-phonon term becomes

$$H_{el\text{-}ph} = \sum_{la} \sum_{q\alpha} A_{q\alpha} \hat{\varepsilon}_{q\alpha}^a \cdot \nabla V_a(r - R_l^a) \quad . \tag{11.14}$$

Fourier analyzing the pseudopotential yields

$$V_a(r) = \frac{1}{wN} \sum_{q'} e^{iq' \cdot r} V_a(q') \qquad (11.15)$$

$$V_a(q) = \frac{1}{\Omega_a} \int d^3r e^{-iq \cdot r} V_a(r) \qquad (11.16)$$

where w is the number of atoms in a cell and Ω_a is the volume per atom. The gradient of the pseudopotential in (11.14) can now be taken

$$\nabla V_a(r) = \frac{i}{wN} \sum_{q} q' e^{iq' \cdot r} V_a(q') \qquad (11.17)$$

$$\nabla V_a(r - R_l^a) = \frac{i}{wN} \sum_{q'} q' e^{iq' \cdot r} V_a(q') \exp(-iq' \cdot R_l^a) \qquad (11.18)$$

giving

$$H_{\text{el-ph}} = \sum_{la} \sum_{q\alpha} \sum_{q'} \frac{i}{Nw} A_{q\alpha} \hat{\varepsilon}_{q\alpha}^a \cdot q' e^{iq \cdot r}$$

$$\exp[i(q - q') \cdot R_l^a] \times V_a(q')(a_{q\alpha} + a_{-q\alpha}^\dagger) \quad . \qquad (11.19)$$

Using $R_l^a = R_l + \tau_a$, the sum over l gives

$$\sum_l \exp[i(q - q') \cdot R_l^a] = N\exp(-iG \cdot \tau_a)\delta_{q',q+G} \quad . \qquad (11.20)$$

In second quantized form, the electron-phonon Hamiltonian, $E_{\text{el-ph}}$, involves the matrix element of $H_{\text{el-ph}}$ between Bloch states $|k'\rangle$ and $|k\rangle$.

$$H_{\text{el-ph}} = \sum_{kq\alpha} M_{q\alpha}(k \to k') C_{k'}^\dagger C_k (a_{q\alpha} + a_{-q\alpha}^\dagger) \qquad (11.21)$$

where

$$M_{q\alpha}(k \to k') = \frac{i}{w} \sum_{aG} \sqrt{\frac{h}{2MN\omega_{q\alpha}}} \hat{\varepsilon}_{q\alpha}^a \cdot (q + G)$$

$$\exp(-iG \cdot \tau_a) V_a(q + G) \langle k'|e^{i(q+G) \cdot r}|k\rangle \qquad (11.22)$$

and where $C_{k'}^\dagger$ and C_k are the creation and annihilation operators for electrons in the states k' and k.

Equation (11.21) describes the scattering of an electron $|k\rangle$ to $|k'\rangle$ by the absorption of a phonon (q, α) or the emission of a phonon $(-q, \alpha)$. The matrix element for the process is given in (11.22), which is the fundamental expression used for computing electron-phonon coupling.

The result is general within the rigid-ion approximation and is appropriate for calculating electron-phonon coupling for acoustic and optical phonons in metals, semiconductors, and insulators. As an example, we can use (11.22) to compute the Fröhlich coupling for an electron to a longitudinal optical phonon of frequency ω in a binary polar crystal. For small q, $\langle k + q | e^{i(q+G) \cdot r} | k \rangle \approx \delta_{G,0}$ and the potentials can be described using a Coulomb form of opposite charge z for the two atoms in the cell

$$V_1(q) = -V_2(q) = \frac{4\pi z e^2}{\varepsilon_\infty q^2 \Omega_a} \tag{11.23}$$

where ε_∞ is the high frequency dielectric function.

Because the nearest neighbor displacements are opposite for optical phonons,

$$\hat{\varepsilon}_1 = \hat{q} = -\hat{\varepsilon}_2$$

and hence

$$M_{LO}(k \to k + q) = \frac{i}{2} \frac{\hbar}{2MN\omega} q(V_1 - V_2) = i \frac{\hbar}{2MN\omega} \frac{4\pi z e^2}{\varepsilon_\infty q \Omega_a} \quad . \tag{11.24}$$

Using the Lyddane-Sach-Teller relation [11.31] and the sum rule on optical phonons we have

$$1 = \left(\frac{\omega^2 - \omega_{TO}^2}{\omega_p^2} \right)^{1/2} = \frac{\omega}{\Omega_p} \left(1 - \frac{\varepsilon_\infty}{\varepsilon_0} \right)^{1/2} \tag{11.25}$$

where ω_{TO} is the transverse optical phonon frequency

$$\Omega_p = \left(\frac{4\pi z e N}{\varepsilon_\infty M \Omega_a} \right)^{1/2}$$

is the plasma frequency, and ε_0 is the static dielectric constant. Equations (11.24, 25) give

$$M_{LO}(k \to k + q) = i \frac{2\pi e^2}{\Omega q^2} \hbar\omega \left(\frac{1}{\varepsilon_\infty} - \frac{1}{\varepsilon_0} \right)^{1/2} \tag{11.26}$$

which is the standard form for the Fröhlich coupling (11.29). This interaction is used to explain polaron formation in ionic crystals.

The simplification expressed in (11.23) serves to show the physical consequences of (11.22). In general, however, the simple Coulomb potentials of (11.23) do not apply and pseudopotential form factors are used.

12. Triatomic, Layer, Chain, and Amorphous Models

In the late 1960s, the successful application of the EPM to elemental and binary compounds and the availability of model potentials [12.1] for many elements helped established the idea that a pseudopotential could be associated with an ion core independent of its chemical state. Pseudopotentials for metallic elements could then be used for semiconductor compounds. It was therefore realized that the EPM was capable of predicting electronic and optical properties of materials having complex crystal structures.

One of the earliest applications to a triatomic system was a study of Mg_2Si, Mg_2Ge, and Mg_2Sn. The pseudopotential form factors for Si, Ge, and Sn had been determined and tested for these semiconductors. In addition, Fermi surface studies helped to determine [12.2] the form factors for Mg. These form factors could be extrapolated using the results of the model potential curves to yield new form factors appropriate to the Mg_2X compounds. In principle, no new information is needed, but fine adjustments could be made to assure better comparisons with experiment.

The results were in surprisingly good agreement with experimental measurements of the optical spectra, and this success motivated further work for compound semiconductors having more than two atoms in a unit cell. The results for the three compounds with X = Si, Ge, Sn, were comparable, hence we focus on Mg_2Si [12.3] as a prototype for the series.

Mg_2Si has the cubic fluorite structure with Si occupying the fcc sites and two Mg atoms associated with each Si at $\pm(1/4, 1/4, 1/4)a$ with respect to the Si; a is the lattice constant. The pseudopotential form factors for Mg_2X become

$$V(G) = \frac{1}{\Omega}\{\Omega_X V^X(G) + 2\Omega_{Mg} V^{Mg}(G) \cos[\tfrac{1}{2}\pi(h + k + l)]\} \quad (12.1)$$

where Ω, Ω_X, and Ω_{Mg} are the cell volume and the volume per atom for the X and Mg respectively; $V^X(G)$ and $V^{Mg}(G)$ are the corresponding form factors for $G = (h, k, l)2\pi/a$. The form factors for Si, Ge, Sn, and Mg are given in Fig. 12.1. The fact that smooth curves close to the model potential results can be drawn through the form factor points was considered to be support for the concept of identifying a unique pseudopotential with an element

The band structure for Mg_2Si is shown in Fig. 12.2 and the imaginary part of the dielectric function $\varepsilon_2(\omega)$ is given in Fig. 12.3. Similar results

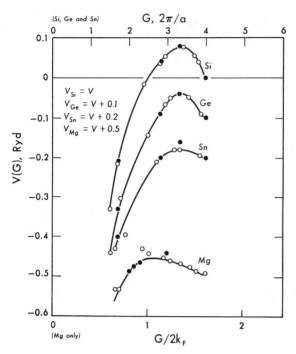

Fig. 12.1. Scaled pseudopotentials for Si, Ge, Sn, and Mg; a is the lattice constant for the semiconductor element and k_F is the Mg Fermi momentum

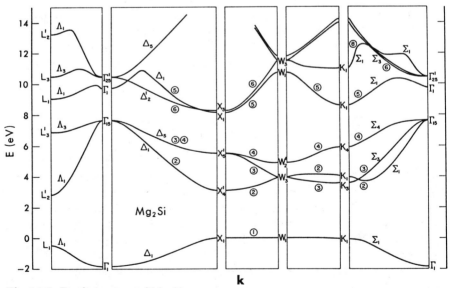

Fig. 12.2. Band structure of Mg$_2$Si

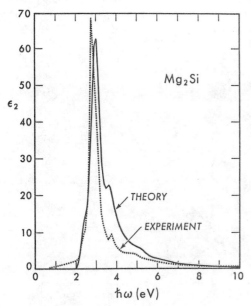

Fig. 12.3. Calculated and experimental imaginary part of the dielectric function $\varepsilon_2(\omega)$ for Mg_2Si

are obtained [12.3] for Mg_2Ge and Mg_2Sn. The agreement between the calculated $\varepsilon_2(\omega)$ and experment is impressive considering the fact that the pseudopotentials were scaled from other studies. A complete critical-point analysis of the optical spectra of the three compounds was made, and the prominent structure in the spectra was identified in terms of interband transitions. The results are given in Table 12.1.

Table 12.1. Calculated transition energies for Mg_2Si, Mg_2Ge, and Mg_2Sn and their identifications. The experimental transition energies, when identified, are shown in parentheses

Transition	Type of singularity Mg_2Si	Mg_2Ge	Mg_2Sn	Energy (eV) Mg_2Si	Mg_2Ge	Mg_2Sn
$\Gamma_{15} \to \Gamma_1$	M_0	M_0	M_0	2.06 (2.1)	1.49 (1.6)	1.06
$L_3' \to L_1$	M_0	M_0	M_0	2.15	1.99 (2.1)	1.97
$\Lambda_3 \to \Lambda_1$	M_3	M_3	M_3	2.39	2.22	2.03
$X_5' \to X_1$	M_0	M_0	M_0	2.62 (2.5)	3.01	2.35 (2.3)
$\Delta_5 \to \Delta_2$	M_3	no cp	no cp	2.81	. . .	. . .
$X_5' \to X_3$	M_0	M_0	M_1	2.74	2.84	3.02
$(K_4 \to K_1)_{45}$	M_0	M_0	M_0	2.74	3.03	2.69 (2.5)
$\Gamma_{15} \to \Gamma_{25}'$	M_0	M_3 or M_0	M_0	2.80	3.20	2.94
$\Sigma_4 \to \Sigma_1$	M_2	M_2	M_2	3.01 (2.7)	3.16 (3.0)	2.83 (2.7)
$L_3' \to L_3$	M_2	M_2	M_2	3.59 (3.7)	4.08 (4.1)	3.52 (3.4)
$\Lambda_3 \to \Lambda_3$	M_3	M_3	M_3	3.79	4.22	3.71
$\Delta_5 \to \Delta_1$	M_3	M_3	M_3	3.87	3.94	3.24
$(K_1 \to K_1)_{25}$	M_0	M_0	M_0	4.59	4.74	4.16
$\Delta_1 \to \Delta_1$	M_0	no cp	M_0	4.60	. . .	4.23
$\Delta_1 \to \Delta_1$	M_1	no cp	M_1	4.63	. . .	4.29
$X_4' \to X_1$	M_1	M_1	M_1	5.03	5.37	4.27
$(K_3 \to K_1)_{35}$	M_0	M_0	M_0	5.06	5.29	4.55

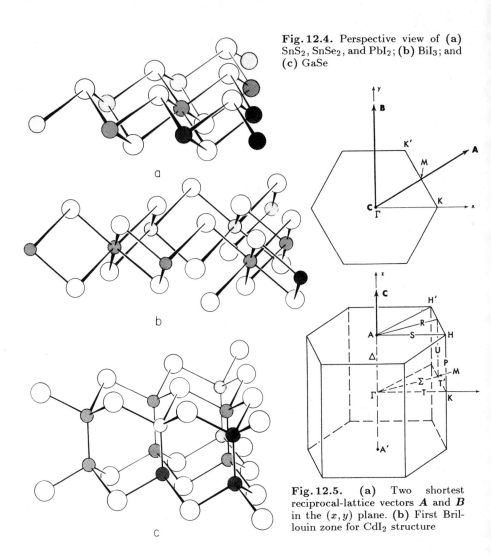

Fig. 12.4. Perspective view of (a) SnS$_2$, SnSe$_2$, and PbI$_2$; (b) BiI$_3$; and (c) GaSe

Fig. 12.5. (a) Two shortest reciprocal-lattice vectors A and B in the (x, y) plane. (b) First Brillouin zone for CdI$_2$ structure

In similar fashion, the EPM was applied to a series of layer componds: SnS$_2$, SnSe [12.4–6], GaSe [12.6–9], GaS [12.9], PbI$_2$ [12.7, 10], and BiI$_3$ [12.7, 11]. Some of the structures of these compounds are illustrated in Fig. 12.4. For SnS$_2$ and SnSe$_2$, the crystal structure is of the CdI$_2$ form, and the Brillouin zone is shown in Fig. 12.5. As in the case of Mg$_2$X, the pseudopotential form factors agree, when scaled, with the model potential [12.1] values. Band structures for these compounds are given in Fig. 12.6. Analysis of the optical spectra [12.6] for SnS$_2$ and SnSe$_2$ in terms of critical points provides identification of the principal optical structure.

Similar calculations were carried out for other layer compounds. In Figs. 12.7, 8 the band structures for GaSe and BiI$_3$ are given. These were

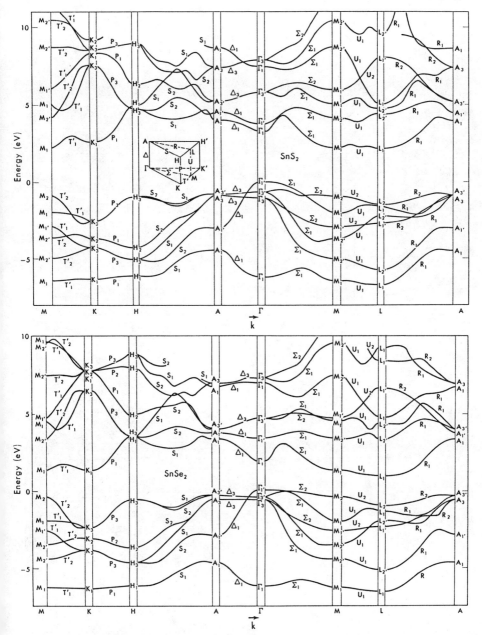

Fig. 12.6. (a) Band structure of SnS₂ and (b) band structure of SnSe₂

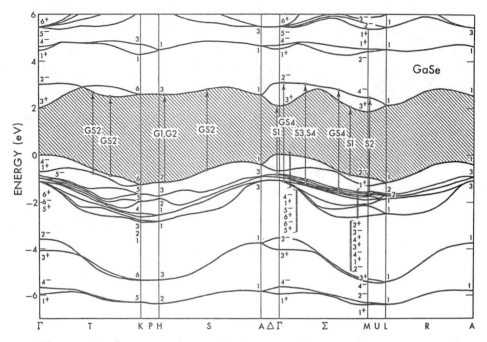

Fig. 12.7. Band structure of GaSe. The lowest Se s-like bands are not shown

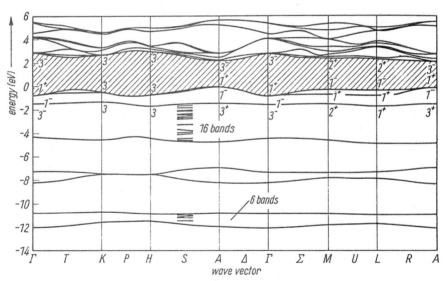

Fig. 12.8. Band structure of BiI$_3$. Spin-orbit effects are not included

used, along with calculated optical spectra, to identify prominent optical structure for these compounds for mixed crystals of GaS and GaSe [12.9]. Valence band density of states spectra were also computed and compared with photoemission results [12.7].

Charge density calculations were performed [12.5, 7] to study the bonding properties of these materials. In particular, $SnSe_2$, PbI_2, BiI_3, and GaSe were examined and compared [12.7]. The crystal structures for these compounds are given in Fig. 12.4, and these layer compounds can be viewed as groups of atoms tightly bound in two-dimensionally extended sandwiches which are several atomic layers thick. The sandwiches are stacked with weak interactions between them. It is the atomic arrangement within the sandwiches which determines the valence band structures of these materials. Interlayer interactions act only as perturbations. Although this view is appropriate for analysis of structural and mechanical properties, individual electronic states are influenced more strongly by interlayer interactions.

Charge density plots are given in Figs. 12.9–12 for $SnSe_2$, PbI_2, BiI_3, and GaSe. These figures illustrate the pile-up of charge around the anion sites for these fairly ionic materials. The relationship between the bonding in these representative layer compounds and an analysis in terms of their structure is given in [12.7].

Fig. 12.9. Charge density contours for the total valence charge of $SnSe_2$ displayed in a (110) plane extending over two half-layers containing anion-cation bonds. The contour values are given in electrons per unit cell

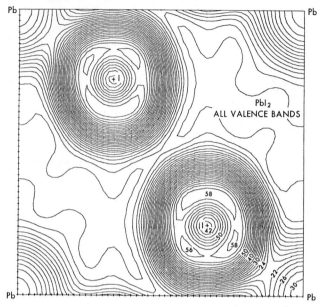

Fig. 12.10. Total valence charge density of PbI$_2$ displayed and labeled as in Fig. 12.9

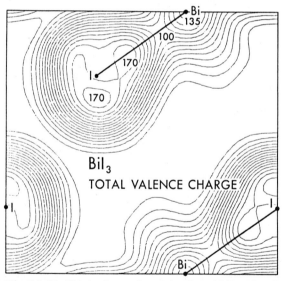

Fig. 12.11. Total valence charge density of BiI$_3$. The charge is displayed in a (100) plane of the BiI$_3$ structure which corresponds to the (110) plane of Figs. 12.9, 10

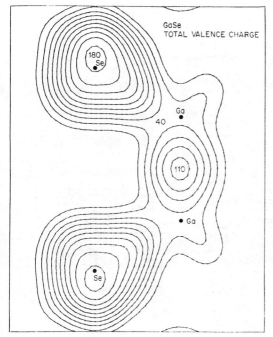

Fig. 12.12. Total valence charge density of GaSe. The charge is displayed in a (110) plane extending over one layer and containing anion-cation as well as cation-cation bonds

Two chain-structured semiconductors, Se and Te, were analyzed [12.12] using the EPM. Although these are monatomic materials, their crystal structure is complicated. Data on both trigonal and amorphous Se and Te were examined. The EPM results were supplemented with tight-binding calculations to obtain analytic expressions for the energy bands. These were used to interpret the EPM band structures in terms of real-space orbital-orbital interactions.

The crystal structure of trigonal Se and Te consists of helical chains which spiral around axes parallel to the crystalline c-axis. The helices are arranged in a hexagonal array. Figure 12.13 illustrates the geometry, and a

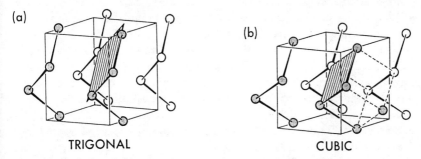

Fig. 12.13. (a) Unit cell of trigonal Se and Te. **(b)** Corresponding simple cubic structure from which the structure of Se and Te can be derived by trigonal distortions

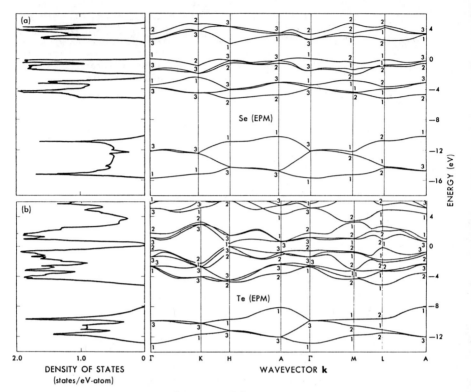

Fig. 12.14. Band structures of (a) Se and (b) Te. The corresponding densities of states are also given

cubic structure is also given for comparison. The crystal unit cell consists of three atoms of a helix (Fig. 12.13). Intrachain bonding is dominant, and a reasonable approximation to the electronic properties can be obtained by treating interchain effects as a perturbation.

Application of the EPM yields the band structures and densities of states shown in Fig. 12.14. The calculated densities of states are compared with photoemission measurements [12.13, 14] in Fig. 12.15. Charge density studies [12.12] were used to examine intra- and interchain interactions. The amorphous modifications were analyzed by monitoring the changes in the densities of states and charge densities with respect to the crystalline phases. Ring statistics, for example, the influence of six-fold and eight-fold rings of bonds, were studied, and the resulting modifications of the densities of states were used to interpret the photoemission of the amorphous phases.

Because the EPM is based on the use of Fourier expansions of the potential and wavefunction, extension of the method to deal with large amorphous-like clusters can most easily be done by creating large unit cells with appropriate structural units. In contrast to tight-binding cluster models, this approach deals with a complex unit which is repeated infinitely. An

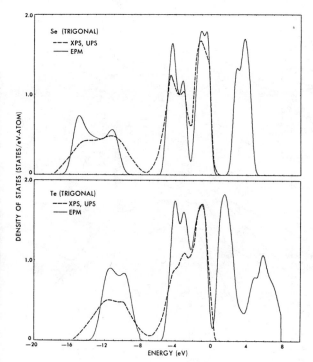

Fig. 12.15. Calculated densities of states and photoemission spectra for **(a)** Se and **(b)** Te

appropriate structure factor and basis vectors are used to place the atoms in their positions in the unit cell, and lattice vectors corresponding to the structure chosen impose the lattice symmetry. In principle, this method can be used to deal with arbitrary collections of atoms, and structural models of amorphous seiconductors can be tested. The limiting feature is that the complexity and hence the computing time increases rapidly with cell size.

The approach used to study amorphous Si and Ge, α-Si and α-Ge, involved investigations [12.15–17] of the electronic and optical properties of these elements in crystal structures which were known to be stable or metastable and semiconducting. The structures studied were, FC-2 (diamond), 2H-4 (homopolar wurtzite or hexagonal diamond), BC-8 (Si-III), and ST-12 (Ge-III). Comparisons of the electronic and optical properties of these structures indicated that despite the increased complexity in the long-ranged structure in this series, some prominent properties could be understood in terms of short-ranged changes in bonding or disorder. Comparisons were also made using tight-binding models, and these results, together with the EPM, allowed interpretation of many features of the amorphous phases of these elements. Extensions [12.18] to III-V compounds were also made.

The FC-2 and 2H-4 (diamond and wurtzite) structures have been discussed earlier and are well known. The metastable phases BC-8 and ST-12, which, when recovered from high pressure, also exist at normal pressures, are less well known. The BC-8 structure is modified bcc with eight atoms

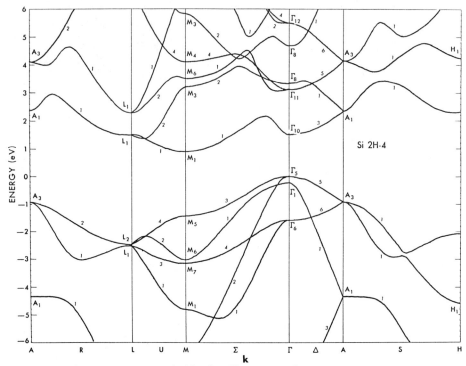

Fig. 12.16. Band structure of Si in the 2H-4 or wurtzite structure

in a unit cell, while ST-12 is a simple tetragonal structure with 12 atoms in the unit cell. For the FC-2, 2H-4, and BC-8 structures, the atoms form six-fold rings of bonds, and each atom has the same type of atomic environment. The ST-12 structure has five-fold rings of bonds and two types of atomic environment. By studying these structures, the role of ring statistics and other changes in structure can be studied systematically. Using Si as an example, the band structures for the 2H-4, BC-8, and ST-12 structures are given in Figs. 12.16–18. The density of states plots for these band structures are given in Fig. 12.19. Results for ε_2, the joint density of states and transitions matrix elements are given in Fig. 12.20.

Two major features of amorphous Si and Ge, the shift of the hump in the density of states at the top of the valence band to high energies and the single broad featureless peak in $\varepsilon_2(\omega)$ are well reproduced by the ST-12 structure. However, the ST-12 structure has not been claimed to be a good structural model for α-Si. Rather, the role of the ST-12 studies was to determine the structural properties necessary to produce the observed spectra for the amorphous case.

Fig. 12.17. Band structure of Si in the BC-8 structure

Fig. 12.18. Band structure of Si in the ST-12 structure

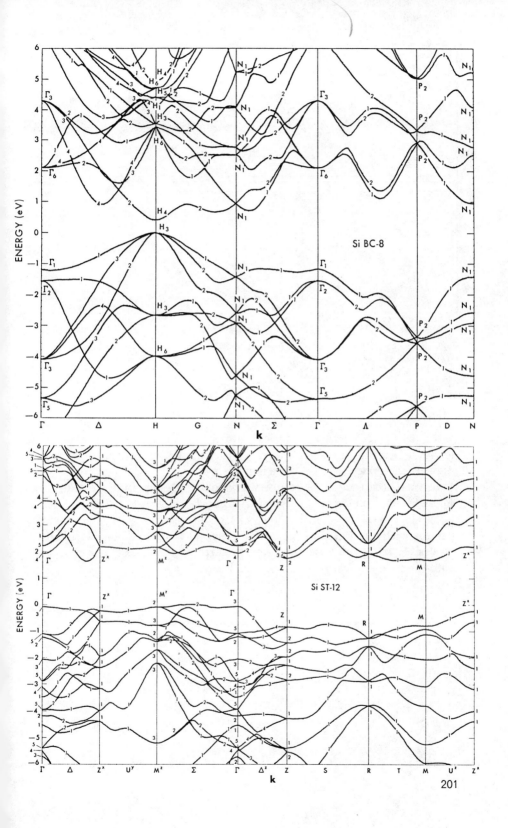

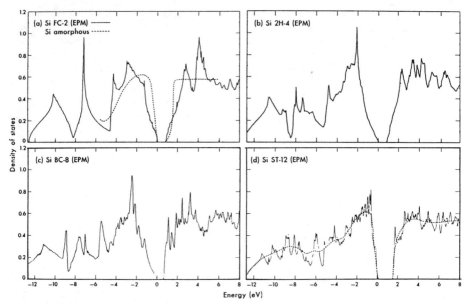

Fig. 12.19. Density of states of Si in the **(a)** FC-2, **(b)** 2H-4, **(c)** BC-8, and **(d)** ST-12 structures. The dotted line in **(a)** is a sketch of the amorphous density of states. The dotted line in **(d)** represents the averaging of Bragg gaps for Si ST-12

Hence, the major result of this study is that the prominent features in the density of states and optical properties of amorphous Si can be understood in terms of a short-range-disorder model. Amorphous systems are often characterized as crystalline materials in which long-range order is lost. However, these studies of complex crystalline models indicate that long-range-disorder effects are of secondary importance. It is the short-range disorder which is essential. In a system with deviations in bond angles and bond lengths, with all bonds satisfied, and with odd-numbered rings of bonds, it is possible to account for both the features of the amorphous density of states and the optical properties.

202

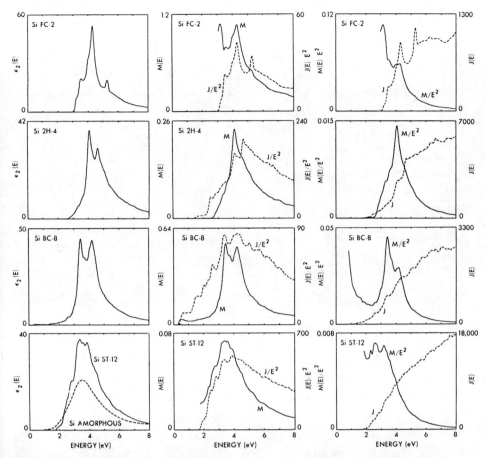

Fig. 12.20. Imaginary part of the dielectric function ε_2, associated average matrix element M, associated joint density of states J/E^2 average dipole matrix element M/E^2, and joint density of states J for Si in the FC-2, 2H-4, BC-8, and ST-12 structures. The amorphous ε_2 is sketched along with the ε_2 for ST-12

References

2.1   C. Kittel: *Introduction to Solid State Physics*, 6th ed. (Wiley, New York 1986)
2.2   F. Bassani, G. Pastori Parravicini: *Electronic States and Optical Transitions in Solids* (Pergamon, Oxford 1975)
2.3   J.C. Slater: Phys. Rev. **51**, 846 (1937)
2.4   C. Herring: Phys. Rev. **57**, 1169 (1940)

3.1   E. Fermi: Nuovo Cimento **11**, 157 (1934)
3.2   H.J. Hellman: J. Chem. Phys. **3**, 61 (1935)
3.3   E. Antoncik: J. Phys. Chem. Solids **10**, 314 (1959)
3.4   J.C. Phillips, L. Kleinman: Phys. Rev. **116**, 287 (1959)
3.5   M.H. Cohen, V. Heine: Phys. Rev. **122**, 1821 (1961)
3.6   P.W. Anderson: *Concepts in Solids* (Benajmin, New York 1963)
3.7   B.J. Austin, V. Heine, L.J. Sham: Phys. Rev. **127**, 276 (1962)
3.8   N.W. Ashcroft: Phys. Lett. **23**, 48 (1966)
3.9   V. Heine, I. Abarankov: Phil. Mag. **9**, 451 (1964)
3.10   A.D.E. Animalu, V. Heine: Phil. Mag. **12**, 1249 (1965)
3.11   M. Appapillai, V. Heine: Technical Report No. 5, Cavendish Laboratory, Cambridge, UK, 1972
3.12   M. Appapillai, A.R. Williams: J. Phys. F**3**, 759 (1973)
3.13   M.L. Cohen, V. Heine: Solid State Phys. **24**, 37 (1970)
3.14   D. Brust, J.C. Phillips, F. Bassani: Phys. Rev. Lett. **9**, 94 (1962)
3.15   D. Brust, M.L. Cohen, J.C. Phillips: Phys. Rev. Lett. **9**, 389 (1962)
3.16   M.L. Cohen, T.K. Bergstresser: Phys. Rev. **141**, 789 (1966)
3.17   P.B. Allen, M.L. Cohen: Phys. Rev. **187**, 525 (1969)
3.18   J.R. Chelikowsky, M.L. Cohen: Phys. Rev. B**14**, 556 (1976)
3.19   J.P. Walter, M.L. Cohen: Phys. Rev. B**2**, 1821 (1970)
3.20   J.A. Appelbaum, D.R. Hamann: Phys. Rev. B**8**, 1777 (1973)
3.21   M.L. Cohen, M. Schlüter, J.R. Chelikowsky, S.G. Louie: Phys. Rev. B**12**, 5575 (1975)
3.22   M. Schlüter, J.R. Chelikowsky, S.G. Louie, M.L. Cohen: Phys. Rev. B**12**, 4200 (1975)
3.23   M.L. Cohen: *Advances in Electronics and Electron Physics*, Vol. 51, eds. L. Marton and C. Marton (Academic, New York 1980), p. 1–62
3.24   E. Wigner: Phys. Rev. **46**, 1002 (1934)
3.25   J.C. Slater: Phys. Rev. **81**, 385 (1951)
3.26   P. Hohenberg, W. Kohn: Phys. Rev. **136**, B863 (1964)
3.27   W. Kohn, L.J. Sham: Phys. Rev. **140**, A113 (1965)
3.28   L. Hedin, B.I. Lundqvist: J. Phys. C**4**, 2064 (1971)
3.29   *Theory of the Inhomogeneous Electron Gas*, ed. by S. Lundqvist, N.H. March (Plenum, New York 1983), and references therein
3.30   T. Starkloff, J.D. Joannopoulos: Phys. Rev. B**16**, 5212 (1977)
3.31   A. Zunger, M.L. Cohen: Phys. Rev. B**20**, 4082 (1979)
3.32   D.R. Hamann, M. Schlüter, C. Chiang: Phys. Rev. Lett. **43**, 1494 (1979)
3.33   G.P. Kerker: J. Phys. C**13**, L189 (1980)
3.34   M.T. Yin, M.L. Cohen: Phys. Rev. B**25**, 7403 (1982)
3.35   S.G. Louie, S. Froyen, M.L. Cohen: Phys. Rev. B**26**, 1738 (1982)

3.36　M.L. Cohen: Phys. Scripta T1, 5 (1982)
3.37　M. Hybertsen, S.G. Louie: Phys. Rev. Lett. **55**, 418 (1985)

4.1　H. Ehrenreich, M.H. Cohen: Phys. Rev. **115**, 786 (1959)
4.2　F. Bassani, G. Pastori Parravicini: *Electronic States and Optical Transitions in Solids* (Pergamon, Oxford 1975)
4.3　M.L. Cohen, J.R. Chelikowsky: *Handbook on Semiconductors*, vol. 1, ed. by W. Paul (North-Holland, Amsterdam, 1982), p. 219
4.4　L. Van Hove: Phys. Rev. **89**, 1189 (1953)
4.5　J.C. Phillips: Phys. Rev. **104**, 1263 (1956)
4.6　D. Penn: Phys. Rev. **128**, 2093 (1962)
4.7　J.P. Walter, M.L. Cohen: Phys. Rev. **B2**, 1821 (1970)
4.8　J.P. Walter, M.L. Cohen: Phys. Rev. **B5**, 3101 (1972)
4.9　S.J. Sramek, M.L. Cohen: Phys. Rev. **B6**, 3800 (1972)
4.10　L. Pauling, *The Nature of the Chemical Bond*, 3rd ed. (Cornell University Press, Ithaca 1960)
4.11　J.P. Walter, M.L. Cohen: Phys. Rev. **B4**, 1877 (1971)
4.12　M.L. Cohen: Science **179**, 1189 (1973)
4.13　L.W. Yang, P. Coppens: Solid State Commun. **15**, 1555 (1974)
4.14　A. Baldlereschi: Phys. Rev. **B7**, 5212 (1973)
4.15　D.J. Chadi, M.L. Cohen: Phys. Rev. **B8**, 5747 (1973)

5.1　C. Kittel: *Introduction to Solid State Physics*, 6th ed. (Wiley, New York 1986)
5.2　B.R. Pamplin: In *CRC Handbook of Chemistry and Physics*, ed. by R.C. West (CRC Press, 1986)
5.3　H.P.R. Federikse: American Institute of Physics Handbook, ed. by D.E. Gray (McGraw-Hill, New York 1972)
5.4　J. Frenkel: Phys. Rev. **37**, 17 and 1276 (1931)
5.5　N.F. Mott: Trans. Faraday Society **34**, 822 (1938)
5.6　G.K. Wannier: Phys. Rev. **52**, 191 (1937)
5.7　M.D. Sturge: Phys. Rev. **127**, 768 (1962)
5.8　J.C. Phillips: Solid State Physics **18**, 56 (1966)
5.9　G. Dresselhaus, A. Kip, C. Kittel: Phys. Rev. **98**, 368 (1955)

6.1　D.E. Aspnes: *Advances in Solid States Physics*, Vol. XVII (Pergamon, Oxford 1976), p. 235
6.2　D.E. Aspnes: Nuovo Cimento **39**, 337 (1977)
6.3　F. Bassani, G. Pastori Parravicini: *Electronic States and Optical Transition in Solids* (Pergamon, Oxford 1975)
6.4　M. Cardona: Solid State Physics (Suppl.) **11**, 1 (1969)
6.5　D.L. Greenaway, K. Harbeke: *Optical Properties and Band Structures of Semiconductors* (Pergamon, Oxford, 1968)
6.6　J.C. Phillips: Solid State Physics **18**, 56 (1966)
6.7　B.O. Seraphin: *Optical Properties of Solids: New Developments* (North-Holland, Amsterdam, 1976)
6.8　J. Tauc: *Optical Properties of Solids* (Academic, New York, 1966)
6.9　H.R. Phllipp, H. Ehrenreich: Phys. Rev. **129**, 1550 (1962)
6.10　R.R. Zucca, Y.R. Shen: Phys. Rev. **B1**, 2668 (1970)
6.11　M. Welkowsky, R. Braunstein: Phys. Rev. **B5**, 497 (1972)
6.12　M.L. Cohen, D.J. Chadi: *Handbook on Semiconductors*, Vol. 2, ed. M. Balkanski (North-Holland, Amsterdam, 1980), p. 155
6.13　P.B. Allen, M. Cardona: Phys. Rev. **B27**, 4760 (1983)
6.14　E. Matatagui, A.G. Thompson, M. Cardona: Phys. Rev. **176**, 950 (1968)
6.15　B. Batz: Solid State Commun. **5**, 985 (1967)
6.16　G. Guizzetti, L. Noxenzo, E. Reguoni, G. Samoygia: Phys. Rev. **B9**, 640 (1974)

6.17 W.E. Engeler, H. Fritsche, M. Garfinkel, J.J. Tiemann: Phys. Rev. Lett. **14**, 1069 (1965)
6.18 G.W. Gobeli, E.O. Kane: Phys. Rev. Lett. **15**, 142 (1965)
6.19 D.D. Sell, E.O. Kane: Phys. Rev. **B5**, 417 (1972)
6.20 F.K. Pollak: Surface Science **37**, 863 (1973)
6.21 J.Koo, Y.R. Shen, R.R. Zucca: Solid State Commun. **9**, 2229 (1971)
6.22 B.O. Seraphin, R.B. Hess: Phys. Rev. Lett. **14**, 138 (1965)
6.23 D.E. Aspnes: Phys. Rev. Lett. **28**, 913 (1972)
6.24 D.E. Aspnes: Surface Science **37**, 418 (1973)
6.25 D.E. Aspnes, A.A. Studna: Phys. Rev. **B7**, 4605 (1973)
6.26 J.B. Theeten, D.E. Aspnes: Thin Film Solids **60**, 183 (1979)
6.27 M. Cardona, K.L. Shaklee, F.K. Pollak: Phys. Rev. **154**, 696 (1967)
6.28 J.W. Grover, P. Handler: Phys. Rev. **B9**, 2600 (1974)
6.29 V. Rehn: Surface Science **37**, 443 (1973)
6.30 S. Zwerding, B. Lax, L.M. Roth: Phys. Rev. **108**, 1402 (1957)
6.31 E. Burstein, G.S. Picus, R.F. Wallis, F. Blatt: Phys. Rev. **113**, 15 (1959)
6.32 E.Y. Wang, W.A. Albers, G.E. Bleil: *Proceedings of the International Conference on II–VI Semiconducting Compounds,* ed. D.G. Thomas (Benjamin, New York 1968) p. 136
6.33 R.E. Nahory, J.L. Shay: Phys. Rev. Lett. **21**, 1569 (1968)
6.34 D.E. Aspnes, C.G. Olson, D.W. Lynch: Phys. Rev. Lett. **36**, 1563 (1976)
6.35 R. Thiry, R. Pincheaux, D. Dagneaux, Y. Petroff: *Proceedings of the 12th International Conference on the Physics of Semiconductors,* ed. Pilkuhn, Stuttgart (1974), p. 1324
6.36 D.E. Aspnes, C.G. Olson, D.W. Lynch: Phys. Rev. Lett. **37**, 766 (1976)
6.37 M.L. Cohen, T.K. Bergstresser: Phys. Rev. **141**, 789 (1966)
6.38 J.B. Gunn: IBM J. Res. Dev. **8**, 141 (1964)
6.39 T.C. Chiang, J.A. Knapp, M. Aono, D.E. Eastman: Phys. Rev. **B21**, 3513 (1980)
6.40 C.N. Bergland, W.E. Spicer: Phys. Rev. **136**, A1030 (1964)
6.41 L. Ley, R.A. Pollak, F.R. McFeely, S.P. Kowalczyk, D.A. Shirley: Phys. Rev. **B9**, 600 (1974)
6.42 D.E. Eastman, W.D. Grobman, J.L. Freeouf, M. Erbudak: Phys. Rev. **B9**, 3473 (1974)
6.43 W.E. Spicer, R.C. Eden: *Proceedings of the 9th International Conference of the Physics of Semiconductors* (Moscow, Nanka, 1968), p. 61
6.44 W.D. Grobman, D.E. Eastman, J.L. Freeouf: Phys. Rev. **B12**, 4405 (1975)
6.45 P.J. Feibelman, D.E. Eastman: Phys. Rev. **B10**, 4932 (1974)
6.46 C. Kunz: T. appl. Phys. **27**, 299 (1979)
6.47 G.J. Lapeyre, J. Anderson, P.L. Gobby, J.A. Knapp: Phys. Rev. Lett. **33**, 1290 (1974)
6.48 G.J. Lapeyre, A. Baer, J. Kermanson, J. Anderson, J.A. Knapp, P.L. Gobby: Solid State Commun. **15**, 1601 (1974)
6.49 D.E. Eastman, J.L. Freeouf: Phys. Rev. Lett. **33**, 1601 (1974)
6.50 N.V. Smith: *Photoelectron Spectroscopy of Solids,* ed. M. Cardona and L. Ley (Springer, Berlin, Heidelberg 1977)
6.51 R.R. Turtle, T.A. Calcott: Phys. Rev. Lett. **34**, 86 (1975)
6.52 M.L. Cohen, J.C. Phillips: Phys. Rev. **139**, A912 (1965)
6.53 J. Daniels, C.V. Festenberg, H. Raether: Springer Tracts in Modern Physics, Vol. 54 (Springer, Berlin, Heidelberg 1970) p. 78
6.54 H. Raether: Springer Tracts in Modern Physics, Vol. 38 (Springer, Berlin, Heidelberg 1965) p. 84
6.55 H. Raether: Springer Tracts in Modern Physics, Vol. 88 (Springer, Berlin, Heidelberg 1980) p. 1
6.56 C.V. Festenberg: Z. Physik **227**, 453 (1969)

7.1   W.L. Bragg: Proc. Cambridge Phil. Soc. **17**, 43 (1913)
7.2   C. Kittel: *Introduction to Solid State Physics,* 6th ed. (Wiley, New York, 1986)

7.3   N.W. Ashcroft, N.D. Mermin: *Solid State Physics* (Holt, Rinehart and Winston, New York 1976)
7.4   M.J. Buerger: *Contemporary Crystallography* (McGraw-Hill, New York 1970)
7.5   B.W. Batterman, D.R. Chipman, J.J. De Marco: Phys. Rev. **122**, 68 (1961)
7.6   S. Gottlicher, E. wolfel: Z. Electrochemie **63**, 891 (1959)
7.7   R. Chen, P. Trucano, R.F. Stewart: Acta Crystallogr. Sect. A**33**, 823 (1977)
7.8   N.A.W. Holzwarth, S.G. Louie, S. Rabii: Phys. Rev. B**26**, 5382 (1982)
7.9   M.L. Cohen: Science **234**, 549 (1986)
7.10 J.F. Vetelino, S.P. Gaur, S.S. Mitra: Phys. Rev. B**5**, 2360 (1972)
7.11 J.B. Roberto, B.W. Batterman, D.J. Keating: Phys. Rev. B**9**, 2590 (1974)
7.12 J.C. Phillips: Phys. Lett. **37A**, 434 (1971)
7.13 J.R. Chelikowsky, M.L. Cohen: Phys. Rev. Lett. **33**, 1339 (1974)
7.14 H. Brooks, S.C. Yu: Ph.D. Thesis of S.C. Yu, Harvard University, 1967

8.1   J.R. Chelikowsky, M.L. Cohen: Phys. Rev. B**14**, 556 (1976); Erratum: Phys. Rev. B**30**, 4828 (1984)
8.2   R.W. Wyckoff: *Crystal Structures*, 2nd ed. (Interscience, New York 1963); B.R. Pamplin, *CRC Handbook of Chemistry and Physics*, ed. R.C. Weast (CRC Press, Boca Raton, 1986)
8.3   A.B. Kunz: Phys. Rev. Lett. **27**, 567 (1971)
8.4   J.S. Kline, F.H. Pollak, M. Cardona: Helv. Phys. Acta **41**, 968 (1968)
8.5   D.E. Aspnes, A.A. Studna: Solid State Commun. **11**, 1375 (1972)
8.6   J.W. Grover, P. Handler: Phys. Rev. B**9**, 2600 (1974)
8.7   H.R. Phillipp, H. Ehrenreich: Phys. Rev. **127**, 1550 (1963)
8.8   H. Ehrenreich, M.H. Cohen: Phys. Rev. **115**, 786 (1959)
8.9   S.L. Adler: Phys. Rev. **126**, 413 (1962); N. Wiser: Phys. Rev. **129**, 62 (1963)
8.10 W.R. Hanke, L.J. Sham: Phys. Rev. Lett. **33**, 582 (1974)
8.11 R.R.L. Zucca, Y.R. Shen: Phys. Rev. B**1**, 2668 (1970)
8.12 E.O. Kane, G.W. Gobeli: Phys. Rev. Lett. **15**, 142 (1965)
8.13 J. Tauc, A. Abraham: J. Phys. Chem. Solids **20**, 190 (1961)
8.14 F.H. Pollak, M. Cardona: Phys. Rev. **172**, 816 (1968)
8.15 J. Koo, Y.R. Shen, R.R. Zucca: Solid State Commun. **9**, 2229 (1971)
8.16 M. Welkowsky, A. Braunstein: Phys. Rev. B**5**, 497 (1972)
8.17 R.R. L. Zucca, J.P. Walter. Y.R. Shen, M.L. Cohen: Solid State Commun. **8**, 627 (1970)
8.18 L. Ley, S.P. Kowalczyk, R.A. Pollak, D.A. Shirley: Phys. Rev. Lett. **29**, 1088 (1972)
8.19 W.D. Grobman, D.E. Eastman: Phys. Rev. Lett. **29**, 1508 (1972)
8.20 W.E. Spicer, R.C. Eden: *Proc. of the 9th Int. Conf. on the Phys. of Semicon.* (Moscow, Nauka 1968) p. 61
8.21 G. Dresselhaus, A. Kip, C. Kittel: Phys. Rev. **98**, 368 (1955)
8.22 E.O. Kane: Phys. Rev. B**4**, 1910 (1971)
8.23 J.C. Hensel, H. Hasegawa, M. Nakagama: Phys. Rev. **138**, 4225 (1965)
8.24 E.B. Hale, T. Castner: Phys. Rev. B**1**, 4763 (1970)
8.25 A. Frova, P. Handler: Phys. Rev. Lett. **14**, 178 (1965)
8.26 J.P. Van Dyke: Phys. Rev. B**5**, 1489 (1972)
8.27 L.W. Yang, P. Coppens: Solid State Commun. **15**, 1555 (1974)
8.28 J.C. Phillips: *Bonds and Bands in Semiconductors* (Academic, New York 1973)
8.29 D.R. Hamann: Phys. Rev. Lett. **42**, 662 (1979)
8.30 J.C. Phillips, K. Pandey: Phys. Rev. Lett. **30**, 787 (1973)
8.31 J.R. Chelikowsky, M.L. Cohen: Phys. Rev. Lett. **31**, 1582 (1973)
8.32 F. Herman, R.L. Kortum, C.D. Kuglin, J.P. Van Dyke: *Methods in Computational Physics*, ed. by B. Adler, S. Fernback, M. Rotenberg, Vol. 8 (Academic, New York 1968) p. 193
8.33 D.E. Aspnes: Phys. Rev. Lett. **31**, 230 (1973)
8.34 D.J. Chadi, M.L. Cohen: Phys. Rev. B**8**, 5747 (1973)
8.35 P. Pollak, L. Ley, S. Kowalczyk, D.A. Shirley, J. Joannopoulos, D.J. Chadi, M.L. Cohen: Phys. Rev. Lett. **29**, 1103 (1973)

8.36   J.R. Chelikowsky, D.J. Chadi, M.L. Cohen: Phys. Rev. B8, 2786 (1973)
8.37   J.E. Fischer: *Proc. of the 10th Int. Conf. on the Phys. of Semicon.*, (Cambridge, Massachusetts, 1970) ed. by S.P. Keller, J.C. Hensel, and F. Stern, p. 427
8.38   J. Halpern, B. Lax: J. Phys. Chem. Sol. 26, 911 (1965)
8.39   W.B. Pearson: *The Crystal Chemistry and Physics of Metals and Alloys* (Wiley, New York 1972)
8.40   M. Cardona, P. McElroy, F.H. Pollak: Solid State Commun. 4, 319 (1966)
8.41   F.H. Pollak, M. Cardona, C.W. Higginbotham, F. Herman, J.P. Van Dyke: Phys. Rev. B2, 352 (1970)
8.42   I.B. Ortenburger, W.E. Rudge: IBM Research Report (RJ-0141), 1972
8.43   L. Pauling: *The Nature of the Chemical Bond*, 3rd ed. (Cornell University Press, Ithaca, 1960)
8.44   D.E. Aspnes, A.A. Studna: Phys. Rev. B7, 4605 (1973)
8.45   V. Rehn, D.S. Kyser: Phys. Rev. Lett. 28, 494 (1972)
8.46   D.D. Sell, R. Dingle, S.E. Stokowski, J.V. Dilarenzo: Phys. Rev. Lett. 27, 1644 (1971)
8.47   D.D. Sell, S.E. Stokowski: *Proc. of the 10th Int. Conf. on the Phys. of Semicon.* (Massachusetts 1970) p. 417
8.48   L. Ley, R.A.Pollak, F.R. McFeely, S.P. Kowalczyk, D.A. Shirley: Phys. Rev. B9, 600 (1974)
8.49   D.E. Eastman, W.D. Grobman, J.L. Freeouf, M. Erbudak: Phys. Rev. B9, 3473 (1974)
8.50   A.M. Gray: Phys. Status. Solidi 37, 11 (1970)
8.51   J.P. Walter, Y. Petroff, M. Balkanski, M.L. Cohen: Phys. Rev. B1, 2661 (1970)
8.52   J.L. Freeouf: Phys. Rev. B7, 3810 (1973)
8.53   C. Varea de Alvarez, J.P. Walter, J. Stokes, Y.R. Shen, M.L. Cohen: Phys. Rev. B6, 1412 (1972)
8.54   S.S. Vishnubhatta, J.C.Woolley: Can. J. Phys. 46, 1769 (1968)
8.55   M. Cardona: J. Appl. Phys. Suppl. 32, 2151 (1961)
8.56   M. Cardona: *Semiconductors and Semimetals*, Vol. 3, ed. R. Willardson and A. Beer (Academic, New York 1967) p. 138
8.57   H. Ehrenreich, H.R. Philipp, J.C. Phillips: Phys. Rev. Lett. 8, 59 (1962)
8.58   D.H. Bilderback, R. Colella: Phys. Rev. Lett. 35, 858 (1975)
8.59   D.J. Chadi, J.P. Walter, M.L. Cohen, Y. Petroff, M. Balkanski: Phys. Rev. B5, 3058 (1972)
8.60   J.P. Walter, M.L. Cohen: Phys. Rev. B4, 1877 (1971)

9.1   R.W. Wyckoff: *Crystal Structures*, 2nd ed. (Interscience, New York 1963)
9.2   T.K. Bergstresser, M.L. Cohen: Phys. Lett. 23, 8 (1966)
9.3   T.K. Bergstresser, M.L. Cohen: Phys. Rev. Lett. 164, 1069 (1967)
9.4   M.L. Cohen: *II–VI Semiconducting Compounds*, ed. D.G.Thomas (Benjamin, New York, 1967), p. 462
9.5   M.L. Cohen, T.K. Bergstresser: Phys. Rev. 141, 789 (1966)
9.6   E.I. Rashba: Soviet Physics Solid State 1, 368 (1959)
9.7   M. Cardona, G. Harbeke: Phys. Rev. 137, A1467 (1965)
9.8   J.L. Birman: Phys. Rev. 115, 1493 (1959)
9.9   J.D. Joannopoulos, M.L. Cohen: J. Phys. C6, 1572 (1973)
9.10   D.J. Chadi, M.L. Cohen: Phys. Rev. B8, 5747 (1973)
9.11   N.G. Stoffel, G. Margaritondo: Phys. Rev. B28, 3306 (1983)
9.12   J.R. Chelikowsky: Solid State Commun. 22, 351 (1977)
9.13   S. Bloom, I. Ortenberger, Phys. Status Solidi (6) 58, 561 (1973)
9.14   L. Ley, R.A. Pollak, F.R. McFeely, S.P. Kowalczyk, D.A. Shirley: Phys. Rev. B9, 600 (1974)
9.15   J.L. Freeouf: Phys. Rev. B7, 3810 (1973)

10.1   C. Varea de Alvarez, M.L. Cohen: Phys. Rev. Lett. **30**, 979 (1973)
10.2   C. Varea de Alvarez, M.L. Cohen, S.E. Kohn, Y. Petroff, Y.R. Shen: Phys. Rev. **B10**, 5175 (1974)
10.3   C. Varea de Alvarez, M.L. Cohen, L. Ley, S.P. Kowalczyk, F.R. McFeely, D.A. Shirley, R.W. Grout: Phys. Rev. **B10**, 596 (1974)
10.4   A. Raudonis, V.S. Grigoreva, D. Prochukhan, A. Shileika: Phys. Status Solidi **B57**, 415 (1973)
10.5   A. Shileika: Surf. Sci. **37**, 730 (1973)
10.6   J.L. Shay, B. Tell, E. Beuhler, J.H. Wernick: Phys. Rev. Lett. **30**, 983 (1973)

11.1   F. Herman, R.L. Kortum, I. Ortenburger, J.P. Van Dyke: J. de Phys. Suppl. **29**, C4–62 (1968)
11.2   L.E. Johnson, J.B. Conklin, Jr., G.W. Pratt, Jr.: Phys. Rev. Lett. **11**, 538 (1963); Phys. Rev. **137**, A1281 (1965)
11.3   L.G. Ferrura: Phys. Rev. **137**, A1601 (1965)
11.4   S. Rabii: Phys. Rev. **107** (1958); **173**, 918 (1968)
11.5   H. Overhof, V. Rosslen: Phys. Status Solidi **37**, 691 (1970)
11.6   P.J. Lin, L. Kleinman: Phys. Rev. **142**, 478 (1966)
11.7   R.L. Bernick, L. Kleinman: Solid State Commun. **8**, 569 (1970)
11.8   Y.W. Tung, M.L. Cohen: Phys. Rev. **180**, 823 (1969); S.E. Kohn, P.Y. Yu, Y. Petroff, Y.R. Shen, Y. Tsang, M.L. Cohen: Phys. Rev. **B8**, 1477 (1973)
11.9   G. Martinez, M. Schlüter, M.L. Cohen: Phys. Rev. **B11**, 651 (1975)
11.10 G. Weisz: Phys. Rev. **149**, 504 (1966)
11.11 S. Bloom, T.K. Bergstresser: Solid State Commun. **6**, 465 (1968)
11.12 F. Herman, C.D. Kuglin, K.F. Cuoff, R.L. Kortum, Phys. Rev. Lett. **11**, 5419 (1963)
11.13 Y.W. Tsang, M.L. Cohen: Solid State Commun. **10**, 871 (1972)
11.14 Y.W. Tung, M.L. Cohen: Phys. Lett. **29A**, 236 (1969)
11.15 Y.W. Tsang, M.L. Cohen: Solid State Commun. **9**, 261 (1971)
11.16 M.L. Cohen, Y.W. Tsang: J. Chem. Phys. Solids **32** (Suppl. 1), 303 (1971)
11.17 G. Martinez, M. Schlüter, M.L. Cohen: Phys. Rev. **B11**, 660 (1975)
11.18 M. Schlüter, G. Martinez, M.L. Cohen: Phys. Rev. **B11**, 3808 (1975)
11.19 M. Schlüter, G. Martinez, M.L. Cohen: Phys. Rev. **B12**, 650 (1975)
11.20 C. Keflfer, T.M. Hayes, A. Bienenstock: Phys. Rev. Lett. **21**, 1677 (1968)
11.21 Y.W. Tsang, M.L. Cohen: Phys. Rev. **B3**, 1254 (1971)
11.22 M.L. Cohen, D.J. Chadi: *Handbook on Semiconductors*, Vol. 2, ed. M. Balkanski (North-Holland, Amsterdam 1980) p. 155
11.23 H.Y. Fan: Phys. Rev. **82**, 900 (1951)
11.24 E. Antonchik: Czech. J. Phys. **5**, 449 (1955)
11.25 H. Brooks, S.C. Yu (unpublished), S.C. Yu: Ph.D. Thesis, Harvard University (1967)
11.26 M.L. Cohen: Phys. Rev. **128**, 131 (1962)
11.27 P.B. Allen, M. Cardona: Phys. Rev. **B27**, 4760 (1983)
11.28 M.L. Cohen: Phys. Rev. **134**, A511 (1964)
11.29 J. Ziman: *Electrons and Phonons* (Oxford University Press, Oxford 1960)
11.30 O.J. Glembocki, F.H. Pollak: Phys. Rev.Lett. **48**, 413 (1982)
11.31 C. Kittel: *Introduction to Solid State Physics*, 6th ed. (Wiley, New York 1986)

12.1   A.O.E. Animalu, V. Heine: Phil. Mag. **12**, 1249 (1965)
12.2   J.C. Kimball, R.W. Stark, F.M. Mueller: Phys. Rev. **152**, 600 (1967)
12.3   M.Y. Au Yang, M.L. Cohen: Phys. Rev. **178**, 1358 (1969)
12.4   C.Y. Fong, M.L. Cohen: Phys. Rev. **B5**, 3905 (1972)
12.5   C.Y. Fong, M.L. Cohen: J. Phys. **C7**, 107 (1974)
12.6   J. Camassel, M. Schlüter, S. Kohn, J.P. Voitchovsky, Y.R. Shen, M.L. Cohen: Phys. Status Solidi (b) **75**, 303 (1976)

12.7   M. Schlüter, M.L. Cohen: Phys. Rev. **B14**, 424 (1976)
12.8   I.Ch. Schlüter, M. Schlüter: Phys. Status Solidi (b) **57**, 145 (1973)
12.9   M. Schlüter, J. Cammassel, S. Kohn, J.P. Voitchovsky, Y.R. Shen, M.L. Cohen:
       Phys. Rev. **B13**, 3534 (1976)
12.10 E. Mooser, I.Ch. Schlüter, M. Schlüter: J. Phys. Chem. Solids **35**, 1269 (1974)
12.11 M. Schlüter, M.L. Cohen, S.E. Kohn, C.Y. Fong: Phys. Status Solidi (b) **78**, 737
       (1976)
12.12 J. D. Joannopoulos, M. Schlüter, M.L. Cohen: Phys. Rev. **B11**, 2186 (1975)
12.13 N.J. Shevchik, J. Tejeda, M. Cardona, D.W. Langer: Solid State Commun. **12**,
       1285 (1973)
12.14 M. Schlüter, J.D. Joannopoulos, M.L. Cohen, L. Ley, S. Kowalczyk, R. Pollak,
       D.A. Shirley: Solid State **15**, 1007 (1974)
12.15 J.D. Joannopoulos, M.L. Cohen: Phys. Rev. **B7**, 2644 (1973)
12.16 J.D. Joannopoulos, M.L. Cohen: Phys. Rev. **B8**, 2733 (1973)
12.17 J.D. Joannopoulos, M.L. Cohen: *Solid State Physics* **31**, 71 (1976)
12.18 J.D. Joannopoulos, M.L. Cohen: Phys. Rev. **B10**, 1545 (1974)

Bibliography

Electronic Structure and Optical Properties of Semiconductors

B.1 Properties of Semiconductors

B.1.1 Charge Densities in Semiconductors

Camp P.E. Van, V.E. Van Doren, J.T. Devreese: Phys. Rev. B **34**, 1314 (1986). First principles calculation of the pressure coefficient of the indirect gap and of the charge density in C and Si

Cohen M.L.: Science **179**, 1189 (1973). Electronic charge densities in semiconductors

Coulson C.A., L.R. Redei, D. Stocker: Proc. R. Soc. Lond. **270**, 357 (1962). The electronic properties of tetrahedral intermetallic compounds: I. Charge distributions

Richardson S.L., M.L. Cohen, S.G. Louie, J.R. Chelikowsky: Phys. Rev. B **33**, 1177 (1986). Electron charge density at conduction band edges of semiconductors

Schlüter M., A. Zunger, G.P. Kerker, K.M. Ho, M.L. Cohen: Phys. Rev. Lett. **42**, 540 (1979). Reliability of pseudopotential charge densities

Walter J.P., M.L. Cohen: Phys. Rev. Lett. **26**, 17 (1971). Electronic charge densities in semiconductors

Walter J.P., M.L. Cohen: Phys. Rev. **4**, 1877 (1971). Pseudopotential calculations of electronic charge densities in seven semiconductors

Wendel H., R.M. Martin: Phys. Rev. Lett. **40**, 950 (1978). Charge density and structural properties of covalent semiconductors

B.1.2 Chemical Trends and Bonding in Semiconductors

Andreoni W., A. Baldereschi, F. Meloni, J.C. Phillips: Solid State Commun. **25**, 245 (1978). Renormalized orbital radii

Camphausen D.L., G.A. Connel, W. Paul: Phys. Rev. Lett. **26**, 184 (1971). Calculation of energy band pressure coefficients from the dielectric theory of the chemical bond

Chadi D.J., W.D. Grobman, M.L. Cohen: Phys. Rev. B **8**, 5587 (1973). Atomic pseudopotentials and the ionicity parameter of Phillips and Van Vechten

Chadi D.J., M.L. Cohen: Phys. Lett. A **49**, 381 (1974). Correlation between the static dielectric constant and the minimum energy gap

Chelikowsky J.R.: Phys. Rev. B **34**, 5295 (1986). Chemical trends in the structural stability of binary compounds

Chelikowsky J.R., J.C. Phillips: Phys. Rev. B **17**, 2453 (1978). Quantum defect theory of heats of formation and structural transition energies of liquid and solid simple metal alloys and compounds

Chelikowsky J.R., J.C. Phillips: Phys. Rev. Lett **36**, 1687 (1977). Orbital model of thermochemical parameters

Grobman W.D., D.E. Eastman, M.L. Cohen: Phys. Lett. A **43**, 49 (1973). A relationship between photoemission-determined valence bank gaps in semiconductors and insulators and ionicity parameters

Harrison W.A.: *Electronic Structure and the Properties of Solids: The Physics of the Chemical Bond* (W.F. Freeman, San Francisco 1980).

Mooser E., W.B. Pearson: Prog. Semicond. **5**, 103 (1960). The chemical bond in semiconductors

Pearson W.B.: *The Crystal Chemistry and Physics of Metals and Alloys* (Wiley, New York 1972)

Pettifor D.G.: Solid State Commun. **51**, 31 (1984). A chemical scale for crystal structure maps

Phillips J.C.: *Bands and Bands in Semiconductors* (Academic, New York 1973).

Phillips J.C.: Science **169**, 1035 (1970). Bonds and bands in semiconductors

Phillips J.C.: Rev. Mod. Phys. **42**, 317 (1970). Ionicity of the chemical bond in crystals

Simons G., A.N. Bloch: Phys. Rev. B **7**, 2754 (1973). Pauli force-model potential for solids

St.John J., A.N. Bloch: Phys. Rev. Lett. **33**, 1095 (1974). Quantum defect electronegativity scale for non-transition metal elements

Tsang Y.W., M.L. Cohen: Phys. Rev. **9**, 3541 (1974). Pseudopotential study of bonding in the zinc-blende and rock-salt structures

Vechten J.A. Van: Phys. Rev. **182**, 891 (1969). Quantum dielectric theory of electronegativity in covalent systems: I. Electronic dielectric constant

Vechten J.A. Van: Phys. Rev. **187**, 1007 (1969). Quantum dielectric theory of electronegativity in covalent systems: II. Ionization potentials and interband transition energies

Vechten J.A. Van: Phys. Rev. B **7**, 1497 (1973). Quantum dielectric theory of electronegativity in covalent systems: III. Pressure-temperature phase diagrams, heats of mixing and distribution coefficients

Varea de Alvarez C., M.L. Cohen: Phys. Rev. B **8**, 1603 (1973). Model pseudopotential calculation of the electronic and bonding properties of group IV elements

Wendel H., R.M. Martin: Phys. Rev. Lett. **40**, 950 (1978). Charge density and structural properties of covalent semiconductors

Zunger A., M.L. Cohen: Phys. Rev. Lett. **41**, 53 (1978). Density functional pseudopotential approach to crystal phase stability and electronic structure

B.1.3 Compilation of Properties of Semiconductors

Bilz H., W. Kress: *Phonon Dispersion Relations in Insulators*, Springer Ser. Solid-State Sci., Vol.10 (Springer, Berlin, Heidelberg 1979)

Gray D.E. (ed.): *American Institute of Physics Handbook*, 3rd ed. (McGraw-Hill, New York 1972).

Gschneidner K.: Solid State Phys. **16**, 275 (1964). Physical constants for the elements

Huntington H.B.: Solid State Phys. **7**, 213 (1962). The elastic constants of crystals

Madelung O., M. Schulz, H. Weis (eds.): *Semiconductors*, Landolt-Börnstein, Group III (Springer, Berlin, Heidelberg 1984 ff)

Pearson W.B.: *The Crystal Chemistry and Physics of Metals and Alloys* (Wiley, New York 1972).

Weast R.C. (ed.): *CRC Handbook of Chemistry and Physics*, 66th ed. (CRC Press, Boca Raton 1986).

Seeger K.: *Semiconductor Physics*, 4th ed., Springer Ser. Solid-State Sci., Vol.40 (Springer, Berlin, Heidelberg 1988)

Willardson R.K., A.C. Beer (eds.): *Semiconductors and Semimetals* (Academic, New York 1968).

Wyckoff R.W.: *Crystal Structures*, 2nd ed. (Interscience, New York 1963).

B.1.4 Electronic Structure of Semiconductors

Austin B.J., V. Heine, L.J. Sham: Phys. Rev. **127**, 276 (1962). General theory of pseudopotentials

Bachelet G.B., H.S. Greenside, G.A. Baraff, M. Schlüter: Phys. Rev. B **24**, 4745 (1981). Structural-energy calculations based on norm-conserving pseudopotentials and localized Gaussian orbitals

Baldereschi A: Phys. Rev. B **7**, 5212 (1973). Mean value point in the Brillouin zone

Bendt P., A. Zunger: Phys. Rev. B **26**, 3114 (1982). New approach for solving the density-functional self-consistent field problem

Blacha A., H. Presting, M. Cardona: Phys. Stat. Sol. b **126**, 11 (1984). Compilation of uniaxial and phonon deformation potentials

Brodsky M.H. (ed.): *Amorphous Semiconductors*, 2nd. ed., Topics Appl. Phys., Vol.36 (Springer, Berlin, Heidelberg 1985)

Cardona M., N.E. Christensen, G. Fasol: Phys. Rev. Lett. **56**, 2831 (1956). Spin splitting of electronic states

Chadi D.J., M.L. Cohen: Phys. Rev. B **8**, 5747 (1973). Special points in the Brillouin zone

Chaney R.C., T.K. Tung, C.C. Lin, E.E. Lafon: J. Chem. Phys. **52**, 361 (1970). Application of Gaussian type orbitals for calculating energy band structures of solids by the methods of tight binding

Chelikowsky J.R., S.G. Louie: Phys. Rev. B **29**, 3470 (1984). First principles linear combination of atomic orbitals for the cohesive and structural properties of solids: application to diamond

Chelikowsky J.R., S.G. Louie, D. Vanderbilt, C.T. Chan: Int'l. J. Quant. Chem. Symp. **18**, 105 (1984). Total energy method for solids and solid surfaces

Cohen M.L., V. Heine: Phys. Rev. **122**, 1821 (1961). Cancellation of kinetic and potential energy in atoms, molecules and solids

Cohen M.L.: Proc. Nat. Acad. Sci. **61**, 6 (1968). Recent pseudopotential calculations in solids

Cohen M.L., V. Heine: Solid State Phys. **24**, 37 (1970). The fitting of pseudopotentials to experimental data and their subsequent application

Cohen M.L.: Proc. of the 11th Int'l. Conf. on the phys. of semiconductors (Warsaw, Poland 1972). Calculations of the electronic structure of semiconductors, p.731

Cohen M.L., M. Schlüter, J.R. Chelikowsky, S.G. Louie: Phys. Rev. B **12**, 5575 (1975). Self-consistent pseudopotential method for localized configurations: molecules

Cohen M.L.: Phys. Today **32**, 40 (July 1979). The pseudopotential panacea

Denteneer P.J.H., W. Van Haeringen: Solid State Commun. **59**, 829 (1986). On energy differences between structurally different crystals

Gygi F., A. Baldereschi: Phys. Rev. B **34**, 4405 (1986). Self-consistent Hartree-Fock and screened exchange calculations in solids: application to silicon

Harrison W.A.: *Pseudopotentials in the Theory of Metals* (Benjamin, New York 1966).

Harrison W.A.: *Electronic Structure and the Properties of Solids* (Freeman, San Francisco 1980).

Harrison W.A., S. Ciraci: Phys. Rev. B **10**, 1516 (1974). Bond orbital method II

Hybertsen M., S.G. Louie: Phys. Rev. B **30**, 5777 (1984). Nonlocal-density-functional approximation for exchange and correlation in semiconductors

Ihm J., A. Zunger, M.L. Cohen: J. Phys. C **12**, 4409 (1979). Momentum space formalism for the total energy of solids

Kittel C.: *Introduction to Solid State Physics*, 6th ed. (Wiley, New York 1986).

Lambrecht W.R.L., O.K. Anderson: Phys. Rev. B **34**, 2439 (1986). Minimal basis sets in the linear muffin tin orbital method: application to the diamond structure crystals C, Si and Ge

Long D.: *Energy Bands in Semiconductors* (Wiley, New York 1968)

Martins J.L., A. Zunger: Phys. Rev. B **32**, 2689 (1985). Structural and chemical changes in binary versus ternary tetrahedral semiconductors

McKelvey J.P.: *Solid State and Semiconductor Physics* (Harper and Rowe, New York 1966).

Moss D.J., E. Ghahramani, J.E. Sipe, H.M. Van Driel: Phys. Rev. B **34**, 8758 (1986). Empirical tight binding calculation of dispersion in the linear optical properties of tetrahedral semiconductors

Phillips J.C.: Phys. Rev. **112**, 685 (1958). Energy band interpolation scheme based on a pseudopotential

Phillips J.C., L. Kleinman: Phys. Rev. **116**, 287 (1959). New method for calculating wave functions in crystals and molecules

Pickett W.E., C.S. Wang: Phys. Rev. B **30**, 4719 (1984). Local-density approximation for dynamical correlation corrections to single-particle excitations in insulators

Ren S.Y., W.A. Harrison: Phys. Rev. B **23**, 762 (1981). Semiconductor properties based upon universal tight-binding parameters

Resta R., K. Kunc: Phys. Rev. B **34**, 7146 (1986). Self-consistent theory of electronic states and dielectric response in semiconductors

Rompa H.W.A.M., M.F.H. Schuurmans, F. Williams: Phys. Rev. Lett. **52**, 675 (1984). Predicted modifications in the direct and the indirect gaps of tetrahedral semiconductors

Linde W. von der, P. Fulde, K.P. Bohnen: Phys. Rev. B **34**, 1063 (1986). Efficient approach to the ab initio Hartree-Fock problem of solids with application to diamond and silicon

Ortenberg M. von: Solid State Commun. **52**, 111 (1984). A new approach to the theory of semimagnetic semiconductors

Shklovskii B., A.L. Efros: *Electronic Properties of Doped Semiconductors*, Springer Ser. Solid-State Sci., Vol.45 (Springer, Berlin, Heidelberg 1984)

Willardson R.K., A.C. Beer (eds.): *Semiconductors and Semimetals* (Academic, New York 1966)

Wood D.M., A. Zunger, R. De Groot: Phys. Rev. B **31**, 2570 (1985). Electronic structure of filled tetrahedral semiconductors

Woodruff T.O.: Solid State Phys. **4**, 367 (1957). The orthogonalized plane wave method

Wulf H.F.: *Semiconductors* (Wiley, New York 1971).

Ziman J.: *Principles of the Theory of Solids* (University Press, Cambridge 1964).

B.1.5 Lattice Forces and Dynamics

Bilz H., W. Kress: *Phonon Dispersion Relations in Insulators*, Springer Ser. Solid-State Sci., Vol.10 (Springer, Berlin, Heidelberg 1979)

Christensen N.E.: Solid State Commun. **49**, 701 (1984). Force theorem and elastic constants of solids

Harrison W.A., J. Chr. Phillips: Phys. Rev. Lett. **33**, 410 (1974). Angular forces in tetrahedral solids

Keating P.N.: Phys. Rev. **149**, 674 (1966). Theory of the third-order elastic constants of diamond-like crystals

Lee D.H., J.D. Joannopoulos: Phys. Rev. Lett. **48**, 1846 (1982). Simple scheme for deriving atomic force constants: application to SiC

McMurray H.C., A.W. Solbrig, Jr., J.K. Boyler, C. Noble: J. Phys. Chem. Solids **28**, 2359 (1967). The use of valence force potentials in calculating crystal vibrations

Pick R.M., M.H. Cohen, R.M. Martin: Phys. Rev. B **1**, 910 (1970). Microscopic theory of force constants in the adiabatic approximation

Sham L.J.: Phys. Rev. **188**, 1431 (1969). Electronic contribution to lattice dynamics in insulating crystals

Sham L.J.: *Dynamical Properties of Solids*, ed. by G.K. Horton, A.A. Maradudin (North Holland, Amsterdam 1974). p.301

B.1.6 Optical and Dielectric Properties of Solids

Ahrenkiel R.K.: J. Opt. Soc. Am. **61**, 1651 (1971). Modified Kramers-Kronig analysis of optical spectra

Aspnes D.E., A. Frova: Solid State Commun. **7**, 155 (1969). Influence of spatially dependent perturbations on modulates reflectance and absorbation of solids

Aspnes D.E., J.E. Rowe: Solid State Commun. **8**, 1145 (1970). Asymptotic convolution integral for the electric field effects on the interband dielectric function

Aspnes D.E., J.E. Rowe: Phys. Rev. B **5**, 4022 (1972). Resonant nonlinear optical susceptibility: electroreflectance in the low field limit

Aspnes D.E., J.E. Rowe: Phys. Rev. Lett. **27**, 188 (1971). High resolution interband energy measurements from electroreflectance spectra

Aspnes D.E.: Phys. Rev. Lett. **28**, 913 (1972). Linearized third derivate spectroscopy with depletion barrier modulation

Aspnes D.E.: Surf. Sci. **37**, 418 (1973). Third derivative modulation spectroscopy with low field electro-reflectance

Aspnes D.E.: J. Opt. Soc. Am. **63**, 1380 (1973). Analysis of modulation spectra of statified media

Aspnes D.E.: Phys. Rev. B **15**, 4228 (1974). Band nonparabolicities, broadening and internal field distributions: the spectroscopy of Franz-Keldysh oscillations

Aspnes D.E., C.G. Olson, D.W. Lynch: J. Appl. Phys. **47**, 602 (1976). Modulation spectroscopy at non-normal incidence with emphasis on vacuum uv spectral region

Aspnes D.E.: Nuovo Cimento **39**, 337 (1977). Modulation spectroscopy in the far uv

Balkanski M. (ed.): *Light Scattering in Solids* (Flammarion, Paris 1971)

Balslev I.: Solid State Commun. **52**, 351 (1984). Optical response of saddle point excitons

Bassani F., G. Pastori Parravicini: *Electronic States and Optical Transitions in Solids* (Pergamon, Oxford 1975)

Bergstresser T.K., G.W. Rubloff: Phys. Rev. Lett. **30**, 794 (1973). Local field effects in the optical properties of solids: the far ultraviolet spectra of ionic crystals

Blossey D.F., Phys. Rev. B **2**, 3976 (1970). Wannier excitation in an electric field: I. Optical absorption by bound and continuum states

Blossey D.F.: Phys. Rev. B **3**, 1382 (1972). Wannier excitation in an electric field: II. Electroabsorption in direct band gap solids

Bottka N., J.E. Fischer: Phys. Rev. B **3**, 2514 (1971). Symmetry analysis of electroreflectance spectra

Bottka N., D.L. Johnson: Phys. Rev. B **11**, 2969 (1975). Theory of band population effects in electroreflectance

Brust D., J.C. Phillips, F. Bassani: Phys. Rev. Lett. **9**, 94 (1962). Critical points and ultraviolet reflectivity of semiconductors

Burstein E., G.S. Picus, R.F. Wallis, F. Blatt: Phys. Rev. **113**, 15 (1959). Zeeman-type magneto-optical studies of interband transitions in semiconductors

Cardona M.: J. Appl. Phys. **32**, 2151 (1961). Fundamental reflectivity spectrum of semiconductors with zinc-blende structure

Cardona M., G. Harbeke: Phys. Rev. Lett. **8**, 90 (1962). Excitons at the L absorption edge in zinc-blende type semiconductors

Cardona M., G. Harbeke: J. Appl. Phys. **34**, 813 (1963). Absorption spectrum of germanium and zinc-blende type materials at energies higher than the fundamental absorption edge

Cardona M.: Solid State Commun. **1**, 109 (1963). Polarization effects in the ultraviolet reflection of crystals with wurtzite structure

Cardona M.: Phys. Rev. **129**, 1068 (1963). Reflectivity of semiconductors with wurtzite structure

Cardona M.: Proc. Int. Conf. Semicond. (Dunod, Paris 1964). Optical properties of semiconductors at energies above the fundamental edge, p.181

Cardona M., G. Harbeke: Phys. Rev. **137**, A1467 (1965). Optical properties and band structure of wurtzite-type crystals and rutile

Cardona M., K.L. Shaklee, F.H. Pollak: Phys. Rev. **154**, 696 (1967). Electroreflectance at a semiconductor-electrolyte interface

Cardona M. (ed.): *Light Scattering in Solids I*, 2nd. ed., Topics Appl. Phys., Vol.8 (Springer, Berlin, Heidelberg 1983)

Cardona M., G. Güntherodt (eds.): *Light Scattering in Solids II-IV*, Topics Appl. Phys., Vols.50-52,54 (Springer, Berlin, Heidelberg 1982,83,84)

Cardona M.: Solid State Phys. (suppl.) **11**, 1 (1969). Modulation spectroscopy

Cardona M., W. Gudat, B. Sonntag, P.Y. Yu: Proc. 10th Int. Conf. on the Phys. of Semicond. (Cambridge, Mass. 1970). Optical absorption of semiconductors from 12 to 200 eV, p.209

Cardona M., R. Haensel: Phys. Rev. B **1**, 2605 (1970). Optical properties of some compound semiconductors in the 36-150 eV region

Cardona M., F. Pollak: *The Physics of Optoelectric Materials*, ed. by W.A. Albers, Jr. (Plenum, New York 1971)

Cardona M.: Solid State Commun. **9**, 819 (1971). Raman tensor of germanium and zinc-blende-type semiconductors

Chakraborty B., P.B. Allen: J. Phys. C **11**, L9 (1978). Theory of temperature dependence of optical properties of solids

Chadi D.J., M.L. Cohen: Phys. Lett A **49**, 381 (1974). Correlation between the static dielectric constant and the minimum energy gap

Cho K.(ed.): *Excitons*, Topics Current Phys. Vol.14 (Springer, Berlin, Heidelberg 1979)

Daniels J., C.V. Festenberg, H. Raether: *Springer Tracts Mod. Phys.* **54**, 78 (Springer, Berlin, Heidelberg 1970). Optical constants of solids by electron spectroscopy

Del Sole R., E. Fiorini: Solid State Commun. **38**, 169 (1981). Local field effects on the optical properties of non-cubic crystals

Dexter D., R.S. Knox: *Excitons* (Wiley, New York 1965)

Dyke J.P. Van: Phys. Rev. B **5**, 1489 (1972). Matrix elements in interband optical transitions

Ehrenreich H., M.H. Cohen: Phys. Rev. **115**, 786 (1959). Self-consistent field approach to the many electron problem

Enderlin R.: *The Anisotropy of Electroreflectance and Band Structure Analysis*, Proc. of the 12th Int'l Conf. on the Phys. of Semicon., ed. by M. Pilkuhn (Teubner, Stuttgart 1974) p.161

Eschrig H., K.A. Kikoin, V.G. Kohn: Solid State Commun. **56**, 773 (1985). On the semiconductor energy gap in density functional theory

Gray J.G.: Phys. Rev. B **4**, 2567 (1971). Screening of Excitons in semiconductors

Gerhardt U., G.W. Rubloff: Appl. Opt. **8**, 305 (1969). A normal incidence scanning reflectometer of high precision

Greenaway D.L., H. Harbeke: *Optical Properties and Band Structures of Semiconductors* (Pergamon, Oxford 1968)

Gudat W., C. Kunz, J. Karlau: Appl. Opt. **13**, 1412 (1974). Rotating beam splitter for extreme vacuum ultraviolet

Guizzetti G., L. Nosenzo, E. Reguzzoni, G. Samoggia: Phys. Rev. **9**, 640 (1974). Thermoreflectance spectra of diamond and zinc-blende semiconductors in the vacuum ultraviolet

Haas M., B.W. Henvis: J. Phys. Chem. Solids **23**, 1099 (1962). Infrared lattice reflection spectra of III-V compound semiconductors

Harrison W.A.: Phys. Rev. B **10**, 767 (1974). Effective charges and piezoelectricity

Horsch S., P. Horsch, P. Fulde: Phys. Rev. B **28**, 5977 (1983). Electronic excitations in semiconductors

Johnson D.L.: Phys. Rev. B **9**, 4475 (1974). Local field effects and the dielectric response matrix of insulators: a model

Johnson E.J., and H.Y. Fan: Phys. Rev. **139**, A1991 (1965). Impurity and exciton effects in the infrared absorption edges of III-V compounds

Kane E.O.: Phys. Rev. **178**, 1368 (1969). Strain effects on optical critical-point structure in diamond-type crystals

Kunz A.B.: J. Phys. C **7**, L231 (1974). Distinction between optical absorption edges and photoemission edges in solids

Kunz C.: J. Appl. Phys. **27**, 299 (1979). Synchrotron radiation: an overview

Kuper C.G., G.D. Whitefield: *Polarons and Excitons* (Plenum, New York 1963)

Levine Z.H., S.G. Louie: Phys. Rev. **25**, 6310 (1982). New model dielectric function and exchange-correlation potential for semiconductors and insulators

Matatagui E., A.G. Thompson, M. Cardona: Phys. Rev. **176**, 950 (1968). Thermoreflectance in semiconductors

Moss D.J., E. Ghahramani, J.E. Sipe, H.M. Van Driel: Phys. Rev. B **34**, 8758 (1986). Empirical tight binding calculation of dispersion in the linear optical properties of tetrahedral semiconductors

Nakajima S., Y. Toyozawa, R. Abe: *The Physics of Elementary Excitations*, Springer Ser. Solid-State Sci., Vol.12 (Springer, Berlin, Heidelberg 1980)

Nilsson P.O., L. Munkby: Phys. Kondens. Materie **10**, 290 (1969). Investigation of errors in the Kramers-Kronig analysis of reflectance data

Penn D.: Phys. Rev. **128**, 2093 (1962). Wave number dependent dielectric function of semiconductors

Philipp H.R., H. Ehrenreich: Phys. Rev. **129**, 1550 (1963). Optical properties of semiconductors

Phillips J.C.: Phys. Rev. **133**, A452 (1964). Ultraviolet absorption of insulators: II. Partially ionic crystals

Phillips J.C.: Solid State Phys. **18**, 56 (1966). Fundamental optical spectra of solids

Pollak F.H.: Surf. Sci. **37**, 863 (1973). Modulation spectroscopy under uniaxial stress

Rehn V.: Surf. Sci. **37**, 443 (1973). Interband critical point symmetry from electroreflectance spectra

Renucci J.B., M.A. Renucci, M. Cardona: Solid State Commun. **9**, 1235 (1971). Resonant Raman scattering in germanium and zinc-blende-type semiconductors: temperature dependence

Resta R., K. Kunc: Phys. Rev. B **34**, 7146 (1986). Self-consistent theory of electronic states and dielectric response in semiconductors

Rode D.L.: Phys. Rev. B **2**, 1012 (1970). Electron mobility in direct gap polar semiconductors

Rodriguez C.O., E.L. Peltzer, Y. Blanca, O.M. Cappannini: Solid State Commun. **56**, 375 (1985). Pressure dependence of energy gaps within the local density approximation

Rompa H.W.A.M., M.F.H. Schuurmans, F. Williams: Phys. Rev. Lett. **52**, 675 (1984). Predicted modifications in the direct and the indirect gaps of tetrahedral semiconductors

Roth L.M.: Phys. Rev. **133**, A542 (1964). Theory of the Faraday effect in solids

Rowe J.E., D.E. Aspens: Phys. Rev. Lett. **25**, 162 (1970). Approximate treatment of exciton effects in electric field modulation via the Slater-Koster interaction

Rubloff G.W., H. Fritzche, U. Gerhardt, J.L. Freeouf: Rev. Sci. Instr. **42**, 1507 (1971). Far ultraviolet spectroscopy of solids in the range of 6-36 eV using synchrotron radiation from an electron storage ring

Seraphin B.O., N. Bottka: Phys. Rev. **145**, 628 (1966). Band structure analysis from electroreflectance studies

Swanson L.R., A.A. Maradudin: Solid State Commun. **8**, 859 (1970). Pseudopotential calculation of the Raman tensor for homopolar semiconductors

Tauc J.: *Optical Properties of Solids* (Academic, New York 1966)

Theeten J.B., D.E. Aspnes: Thin Solid Films **60**, 183 (1979). The determination of interface layers by spectroscopic ellipsometry

Tome T.: Solid State Commun. **59**, 661 (1986). Steady state of photoexcited plasma in semiconductors

Toyozawa Y., J. Hermanson: Phys. Rev. Lett. **21**, 1637 (1968). Exciton-phonon bound state: a new quasiparticle

Vechten J.A. Van: Phys. Rev. **182**, 891 (1969). Quantum dielectric theory of electronegativity in covalent systems: I. Electronic dielectric constant

Vechten J.A. Van: Phys. Rev. **187**, 1007 (1969). Quantum dielectric theory of electronegativity in covalent systems: II. Ionization potentials and interband transition energies

Vechten J.A. Van, M. Cardona, D.E. Aspnes, R.M. Martin: Proc. 10th Int'l Conf. on Physics of Semiconductors (Cambridge, Mass. 1970) p.83. Theory of third order susceptibility of semiconductors

Vishnubhatla S.S., J.C. Woolley: Can. J. Phys. **46**, 1769 (1968). Reflectance spectra of some III-V compounds in the vacuum ultraviolet

Wang C.S., W.E. Pickett: Phys. Rev. Lett. **51**, 597 (1983). Density-functional theory of excitation spectra of semiconductors: application to Si

Wang E.Y., W.A. Albers, C.E. Beil: Light modulated reflectance of semiconductors, in *Proc. of the Int'l Conf. on II-VI Semicond. Compounds* (1967), ed. by D.G. Thomas (Benjamin, Elmsford, NY 1968) p. 136

Wiser N.: Phys. Rev. **129**, 62 (1963). Dielectric constant with local field effects included

Zucca R.R., Y.R. Shen: Phys. Rev. B **1**, 2668 (1970). Wavelength modulation of some semiconductors

Zwerdling S., B. Lax, L.M. Roth: Phys. Rev. **108**, 1402 (1957). Oscillatory magnetoabsorption in semiconductors

B.1.7 Photoemission and Electron Spectroscopies

Berglund C.N., W.E. Spicer: Phys. Rev. **136**, A1030 (1964). Photoemission studies of copper and silver: theory

Brown F.C.: Solid State Phys. **29**, 1 (1974). Ultraviolet spectroscopy of solids with the use of synchrotron radiation

Cardona M., L. Ley (eds.): *Photoemission in Solids I and II*, Topics Appl.Phys., Vols.26 and 27 (Springer, Berlin, Heidelberg 1978, 79)

Daniels J., C.V. Festenberg, H. Raether: Optical contants of solids by electron spectroscopy, in *Springer Tracts Mod. Phys.* **54**, 78 (Springer, Berlin, Heidelberg 1970)

Feibelman P.J., D. Eastman: Phys. Rev. B **10**, 4932 (1974). Photoemission spectroscopy correspondence between quantum theory and experimental phenomenology

Gelius U.: In *Electron Spectroscopy*, ed. by D.A. Shirley (North-Holland, Amsterdam 1972)

Kane E.O.: Phys. Rev. **127**, 131 (1962). Theory of photoelectron emission from semiconductors

Kane E.O.: Phys. Rev. **175**, 1039 (1968). Critical-point structure in photoelectron emission energy distributions

Kunz A.B.: J. Phys. C **7**, L231 (1974). Distiction between optical absorption edges and photoemission edges in solids

Raether H.: In *Springer Tracts Mod. Phys.* **38**, 84 (Springer, Berlin, Heidelberg 1965). Solid state excitations by electrons

Raether H.: *Excitations of Plasmons and Interband Transition by Electrons*, Springer Tracts Mod. Phys., Vol.88 (Springer, Berlin, Heidelberg 1980)

Spicer W.E.: Phys. Rev. **154**, 385 (1967). Possible non-one-electron effects in the fundamental optical excitation spectra of certain cristalline solids and their effect on photoemission

Spicer W.E.: Comments Solid State Phys. **5**, 105 (1973). Ultraviolet photoemission spectroscopy

Straub D., L. Ley, F.J. Himpsel: Phys. Rev. B **33**, 2607 (1986). Inversion photoemission study of unoccupied electronic states in Ge and Si: Bulk energy bands

Williams R.H., P.C. Kemeny, L. Ley: Solid State Commun. **19**, 495 (1976). Spatial symmetries of valence band structures by angle-resolved x-ray photoelectron spectroscopy

B.1.8 Temperature and Pressure Effects in Semiconductors

Allen P.B., M. Cardona: Phys. Rev. B **27**, 4760 (1983). Temperature dependence of the direct gap of Si and Ge

Allen P.B., M. Cardona: Phys. Rev. B **23**, 1495 (1981). Theory of the temperature of the direct gap of germanium

Allen P.B., V. Heine: J. Phys. C **9**, 2305 (1976). Theory of temperature dependence of electronic band structures

Bauman K.: Phys. Status Solidi B **63**, K71 (1974). Temperature dependence of band gap in semiconductors

Brooks H., S.C. Yu: Temperature Effects in Solids, Ph.D. Thesis of S.C. Yu (Harvard University, 1967)

Camp P.E.Van, V.E. Van Doren, J.T. Devreese: Phys. Rev. B **34**, 1314 (1986). First principles calculation of the pressure coefficient of the indirect gap and of the charge density in C and Si

Camphausen D.L., G.A. Connel, W. Paul: Phys. Rev. Lett. **26**, 184 (1971). Calculation of energy band pressure coefficients from the dielectric theory of the chemical bond

Chakraborty B., P.B. Allen: J. Phys. C -**11**, L9 (1978). Theory of temperature dependence of optical properties of solids

Cohen M.L., D.J. Chadi: In *Handbook on Semiconductors*, Vol.II, ed. by M. Balkanski (North-Holland, Amsterdam 1980) p.155

Froyen S., M.L. Cohen: Solid State Commun. **43**, 447 (1982). High pressure phases of III-V semiconductors: a microscopic theory

Hess K., J. Dow: Solid State Commun. **40**, 371 (1981). Deformation potentials of bulk semiconductors

Rodriguez C.O., E.L. Peltzer, Y. Blanca, O.M. Cappannini: Solid State Commun. **56**, 375 (1985). Pressure dependence of energy gaps within the local densit approximation

Ves S., M. Cardona: Solid State Commun. **38**, 1109 (1981). A new application of the diamond anvil cell: Measurements under uniaxial stess

Ves S., D. Glotzel, M. Cardona, H. Overhof: Phys. Rev. B **24**, 3073 (1981). Pressure dependence of the optical properties and band structures of the copper and silver halides

Yin M.T., M.L. Cohen: Phys. Rev. Lett. **50**, 1172 (1983). Valence-electron density of silicon under high pressure

B.2 General Semiconductor Articles

B.2.1 II–VI Semiconductors

Adler S.L.: Phys. Rev. **126**, 118 (1962). Theory of the valence band splittings at k=0 in zinc-blende and wurzite structures

Auvergne D., J. Camassel, H. Mathieu, M. Cardona: Phys. Rev. B **9**, 5168 (1974). Temperature dependence of the band structure of germanium and zinc-blende-type semiconductors

Birman J.L.: Phys. Rev. **115**, 1493 (1959). Simplified LCAO method for for zinc-blende, wurtzite and mixed crystal structures

Burst D.: Solid State Commun. **9**, 481 (1971). The band structure of several zinc-blende semiconductors from a self-consistent pseudopotential approach

Cardona M.: J. Appl. Phys. **32**, 2151 (1961). Fundamental reflectivity spectrum of semiconductors with zinc-blende structure

Cardona M., G. Harbeke: Phys. Rev. Lett. **8**, 90 (1962). Excitons at the L absorption edge in zinc-blende-type semiconductors

Cardona M.: Solid State Commun. **1**, 109 (1963). Polarization effects in the ultraviolet reflection of crystals with wurtzite structure

Cardona M.: Phys. Rev. **129**, 1068 (1963). Reflectivity of semiconductors with wurtzite structure

Cardona M.: J. Phys. Chem. Solids **24**, 1543 (1963). Band parameters of semiconductors with zinc-blende, wurtzite and germanium structure

Cardona M., G. Harbeke: Phys. Rev. **137**, A1467 (1965). Optical properties and band structure of wurtzite-type crystals and rutile

Cerdeira F., J.S. de Witt, U. Rossler, M. Cardona: Phys. Status Solidi B **41**, 735 (1970). Hydrostatic pressure coefficients and deformation potentials for II–VI compounds

Chelikowsky J.R., D.J. Chadi, M.L. Cohen: Phys. Rev. B **8**, 2786 (1973). Calculated valence band densities of states and photoemission spectra of diamond and zinc-blende semiconductors

Chelikowsky J.R., M.L. Cohen: Phys. Rev. Lett. **36**, 229 (1976). Pseudopotential valence charge densities in homopolar and heteropolar semiconductors

Cohen M.L.: In *II-VI Semiconducting Compounds*, ed. by D.G. Thomas (Benjamin, Elmsford, NY 1967). Pseudopotential calculations for II–VI compounds, p.462

Euwema R.N., D.J. Stukel: Phys. Rev. B **1**, 4692 (1970). Orthogonalized plane wave convergence study for some tetrahedral semiconductors

Guizzetti G., L. Nosenzo, E. Reguzzoni, G. Samoggia: Phys. Rev. B **9**, 640 (1974). Thermodreflectance spectra of diamond and zinc-blende semiconductors in the vacuum ultraviolet

Harrison W.A.: Phys. Rev. B **8**, 4487 (1973). Bond-orbital-model and the properties of tetrahedrally coordinated solids

Lawaetz P.: Phys. Rev. B **4**, 3460 (1971). Valence band parameters in cubic semiconductors

Lawaetz P.: Phys. Rev. B **5**, 4039 (1972). Stability of wurtzite structures

Martin R.M.: Phys. Rev. B **1**, 4005 (1970). Elastic properties of ZnS structure semiconductors

Pantelides S.T., W.A. Harrison: Phys. Rev. B **11**, 3006 (1975). Structure of the valence bands of zinc-blence type semiconductors

Pamenter R.H.: Phys. Rev. **100**, 573 (1955). Symmetry properties of the energy bands of the zinc-blence structure

Renucci J.B., M.A. Renucci, M. Cardona: Solid State Commun. **9**, 1235 (1971). Resonant Raman

Reynolds D.C., C.W. Litton, T.C. Collins: Phys. Status Solidi **9**, 645 (1965). Some optical properties of group II-VI semiconductors

Rössler U.: Phys. Rev. **184**, 733 (1969). Energy bands of hexagonal II-VI semiconductors

Shevchik N.J., J. Tejeda, M. Cardona: Phys. Rev. B **9**, 2627 (1974). Densities of valence states of amorphous in crystalline III-V and II-VI semiconductors

Tomoda T., M. Mannami: J. Phys. Soc. Japan **27**, 1204 (1969). Charactristic energy loss spectra of II-VI compounds

Tsang Y.W., M.L. Cohen: Phys. Rev. B **9**, 3541 (1974). Pseudopotential study of bonding in the zinc-blende and rocksalt structures

Wepfer G.C., T.C. Collins, R.N. Euwema: Phys. Rev. B **4**, 1296 (1971). Calculated spin-orbit splittings of some group IV, III-V and II-VI semiconductors

Vesely C., D. Langer: Phys. Rev. B **4**, 451 (1971). Electronic core levels of IIB-VIA compounds

Vesely C.J., R.L. Hengehold, D.W. Langer: Phys. Rev. B **5**, 2296 (1972). UV photoemission measurements of the upper d levels in the IIB-VIA compounds

Vetelino J.F., S.P. Gaur, S.S. Mitra: Phys. Rev. B **5**, 2360 (1972). Debye Waller factor for zinc-blende type crystals

Wang E.Y., W.A. Albers, C.E. Bleil: *Proc. of the Int'l Conf. on II-VI Semicond. Compounds 1967*, ed. by D.G. Thomas (Benjamin, Elmsford, NY 1968). Light modulated reflectance of semicondutors, p.136

Yu P.Y., M. Cardona: Phys. Rev. B **2**, 3193 (1970). Temperature coefficient of the refractive index of diamond and zinc-blende type semiconductors

B.2.2 III-V Semiconductors

Adler S.L.: Phys. Rev. **126**, 118 (1962). Theory of the valence band splittings at k=0 in zinc-blende and wurtzite structures

Auvergne D., J. Camassel, H. Mathieu, M. Cardona: Phys. Rev. B **9**, 5168 (1974). Temperature dependence of the band structure of germanium and zinc-blende type semiconductors

Bassani F., M. Yoshimine: Phys. Rev. **130**, 20 (1963). Electronic band structure of group IV and of III-V compounds

Birman J.L.: Phys. Rev. **115**, 1493 (1959). Simplified LCAO method for zinc-blende wurtzite and mixed crystal structures

Brust D.: Solid State Commun. **9**, 481 (1971). The band structure of several zinc-blende semiconductors from a self-consistent pseudopotential approach

Cardona M.: J. Appl. Phys. **32**, 2151 (1961). Fundamental reflectivity spectrum of semiconductors with zinc-blende structure

Cardona M., G. Harbeke: Phys. Rev. Lett. **8**, 90 (1962). Excitons at the L absorption edge in zinc-blende type semiconductors

Cardona M.: Solid State Commun. **1**,109 (1963). Polarization effects in the ultraviolet reflection of crystals with wurtzite structure

Cardona M.: Phys. Rev. **129**, 1068 (1963). Reflectivity of semiconductors with wurtzite structure

Cardona M.: J. Phys. Chem. Solids **24**, 1543 (1963). Band parameters of semiconductors with zinc-blende wurtzite and germanium structure

Cardona M., Harbeke G.: Phys. Rev. **137**, A1467 (1965). Optical properties and band structure of wurtzite type crystals and rutile

Cardona M., W. Gudat, E.E. Koch, M. Skibowski, B. Sonntag, P.Y. Yu: Phys. Rev. Lett. **25**, 659 (1970). Core transitions and density of conduction states in III-V semiconductors

Chelikowsky J.R., D.J. Chadi, M.L. Cohen: Phys. Rev. B **8**, 2786 (1973). Calculated valence band densities of states and photoemission spectra of diamond and zinc-blende semiconductors

Chelikowsky J.R., M.L. Cohen: Phys. Rev. Lett. **36**, 229 (1976). Pseudopotential valence charge densities in homopolar and heteropolar semiconductors

Ehrenreich H.: J. Appl. Phys. **32**, 2155 (1961). Band structure and transport properties of some III-V compounds

Euwema R.N., D.J. Stukel: Phys. Rev. B **1**, 4692 (1970). Orthogonalized plane wave convergence study for some tetrahedral semiconductors

Froyen S., M.L. Cohen: Solid State Commun. **43**, 447 (1982). High pressure phases of III-V semiconductors: a microscopic theory

Gudat W., E.E. Koch, P.Y. Yu, M. Cardona, C.M. Penchina: Phys. Stat. Sol. B **52**, 505 (1972). Core levels of III-V semiconductors

Guizzetti G., L. Nosenzo, E. Reguzzoni, G. Samoggia: Phys. Rev. B **9**, 640 (1974). Thermoreflectance spectra of diamond and zinc-blence semiconductors in the vacuum ultraviolet

Gunn J.B.: IBM J. Res. Develop. **8**, 141 (1964). Instabilities of current in II-V semiconductors

Haas M., B.W. Henvis: J. Phys. Chem. Solids **23**, 1099 (1962). Infrared lattice reflection spectra of III-V compound semiconductors

Harrison W.A.: Phys. Rev. B **8**, 4487 (1973). Bond-orbital model and the properties of tetrahedrally coordinated solids

Joannopoulos J.D., M.L. Cohen: Solid state Commun. **15**, 105 (1974). Electronic density of states of amorphous III-V semiconductors

Joannopoulos J.D., M.L. Cohen: Phys. Rev. B **10**, 1545 (1974). Effects of disorder on the electronic density of states of III-V compounds.

Joannopoulos J.D., G. Lucovsky (eds.): *The Physics of Hydrogenated Amorphous Silicon I and II*, Topics Appl. Phys., Vols.55 and 56 (Springer, Berlin, Heidelberg 1983 and 1984)

Johnson E.J., H.Y. Fan: Phys. Rev. **139**, A1991 (1965). Impurity and exciton effects on the infrared absorption edges of III-V compounds

Koplov A.A.: Solid state Commun. **56**, 1 (1985). The X_1 camel's back parameters for cubic III-V semiconductors

Lawaetz P.: Phys. Rev. B **4**, 3460 (1971). Valence band parameters in cubic semiconductors

Lawaetz P.: Phys. Rev. B **5**, 4039 (1972). Stability of wurtzite structures

Minomura S., H.G. Drickamer: J. Phys. Chem. Solids **23**, 451 (1962). Pressure induced phase transitions in silicon, germanium and some III-V compounds

Madelung O., M. Schulz, H. Weiss (eds.): *Semiconductors*, Landolt-Börnstein, Group III (Springer, Berlin, Heidelberg 1984 ff)

Pantelides S.T., W.A. Harrison: Phys. Rev. B **11**, 3006 (1975). Structure of the valence bands of zinc-blence type semiconductors

Pamenter R.H.: Phys. Rev. **100**, 573 (1955). Symmetry properties of the energy bands of the zinc-blende structure

Renucci J.B., M.A. Renucci, M. Cardona: Solid State Commun. **9**, 1235 (1971). Resonant Raman scattering in germanium and zinc-blende type semiconductors temperature dependence

Sen P.K.: Solid State Commun. **43**, 141 (1982). Third order susceptibility of III-V semiconductors in the true continuum near the band edge

Shevchik N.J., J. Tejeda, M. Cardona: Phys. Rev. B **9**, 2627 (1974). Densities of valence states of amorphous and crystalline III-V and II-VI semiconductors

Thiry P., Y. Petroff, R. Pincheaux, J.R. Chelikowsky, M.L. Cohen: Solid State Commun. **20**, 1107 (1976). Electron hole interaction of the d-core levels in III-V semiconductors

Tsang Y.W., M.L. Cohen: Phys. Rev. B **9**, 3541 (1974). Pseudopotential study of bonding in the zinc-blende and rocksalt structures

Wepfer G.C, T.C. Collins, R.N. Euwema: Phys. Rev. B **4**, 1296 (1971). Calculated spin-orbit splittings of some group IV, III-V and II-VI semiconductors

Wood D.M., A. Zunger: Phys. Rev. B **34**, 4105 (1986). Electronic structure of generic semiconductors: antifluorite silicide and III-V compounds

Vetelino J.F., S.P. Gaur, S.S. Mitra: Phys. Rev. B **5**, 2360 (1972). Debye Waller factor for zinc-blende type crystals

Vishnubhatla S.S., J.C. Woolley: Can. J. Phys. **46**, 1769 (1968). Reflectance spectra of some III-V compounds in the vacuum ultraviolet

Yu P.Y., M. Cardona: Phys. Rev. B **2**, 3193 (1970). Temperature coefficient of the refractive index of diamond and zinc-blende type semiconductors

B.2.3 IV-IV Semiconductors

Auvergne D., J. Camassel, H. Mathieu, M. Cardona: Phys. Rev. B **9**, 5168 (1974). Temperature dependence of the band structure of germanium and zinc-blende type semiconductors

Bassani F., M. Yoshimine: Phys. Rev. **130**, 20 (1963). Electronic band structure of group IV and of III-V compounds

Birman J.L.: Phys. Rev. **115**, 1493 (1959). Simplified LCAO method for zinc-blende, wurtzite and mixed crystal structures

Brinkman W., B. Goodman: Phys. Rev. **149**, 597 (1966). Crystal potential and correlation for energy bands in valence semiconductors

Brust D.: Phys. Lett. A **32**, 114 (1970). Effect of pressure on the elctronic structure and atomic from factors of group in semiconductors: A self-consistent pseudopotential approach

Cardona M., G. Harbeke: J. Appl. Phys. **34**, 813 (1963). Absorption spectrum of germanium and zinc-blende type materials at energies higher than the fundamental absorption edge

Cardona M.: J. Phys. Chem. Solids **24**, 1543 (1963). Band parameters of semiconductors with zinc-blende, wurtzite and germanium structure

Cardona M.: In *Atomic Structure and Properties of Solids*, ed. by E. Burstein (Academic, New York 1972) p.514

Chadi D.J., M.L. Cohen: Phys. Status Solidi B **68**, 405 (1975). Tight binding calculations of the valence bands of diamond and zinc-blende crystals

Chadi D.J., M.L. Cohen: Phys. Status Solidi B **62**, 235 (1974). Analytic expression for the electronic charge density distribution in diamond structure crystals

Chelikowsky J.R., D.J. Chadi, M.L. Cohen: Phys. Rev. B **8**, 2786 (1973). Calculated valence band densities of states and photoemission spectra of diamond and zinc-blende semiconductors

Chelikowsky J.R., M.L. Cohen: Phys. Rev. Lett. **36**, 229 (1976). Pseudopotential valence charge densities in homopolar and heteropolar semiconductors

Euwema R.N., D.J. Stukel: Phys. Rev. B **1**, 4692 (1970). Orthogonalized plane wave convergence study for some tetrahedral semiconductors

Guizzetti G., L. Nosenzo, Reguzzoni E., Samoggia G.: Phys. Rev. B **9**, 640 (1974). Thermoreflectance spectra of diamond and zinc-blende semiconductors in the vacuum ultraviolet

Harrison W.A.: Phys. Rev. B **8**, 4487 (1973). Bond-orbital model and the properties of tetrahedrally coordinated solids

Heine V., R.O. Jones: J. Phys. C **2**, 719 (1969). Electronic band structure and covalency in damond type semiconductors

Joannopoulos J.D., M.L. Cohen: In *Tetrahedrally Bonded Amorphous Semiconductors*, ed. by M.H. Brodsky, S. Kirkpatrick, D.Weaire (AIP, New York 1974) p.85

Joannopoulos J.D., M.L. Cohen: Phys. Rev. B **10**, 1545 (1974). Effects of disorder on the elctronic density of states of III-V compounds

Joannopoulos J.D., M.L. Cohen: Solid State Phys. **31**, 71 (1976). Theory of short-range order and disorder in tetrahedrally bonded semiconductors

Kane E.O.: Phys. Rev. **178**, 1368 (1969). Strain effects on optical critical point structure in diamond type crystals

Lawaetz P.: Phys. Rev. B **4**, 3460 (1971). Valence band parameters in cubic semiconductors

Madelung O., M. Schulz, H. Weiss (eds.): *Semiconductors*, Landolt-Börnstein, Group III (Springer, Berlin, Heidelberg 1984 ff)

Martin R.M.: Phys. Rev. **186**, 871 (1969). Dielectric screening model for lattice vibrations of diamond structure crystals

Minomura S., H.G. Drickamer: J. Phys. Chem. Solids **23**, 451 (1962). Pressure induced phase transitions in silicon, germanium and some III-V compounds

Renucci J.B., M.A. Renucci, M. Cardona: Solid State Commun. **9**, 1235 (1971). Resonant Raman scattering in germanium and zinc-blende type semiconductors, temperature dependence

Tsay Y.F, S.S. Mitra, B. Bendow: Phys. Rev. B **10**, 1476 (1974). Pressure dependence of energy gaps and refractive indices of tetrahedrally bonded semiconductors

Wepfer G.C., T.C. Collins, R.N. Euwema: Phys. Rev. B **4**, 1296 (1971). Calculated spin-orbit splittings of some group IV, III-V and II-VI semiconductors

Yu P.Y., M. Cardona: Phys. Rev. B **2**, 3193 (1970). Temperature coefficient of the refractive index of diamond and zinc-blende type semiconductors

B.2.4 IV-VI Semiconductors

Bernick R.L., L. Kleinman: Solid State Commun. **8**, 569 (1970). Energy bands, effective masses and g-factors of the lead salts and SnTe

Cardona M., D.L. Greenaway: Phys. Rev. **133**, A1685 (1964). Optical properties and band structure of group IV-VI and group V materials

Cardona M., C.M. Penchina, E.E. Koch, P.Y. Yu: Phys. Status Solidi B **53**, 327 (1972). Optical and photoelectric properties of lead chalcogenides

Cohen M.L., Y.W. Tsang: J. Chem. Phys. Sol. (Suppl.1) **32**, 303 (1971). Theory of electronic structure of some IV-VI semiconductors

Madelung O., M. Schulz, H. Weiss: *Semiconductors*, Landolt-Börnstein, Group III (Springer, Berlin, Heidelberg 1984 ff)

Martinez G., M. Schluter, R. Pinchaux, P. Thiry, D. Dagneaux, Y. Petroff, M.L. Cohen: Solid State Commun. **17**, 5 (1975). Synchroton radiation measurements and calculations of core to conduction level transitions in lead chalcogenides

Trzeciakowski W., M. Baj: Solid State Commun. **52**, 669 (1984). The dielectric constant in narrow gap semiconductors

Tsang Y.W., M.L. Cohen: J. Phys. Chem. Solids **32**, 303 (1971). Theory of electronic structure of some IV-VI semiconductors

B.3 Chalcopyrite Semiconductors

Jaffe J., A. Zunger: Phys. Rev. B **27**, 5176 (1983). Anion displacements and the band-gap anomaly in ternary ABC_2 chalcopyrite semiconductors

Jaffe J., A. Zunger: Phys. Rev. B **28**, 5822 (1983). Electronic structure of the ternary chalcopyrite semiconductors $CuAlS_2$, $CuGaS_2$, $CuInS_2$, $CuAlSe_2$, $CuGaSe_2$ and $CuInSe_2$

Jaffe J., A. Zunger: Phys. Rev. B **30**, 741 (1984). Electronic structure of the ternary pnictide semiconductors $ZnSiP_2$., $ZnGeP_2$, $ZnSiAs_2$ and $MgSiP_2$

Kidal H.: Phys. Rev. B **10**, 5082 (1974). Band structure of $CdGeAs_2$ near k=0

Shay J.L., E. Buehler, J.H. Wernick: Phys. Rev. B **2**, 4104 (1970) Electroreflectance study of the energy band structure of $CdSnP_2$

Varea de Alvarez C., M.L. Cohen: Phys. Rev. Lett. **30**, 979 (1973). Calculated band structure and reflectivity spectra of $ZnGeP_2$

Varea de Alvarez C., M.L. Cohen, S.E. Kohn, Y. Petroff, Y.R. Shen: Phys. Rev. B**10**, 5175 (1974). Calculated and measured reflectivity of $ZnGeP_2$

Varea de Alvarez C., M.L. Cohen, L. Ley, S.P. Kowalczyk, F.R. McFeely, D.A. Shirely, R.W. Grant: Phys. Rev. B **10**, 596 (1974). Electronic density of states and bonding in chalcopyrite-type semiconductors

B.4 Properties of Specific Semiconductors

B.4.1 Aluminum Antimonide

Cohen M.L., T. K. Bergstresser: Phys. Rev. **141**, 789 (1966). Band structures and pseudopotential form factors for fourteen semiconductors of the diamond and zinc-blende structures

Fischer T.E.: Phys. Rev. **139**, A1228 (1965). Reflectivity photoelectric emission and work function of AlSb

Joullie A., B. Girault, A.M. Joullie and A. Zien-Eddine: Phys. Rev. B **25**, 7830 (1982). Determination of the first five interband transitions above the lowest indirect gap of the aluminum antominide

Kagaya H.-K., T. Soma: Solid State Commun. **48**, 785 (1983). Interatomic force constants and lattice vibrations of AlP, AlAs and AlSb

Shileika A.Y., M. Cardona, F.H. Pollak: Solid State Commun. 7, 1113 (1969). Intrinsic Piezobirefringence of AlSb

Strössner K., S. Ves, C.K. Kim and M. Cardona: Phys. Rev. B 33, 4044 (1986). Dependence of the direct and indirect gap of AlSb on hydrostatic pressure

Ves S., K. Strössner, M. Cardona: Solid State Commun. 57, 483 (1986). Pressure dependence of the optical phonon frequencies and the transverse effective charge of AlSb

Welkowsky M., R. Braunstein: Phys. Rev. 5, 497 (1972). Interband transitions and exciton effects. Band structures of Ge, Si, GaAs, GaP, GaSb, InAs, InP, InSb and AlSb

B.4.2 Beryllium Oxide

Walker W.C., D.M. Roessler, E. Loh: Phys. Rev. Lett. 20, 847 (1968). Phonon induced splitting of exciton lines in MgO and BeO

B.4.3 Bismuth Triiodide

Kowalczyk S.P., L. Ley, F.R. McFeely, D.A. Shirley: Solid State Commun. 17, 463 (1975). A high resolution x-ray photoemission study of the total valence band densities of states of GaSe and BiI_3

Schlüter M., M.L. Cohen, S.E. Kohn, C.Y. Fong: Phys. Status Solidi B 78, 737 (1976). Electronic structure of BiI_3.

Schlüter M., M.L. Cohen: Phys. Rev. B 14, 424 (1976). Valence band density of states and chemical bonding for several non-transition metal layer compounds: $SnSe_2$, PbI_2, BiI_3, GaSe

B.4.4 Cadmium Germanium Arsenide

Kidal H.: Phys. Rev. B 10, 5082 (1974). Band structure of $CdGeAs_2$ near k=0

B.4.5 Cadmium Oxide

Altwein M., H. Finkenrath, C. Konak, J. Stuke, J. Zimmerer: Phys. Status Solidi 29, 203 (1968). The electronic structure of CdO: II. Spectral distribution of optical constants

Boettger J.C., A.B. Kunz: Phys. Rev. B 27, 1359 (1983). Ab initio energy bands for CdO

Maschke K., U. Rossler: Phys. Status Solidi 28, 577 (1968). The electronic structure of CdO I. The energy band structure

B.4.6 Cadmium Selenide

Bergstresser T.K., M.L. Cohen: Phys. Rev. 164, 1069 (1967). Electronic structure and optical properties of hexagonal CdSe, CdS and ZnS

Hengehold R.L., C.R. Fraime: Phys. Rev. 174, 808 (1968). Ultraviolet reflectivity spectra of $CdS_{1-x}Se_x$ single crystals

Hengehold R.L., F.L. Pedrotti: Phys. Rev. B 6, 2262 (1972). Electron energy loss spectra of CdS, CdSe and CdTe

Kobayashi A., O.F. Sankey, S.M. Volz, J.D. Dow: Phys. Rev. B 28, 935 (1983). Semiempirical tight-binding band structures of wurtzite semiconductors: AlN, CdS, ZnS, and ZnO

Ley L., R.A.Pollak, F.R. McFeely, S.P. Kowalczyk, D.A. Shirley: Phys. Rev. B **9**, 600 (1974). Total valence band densities of states of III-V and II-VI compounds from x-ray photoemission spectroscopy

Logothethidis S., M. Cardona, P. Lautenschlager, M. Garriga: Phys. Rev. B **34**, 2458 (1986). Temperature dependence of the dielectric function and the interband critical points of CdSe

Mei J.R., V. Lemos: Solid State Commun. **52**, 785 (1984). Photoluminescence of CdSe and CdTe under hydrostatic pressure

Shay J.L., W.E. Spicer: Phys. Rev. **169**, 650 (1968). Photoemission study of the electronic structure of wurtzite CdSe and CdS

Shevchik N.J., J. Tejeda, D.W. Langer, M. Cardona: Phys. Status Solidi B **59**, 87 (1973). Photoemission and density of valence states of II-VI compounds: I. ZnTe, CdSe, CdTe, HgSe and HgTe

Wheeler R.G., J. Dimmock: Phys. Rev. **125**, 1805 (1962). Exciton structure and Zeeman effects in cadmium selenide.

B.4.7 Cadmium Sulphide

Bergstresser T.K., M.L. Cohen: Phys. Rev. **164**, 1069 (1967). Electronic structure and optical properties of hexagonal CdSe, CdS and ZnS

Cardona M., M. Weinstein, G.A. Wolff: Phys. Rev. **140**, A633 (1965). Ultraviolet reflection spectrum of cubic CdS

Chang K.J., S. Froyen, M.L. Cohen: Phys. Rev. B **28**, 4736 (1983). Electronc band structures for zinc-blende and wurtzite CdS

Drews R.E., E.A. Davis, A.G. Leign: PHys. Rev. Lett. **18**, 1194 (1967). Reflectivity spectra of $Cd_{1-k}Zn_kS$ single crystals

Euwema R.N., T.C. Collins, D.G. Shankland, J.S. Dewitt: Phys. Rev. **162**, 710 (1967). Convergence study of a self-consistent orthogonalized plane wave band calculationfor hexagonal CdS

Hengehold R.L., C.R. Fraime: Phys. Rev. **174**, 808 (1968). Ultraviolet reflectivity spectra of $CdS_{1-x}Se_x$ single crystals

Hengehold R.L., F.L. Pedrotti: Phys. Rev. B **6**, 2262 (1972). Electron energy loss spectra of CdS, CdSe and CdTe

Kindig N.B., W.E. Spicer: Phys. Rev. **138**, A561 (1965). Band structure of cadmium sulfide photoemission studies

Kobayashi A., O.F. Sankey, S.M. Volz, J.D. Dow: Phys Rev. B **28**, 935 (1983). Semiempirical tight-binding band structures of wurtzite semicodnuctors: AlN, CdS, ZnS, and ZnO

Ley L., R.A. Pollak, F.R. McFeely, S.P. Kowalczyk, D.A. Shirley: Phys. Rev. B **9**, 600 (1974). Total valence band densities of states f_0 III-V and II-VI compounds from x-ray photoemission spectroscopy

Magnusson K.O., S.A. Flodstrom, P. Martensson, J.M. Nicholls, U.O. Karlsson, R. Engelhardt, E.E. Koch: Solid State Commun. **55**, 643 (1985). The electronic structure of wurtzite CdS studied using angle resolved uv photoelectron spectroscopy

Majumder M.A.: Solid State Commun. **43**, 13 (1982). Dipole selection rules for wurtzite structure and reflection spectra of hexagonal CdS

Minami F., K. Era: Solid State Commun. **53**, 187 (1985). Lifetimes of bound excitions in CdS

Shay J.L., W.E. Spicer: Phys. Rev. **169**, 650 (1968). Photoemission study of the electronic structure of wurtzite CdSe and CdS

Shevchik N.J., J. Tejeda, D.W. Langer, M. Cardona: Phys. Status Solidi B **60**, 345 (1973). Photoemission and density of valence states of II-VI compounds: II. ZnSe, CdS, and HgS

Stukel D., R. Euwema, T.C. Collins, F. Herman, R. Kortum: Phys. Rev. 179, 740 (1969). Self-consistent orthogonalized plane wave and empirically refined OPW energy band models for cubic ZnS, ZnSe, CdS and CdSe

Thomas D.G., J.J. Hopfield: Phys. Rev. 116, 573 (1959). Exciton spectrum of cadmium sulfide.

Walker W.C., J. Osantowski: J. Phys. Chem. Solids 25, 778 (1964). The ultraviolet reflection spectrum of cadmium sulfide

Walker W.C.: Phys. Rev. Lett. 13, 51 (1964). Polarization dependence of the far ultraviolet optical transitions in CdS

B.4.8 Cadmium Telluride

Bloom S., T.K. Bergstresser: Solid State Commun. 6, 465 (1968). Band structure of α-Sn, InSb and CdTe inluding spin orbit effects

Cade N.A., P.M. Lee: Solid State Commun. 56, 673 (1985). Self-consistent energy band structures for HgTe and CdTe

Cardona M., D.L. Greenaway: Phys. Rev. 131, 98 (1963). Fundamental reflectivity and band structure of ZnTe, CdTe and HgTe

Chadi D.J., J.P. Walter, Y. Petroff, M. Balkanski, M.L. Cohen: Phys. Rev. B 5, 3058 (1972). Reflectivities and electronic band structures of CdTe and HgTe

Chadi D.J., M.L. Cohen: Phys. Rev. B 7, 692 (1973). Electronic structure of $Hg_{1-x}Cd_x$Te alloys and charge density calculations using representative k-points

Chelikowsky J.R., M.L. Cohen: Phys. Rev. B 14, 556 (1976). Nonlocal pseudopotential calculations for the electronic structure of eleven diamond and zinc-blende semiconductors

Cohen M.L., T.K. Bergstresser: Phys. Rev. 141, 789 (1966). Band structures and pseudopotential form factors for fourteen semiconductors of the diamond and zinc-blende structures

Eastman D.E., W.D. Grobman, J.L. Freeouf, M. Erbudak: Phys. Rev. B 9, 3473 (1974). Photoemission spectroscopy using synchtron radiation: I. Overviews of valence band structure for Ge, GaAs, GaP, InSb, ZnSe, CdTe, and AgI

Eckelt P.: Phys. Status Solidi 23, 307 (1967). Energy band structures of cubic ZnS, ZnSe, ZnTe and CdTe

Hengehold R.L., F.L. Pedrotti: Phys. Rev. B 6, 2262 (1972). Electron energy loss spectra of CdS, CdSe and CdTe

Ley L., R.A. Pollak, F.R. McFeely, S.P. Kowalczyik, D.A. Shirley: Phys. Rev. B 9, 600 (1974). Total valence band densities of states of III-V and II-VI compounds from x-ray photoemission spectroscopy

Marple D.T., H. Ehrenreich: Phys. Rev. Lett. 8, 87 (1962). Dielectric constant behavior near band edges in CdTe and Ge

Mei J.R., V. Lemos: Solid State Commun. 52, 785 (1984). Photoluminescence of CdSe and CdTe under hydrostatic pressure

Melz P.: J. Phys. Chem. Solids 32, 209 (1971). Energy band structure of strained crystals pseudopotential calculations for Ge and Si with trial calcualtions for GaAs and CdTe

Shay J.L., W.E. Spicer: Phys. Rev. 161, 799 (1967). Photoemission studies of CdTe

Shay J.L., W.E. Spicer, F. Herman: Phys. Rev. Lett. 18, 649 (1967). Photoemission study of CdTe

Shevchik N.J., J. Tejeda, D.W. Langer, M. Cardona: Phys. Status Solidi B 59, 87 (1973). Photoemission and density of valence states of II-VI compounds: I. ZnTe, CdSe, CdTe, HgSe and HgTe

Vaidyanathan A., A.H. Guenther, S.S. Mitra: Phys. Rev. B **24**, 2259 (1981). Band-structure calculations of the two phonon absorption coefficients of GaAs, InP, CdTe and ZnSe

Walter J.P., M.L. Cohen: Phys. Rev. B **4**, 1877 (1971). Pseudopotential calculations of electronic charge densities in seven semiconductors

B.4.9 Carbon

Armon H., J.P.F. Selleschop: Phys. Rev. B **26**, 3114 (1982). Angular dependence of electron-energy-loss spectroscopy: application to diamond

Bassani F., G.P. Parravicini: Nuovo Cimento B **50**, 95 (1967). Band structure and optical properties of graphite and the layered compounds GaS and GaSe

Biswas R., R.M. Martin, R.J. Needs, O.H. Nielsen: Phys. Rev. B **30**, 3210 (1984). Complex tetrahedral structures of silicon and carbon under pressure

Bullet D.W.: J. Phys. C **8**, 2707 (1975). Chemical pseudoptotential approach to covalent bonding: bond lengths and bond energies in diamond, silicon and graphite

Cardona M., N.E. Christensen: Solid State Commun. **58**, 421 (1986). Deformation potentials of the direct gap of diamond

Cavell R.G., S.P. Kowalczyk, L. Ley, R.A. Pollak, B. Mills, D.A. Shirley, W. Perry: Phys. Rev. B **7**, 5313 (1973). X-ray photoemission cross section modulation in diamond, silicon, germanium, methane, silane and germane

Camp P.E.Van, V.E. Van Doren, J.T. Devreese: Phys. Rev. B **34**, 1314 (1986). First principles calculation of the pressure coefficient of the indirect gap and of the charge density in C and Si

Chadi D.J., R.M. Martin: Solid State Commun. **19**, 643 (1976). Calcualtion of lattice dynamical properties from electronic energies: application to C, Si and Ge

Chaney R.C., C.C. Lin, E.E. Lafon: Phys. Rev. B **3**, 459 (1971). Application of the method of tight binding to the calculation of the energy band structures of diamond, silicon and sodium crystals

Chelikowsky J.R., S.G. Louie: Phys. Rev. B. **29**, 3470 (1984). First principles linear combination of atomic orbitals for the cohesive and structural properties of solids: application to diamond

Goroff I., L. Kleinman: Phys. Rev. B. **1**, 2574 (1970). First principles calculation of the bulk modulus of diamond

Hanke W.R., L.J. Sham: Phys. Rev. Lett. **33**, 582 (1974). Dielectric response in Wannier representation: application to the optical spectrum of diamond

Hemstreet L.A., C.Y. Fong, M.L. Cohen: Phys. Rev. B **2**, 2054 (1970). Calculation of the band structure and optical constants of diamond using the nonlocal pseudopotential method

Herman F.: Phys. Rev. **88**, 1210 (1952). Electronic structure of the diamond crystal

Herman F.: Phys. Rev. **93**, 1214 (1954). Calculation of the energy band structures of the diamond and germanium crystals by the method of orthogonalized plane waves

Lambrecht W.R.L., O.K. Anderson: Phys. Rev. B **34**, 2439 (1986). Minimal basis sets in the linear muffin tin orbital method: application to the diamond structure crystals: C,Si and Ge

Linde W.von der, P. Fulde, K.P. Bohnen: Phys. Rev. B **34**, 1063 (1986). Efficient approach to the Ab initio Hartree-Fock problem of solis with application to diamond and silicon

McFeely F.R., S.P. Kowalczyk, L. Ley, R.G. Cavell, R.A. Pollak and D.A. Shirley: Phys. Re. B **9**, 5268 (1974). X-ray photoemission studies of diamond, graphite and glassy carbon valence bands

Nielson O.H.: Phys. Rev. **34**, 5808 (1986). Optical phonons and elasticity of diamond at megabar stress

Raccah P.M., R.N. Euwema, D.J. Stuckel, T.C. Collins: Phys. Rev. B 1, 756 (1970). Comparison of theoretical and experimental charge densities for C, Si, Ge and ZnSe

Saslow W., T.K. Bergstresser, M.L. Cohen: Phys. Rev. Lett. 16, 354 (1966). Band structure and optical properties of diamond

Tubino R., L. Piseri, C. Zerbi: J. Chem. Phys. 56, 1022 (1972). Lattice dynamics and spectroscopic properties by a valence force potential of diamond like crystals: C, Si, Ge and Sn

Vechten J.A.Van, R.M. Martin: Phys. Rev. Lett 28, 446 (1972). Calculation of local effective fields: optical spectrum of diamond

Weber W.: Phys. Rev. B 15, 4789 (1977). Adiabatic bond charge model for phonons in diamond, Si, Ge and α-Sn

Yin M.T., M.L. Cohen: Phys. Rev. B 24, 6121 (1981). Ground state properties of diamond

B.4.10 Copper Bromide

Blacha A., N.E. Christensen, M. Cardona: Phys. Rev. B 33, 2413 (1986). Electronic structure of high pressure modifications of CuCl, CuBr

Blacha A., S. Ves, M. Cardona: Phys. Rev. B 27, 6345 (1983). Effects of uniaxial strain on the exciton spectra of CuCl, CuBr and CuI

Song K.: J. Phys. Chem. Solids 28, 2003 (1967). Structure des bands des halogenures de cuiver: CuCl, CuBr, et CuI

Ves S., D. Glotzel, M. Cardona, H. Overhof: Phys. Rev. B 24, 3073 (1981). Pressure dependence of the optical properties and band structures of the copper and silver halides

B.4.11 Copper Chloride

Blacha A., N.E. Christensen, M. Cardona: Phys. Rev. B 33, 2413 (1986). Electronic structure of high pressure modifications of CuCl, CuBr and CuI

Blacha A., S. Ves, M. Cardona: Phys. Rev. B 27, 6345 (1983). Effects of uniaxial strain on the exciton spectra of CuCl, CuBr and CuI

Frohlich D., H. Volkenendt: Solid State Commun. 43, 189 (1982). Determination of Γ_3 valence band in CuCl by two photon absorption

Guimaraes P.S.: Solid State Commun. 52, 5 (1984). A calculation of the pressure dependence of the energy bands of copper chloride

Lewonczuk S., J.G. Gross, J. Ringeissen, M.A. Kahn, R. Riedinger: Phys. Rev. B 27, 1259 (1983). Relativistic band structure of cuprous chloride

Song K.: J. Phys. Chem. Solids 28, 2003 (1967). Structure des bands des halogenures de cuiver: CuCl, CuBr et CuI

Ves S., D. Glotzel, M. Cardona, H. Overhof: Phys. Rev. B 24, 3073 (1981). Pressure dependence of the optical properties and band structures of the copper and silver halides

Zunger A., M.L. Cohen: Phys. Rev. B 20, 1189 (1979). Electronic structure of CuCl

B.4.12 Copper Iodide

Blacha A., N.E. Christensen, M. Cardona: Phys. Rev. B 33, 2413 (1986). Electronic structure of high pressure modifications of CuCl, CuBr and CuI

Blacha A., S. Ves, M. Cardona: Phys. Rev. B 27, 6345 (1983). Effects of uniaxial strain on the exciton spectra of CuCl, CuBr and CuI

Song K: J. Phys. Chem. Solids **28**, 2003 (1967). Structure des bands des halogenures de cuiver: CuCl, CuBr et CuI

Ves S., D. Glötzel, M. Cardona, H. Overhof: Phys. Rev. B **24**, 3073 (1981). Pressure dependence of the optical properties and band structures of the copper and silver halides

B.4.13 Gallium Antimonide

Alibert C., G. Bordure: Phys. Status Solidi **40**, 687 (1970). Etude des spectres d'eletroreflexion du GaSb

Aoki M., A.K. Sood, H. Presting, M. Cardona: Solid State Commun. **50**, 287 (1984). Pressure dependence of the E_1 gap in GaSb: resonant Raman technique

Aspnes D.E., C.G. Olson, D.W. Lynch: Phys. Rev. B **14**, 4450 (1976). Electroreflectance of GaSb from 0.6 to 26 eV

Aspnes D.E., M. Cardona, V. Saile, M. Skibowski, G. Spruessel: Solid State Commun. **31**, 99 (1979). Fine structure in optical transitions from 3d and 4d core levels to the lower conduction band in Ga-V and In-V compounds

Cahn R.N., M.L. Cohen: Phys. Rev. B **1**, 2569 (1970). A local pseudopotential model for GaSb: electronic and optical properties

Cardona M., V.A. Maruschak, A.N. Titkov: Solid State Commun. **50**, 701 (1984). Stress induced splitting of the conduction bands of GaAs and GaSb

Chelikowsky J.R., M.L. Cohen: Phys. Rev. B **14**, 556 (1976). Nonlocal pseudopotential calculations for the electronic structure of eleven diamond and zinc-blende semiconductors

Cohen M.L., J.C. Phillips: Phys. Rev. **139**, A912 (1965). Spectral analysis of photoemissive yields in Si, Ge, GaAs, GaSb, InAs, and InSb

Cohen M.L., T.K. Bergstresser: Phys. Rev. **141**, 789 (1966). Band structures and pseudopotential form factors for fourteen semiconductors of the diamond and zincblende structures

Gobeli G.W., F.G. Allen: Phys. Rev. **137**, A245 (1965). Photoelectric properties of cleaved GaAs, GaSb, InAs and InSb surfaces: comparisons with Si and Ge

Groves S.H., C.R. Pidgeon, J. Feinleib: Phys. Rev. Lett. **17**, 643 (1966). Infrared magnetoelectroreflectance in Ge, GaSb and InSb

Kosicki B.B., A. Jararaman, W. Paul: Phys. Rev. **172**, 764 (1968). Conduction band structure of GaSb from pressure experiments to 50 kbar

Ley L., R.A. Pollak, F.R. McFeely, S.P. Kowalczyk, D.A. Shirley: Phys. Rev. B **9**, 600 (1974). Total valence band densities of states of III-V and II-VI compounds from x-ray photoemission spectroscopy

Parsont B.J., H. Piller: Solid State Commun. **9**, 767 (1971). An electroreflectance study of gallium antimonide in the 3.0-4.2 eV region

Reine M., R.L. Aggarwal, B. Lax: Phys. Rev. B **5**, 3033 (1972). Stress modulated magnetoreflectivity of gallium antimonide and gallium arsenide

Sagar A.: Phys. Rev. **117**, 93 (1960). Experimental investigation of the conduction bands of GaSb

Tuomi T., M. Cardona, F.H. Pollak: Phys. Status Solidi **40**, 227 (1970). Stress dependence of E_1 and $E_1+\Delta_1$ transitions in InSb and GaSb

Welkowsky M., R. Braunstein: Phys. Rev. B **5**, 497 (1972). Interband transitions and exciton effects. Band structures of Ge, Si, GaAs, GaP, GaSb, InAs, InP, InSb and AlSb

Yu P.Y., M. Cardona, F.H. Pollak: Phys. Rev. B **3**, 340 (1971). Intrinsic piezobirefringence in GaSb, InAs and InSb

Zhang H.I., J. Callaway: Phys. Rev. **181**, 1163 (1969). Energy band structure and optical properties of GaSb

Zucca R.R., Y.R. Shen: Phys. Rev. B **1**, 2668 (1970). Wavelength modulation of some semiconductors

B.4.14 Gallium Arsenide

Aspnes D.E., A.A. Studna: Phys. Rev. B **7**, 4605 (1973). Schottky barrier electroreflectance: application to GaAs

Aspnes D.E., C.G. Olson, D.W. Lynch: Phys. Rev. B **12**, 2527 (1975). Electroreflectance of GaAs and GaP to 27 eV using synchrotron radiation

Aspnes D.E., C.G. Olson, D.W. Lynch: Phys. Rev. Lett. **37**, 766 (1976). Ordering and absolute energies of the L_6^c and X_6^c conduction band minima in GaAs

Aspnes D.E.: Phys. Rev. B **14** 5331 (1976). GaAs lower conduction band minima: ordering and properties

Aspnes D.E., M. Cardona, V. Saile, M. Skibowski, G. Spruessel: Solid State Commun. **31**, 99 (1979). Fine structure in optical transitions from 3d and 4d core levels to the lower conduction band in Ga-V and In-V compounds

Bachelet G.B., N.E. Christensen: Phys. Rev. B **31**, 879 (1985). Relativistic and core-relaxation effects on the energy bands of gallium arsenide and germanium

Balslev I.: Phys. Rev. **173**, 762 (1968). Optical Absorption due to inter-conduction-minimum transitions in gallium arsenide

Bergstresser T.K., M.L. Cohen, E.W. Williams: Phys. Rev. Lett. **15**, 662 (1965). Reflectivity and band structure of GaAs, GaP and Ga(As,P) alloys

Blood P.: Phys. Rev. Lett. B **6**. 2257 (1972). Epitaxial GaAs at high temperature

Cardona M., V.A. Maruschak, A.N. Titkov: Solid State Commun. **50**, 701 (1984). Stress induced splitting of the conduction bands of GaAs and GaSb

Cardona M., C.M. Penchina, N. Shevchik, J. Tejeda: Solid State Commun. **11**, 1655 (1972). Photoemission of GaAs and InSb core levels

Chandrasekhar M., F.H. Pollak: Phys. Rev. B **15**, 2127 (1977). Effects of uniaxial stress on the electroreflectance spectrum of Ge and GaAs

Chelikowsky J.R., M.L. Cohen: Phys. Rev. Lett. **32**, 674 (1974). Electronic structure of GaAs

Chelikowsky J.R., M.L. Cohen: Phys. Rev. B **14**, 556 (1976). Nonlocal pseudopotential calculations for the electronic structure of eleven diamond and zinc-blende semiconductors

Christensen N.E.: Phys. Rev. B **30**, 5753 (1984). Electronic structure of GaAs under strain

Christensen N.E., M. Cardona: Solid State Commun. **51**, 491 (1984). Splitting of the conduction bands of GaAs for **k** along [110]

Cohen M.L., J.C. Phillips: Phys. Rev. **139**, A912 (1965). Spectral analysis of photoemisive yields in Si, Ge, GaAs, GaSb, InAs, and InSb

Cohen M.L., T.K. Bergstresser: Phys. Rev. **141**, 789 (1966). Band structures and pseudopotential form factors for fourteen semiconductors of the diamond and zinc-blende structures

Collins C.L., P.Y Yu: Phys. Rev. B **30**, 4501 (1984). Generation of nonequilibrium optical phonons in GaAs and their application in studying intervalley electron-phonon scattering

Collins T.C., D.J. Stukel, R.N. Euwema: Phys. Rev. B **1**, 724 (1970). Self-consistent orthogonalized plane wave calculation on GaAs

Eastman D.E., W.D. Grobman, J.L. Freeouf, M. Erbudak: Phys. Rev. B **9**, 3473 (1974). Photoemission spectroscopy using synchrotron radiation. I. Overviews of valence band structure for Ge, GaAs, GaP, InSb, ZnSe, CdTe, and AgI

Eastman D.E., J.L. Freeouf: Phys. Rev. Lett. **33**, 1601 (1974). Photoemission partial yield measurements of unoccupied intrinsic surface states for Ge(111) and GaAs (110)

Ehrenreich H.: Phys. Rev. **120**, 1951 (1960). Band structure and electron transport of GaAs

Fawcett W., A.D. Boardman, S.W. Swain: J. Phys. Chem. Solids **31** 1963 (1970). Monte Carlo determination of electronic transport in gallium arsenide

Gobeli G.W., F.G. Allen: Phys. Rev. **137**, A245 (1965). Photoelectric properties of cleaved GaAs, GaSb, InAs and InSb surfaces: comparisons with Si and Ge

Gray A.M.: Phys. Status Solidi **37**, 11 (1970). Evaluation of the electronic energy band structures of GaAs and GaP

Greenaway D.L.: Phys. Rev. Lett. **9**, 97 (1962). Fundamental reflectivity of GaAs at low temperature

Harris J.S., J.L. Moll, G.L. Pearson: Phys. Rev. B **1**, 1660 (1971). Effects of uniaxial stress on the electrical resistivity and the Gunn effect in n-type GaAs

Herman F., W.E. Spicer: Phys. Rev. **174**, 906 (1968). Spectral analysis of photoemissive yields in GaAs and related crystals

Higginbotham C.W., M. Cardona, F.H. Pollak: Phys. Rev. **184**, 821 (1969). Intrinsic piezobirefringence of Ge, Si and GaAs

Ihm J., J.D. Joannopoulos: Phys. Rev. B **24**, 4191 (1981). Ground-state properties of GaAs and AlAs

James L.W., R.C. Eden, J.L. Moll, W.E. Spicer: Phys. Rev. **174**, 909 (1968). Location of the L_1 and X_3 minima in GaAs as determined by photoemission studies

James L.W., J.L. Moll: Phys. Rev. **183**, 740 (1969). Transport properties of GaAs obtained from photoemission measurements

Joullie A., A. Zein Eddin, B. Girault: Phys. Rev. B **23**, 928 (1981). Temperature dependence of the $L_6{}^c$-$\Gamma_6{}^c$ energy gap in gallium arsenide

Kim C.K., P. Lautenschlager, M. Cardona: Solid State Commun. **59**, 797 (1986). Temperature dependence of the fundamental energy gap in GaAs

Lane T., C.J. Vesley, D.W. Langer: Phys. Rev. B **6**, 3770 (1972). X-ray photoemission measurements of GaP, GaAs, InAs and InSb

Lapeyre G.J., J. Anderson: Phys. Rev. Lett. **35**, 117 (1975). Evidence for a surface state exciton on GaAs (110)

Ley L., R.A. Pollak, F.R. McFeely, S.P. Kowalczyk, D.A. Shirley: Phys. Rev. B **9**, 600 (1974). Total valence band densities of states of III-V and II-VI compounds from x-ray photoemission spectroscopy

Manghi F., G. Reigler, C.M. Bertoni, G.B. Bachelet: Phys. Rev. B **31**, 3680 (1985). Band structure calculation for GaAs and Si beyond the local density approximation

Melz P.: J. Phys.Chem. Solids **32** 209 (1971). Energy band structure of strained crystals: pseudopotential calculations for Ge and Si with trial calculations for GaAs and CdTe

Menendez J., M. Cardona: Phys. Rev. Lett. **51**, 1297 (1983). Interference between allowed and forbidden Raman scattering by longitudinal-optical phonons in GaAs

McSkimin H.J., A. Jayaraman, J. Andreath: J. Appl. Phys. **38**. 2362 (1967). Elastic moduli of GaAs at moderate pressures and the evaluation of compression to 250 kbar

Nahory R.E., J.L. Shay: Phys. Rev. Lett. **21**, 1569 (1968). Reflectance modulation by the surface field in GaAs

Onton A., R.J. Chicotka, Y. Yacoby: *11th Int. Conf. on the Phys. of Semicond. Warsaw* (Warszawa, 1972), Subsidiary indirect conduction band minima and their donor levels in GaAs and InP, p.1023

Pandrey K.C., J.C. Phillips: Phys. Rev. B **9**, 1552 (1974). Nonlocal pseudopotentials for Ge and GaAs

Panish M.B., H.C. Casey: J. Appl. Phys. **40**, 163 (1969). Temperature dependence of the energy gap in GaAs and GaP

Pietsch U., V.G. Tsirelson, R.P. Ozeror: Phys. Status Solidi B **138**, 47 (1986). X-ray electron density of GaAs

Pitt G.D., J. Lees: Phys. Rev. B **2**, 4144 (1970). Electrical properties of the GaAs X_1^c minima at low electric fields from a high pressure experiment

Pitt G.D.: J. Phys. C **6**, 1586 (1973). Conduction band structures of GaAs and InP

Pitt G.D., J. Lees, R.A. Hoult, R.A. Stradling: J. Phys. C **6**, 3282 (1973). Magneto-phonon effect in GaAs and InP to high pressures

Pollak F.H., M. Cardona: Phys. Rev. **172**, 816 (1968). Piezo-electroreflectance in Ge, GaAs, and Si

Pollak R., L. Ley, S. Kowalcyzk, D.A. Shirley, J. Joannopoulos, D.J. Chadi, M.L. Cohen: Phys. Rev. Lett. **29**, 1103 (1973). X-ray photoemission valence band spectra and theoretical valence band densities of states for Ge, GaAs, and ZnSe

Pond S.F., P. Handler: Phys. Rev. B **6**, 2248 (1972). Flatband electroreflectance of gallium arsenide: I. Experimental results

Rehn V., D.S. Kyser: Phys. Rev. Lett. **28**, 494 (1972). Symmetry of the 4.5 eV optical interband transition in GaAs

Reine M., R.L. Aggarwal, B. Lax: Phys. Rev. B **5**, 3033 (1972). Stress modulated magnetoreflectivity of gallium antimonide and gallium arsenide

Rode D.L., S. Knight: Phys. Rev. B **3**, 2534 (1971). Electron transport in GaAs

Rogers D.L., C.Y. Fong: Phys. Rev. Lett. **34**, 660 (1975). Theoretical analyses of the angular dependent photoemission from GaAs

Saslow W., T.K. Bergstresser, C.Y. Fong, M.L. Cohen, D. Brust: Solid State Commun. **5**, 667 (1967). Pseudopotential calculation of ϵ_2 for the zinc-blende structure: GaAs

Sell D.D., S.E. Stokowski: Proc. 10th. Int. Conf. on Physics of Semiconductors (Oak Ridge, USAEC 1970) p.417, Modulated piezoreflectance and reflectance studies of GaAs

Sell D.D., R. Dingle, S.E. Stokowski, J.V. Dilorenzo: Phys. Rev. Lett. **27**, 1644 (1971). Observation of polaritons in GaAs: a new interpretation of the free exciton reflectance and luminescence

Sell D.D., S.E. Stokowski, R. Dingle, J.V. Dilorenzo: Phys. Rev. B. **7**, 4568 (1973). Polariton reflectance and photoluminescence in high purity GaAs

Sell D.D., H.C. Casey, Jr., K.W. Wecht: J. Appl. Phys. **45**, 2650 (1974). Concentration dependence of refractive index for n-type and p-type GaAs between 1.2 and 1.8 eV

Smith N.V., M.M. Traum: Phys. Rev. Lett. **31**, 1247 (1973). Angular dependence of photoemission from the (110) face of GaAs

Soma T., J. Satoh, H. Matsuo: Solid State Commun. **42**, 889 (1982). Thermal expansion coefficients of GaAs and InP

Sramek S.J., M.L. Cohen: Phys. Rev. B **6**, 3800 (1972). Frequency and wave-vector-dependent dielectric function for Ge, GaAs and ZnSe

Thomson A.G., J.C. Woolley, M. Rubenstein: Can. J. Phys. **44**, 2927 (1966). Reflectance of GaAs, GaP and GaAs$_{1-x}$P$_x$ alloys

Trommer R., M. Cardona: Solid State Commun. **21**, 153 (1977). Resonant Raman scattering by 2 TO phonons and the ordering of conduction band minima in GaAs

Tsay Y.F., B. Bendow: Phys. Rev. B **14**, 2681 (1976). Pressure dependence of the direct energy gap of GaAs

Vaidyanathan A., A.H. Guenther, S.S. Mitra: Phys. Rev. B **24**, 2259 (1981). Band-structure calculations of the two phonon absorption coefficients of GaAs, InP, CdTe and ZnSe

Vinson P.J., C. Pickering, A.R. Adams, W. Fawcett, G.D. Pitt: *Proc. of the 13th Int.*

Conf. on the Phys. of Semicond., ed. by F.G. Fermi (Rome 1970). Band structure of GaAs from transferred electron effects at high pressure, p. 1243

Vrehon Q.H.: J. Phys. Chem. Solids **29**, 129 (1968). Interband magneto-optical absorption in gallium arsenide

Walter J.P., M.L. Cohen: Phys. Rev. **183**, 763 (1969). Calculation of the reflectivity, modulated reflectivity and band structure of GaAs, GaP, ZnSe and ZnS

Walter J.P., R.R. Zucca, Y.R. Shen, M.L. Cohen: Phys. Rev. Lett. **24**, 102 (1970). Temperature dependence of the wavelength modulation spectra of GaAs

Walter J.P., M.L. Cohen: Phys. Rev. B **2**, 1821 (1970). Wave vector dependent dielectric function for Si, Ge, GaAs and ZnSe

Walter J.P., M.L. Cohen: Phys. Rev. B **4**, 1877 (1971). Pseudopotential calculations of electronic charge densities in seven semiconductors

Walton A.K., S.F. Metcalfe: J. Phys. C **9**, 3605 (1976). Free carrier absorption of low temperature uniaxially stressed n-type Ge, Si and GaAs

Wang C.S., B.M. Klein: Phys. Rev. B **24**, 3393 (1981). First principles electronic structure of Si, Ge, GaP, GaAs, ZnS and ZnSe: I. Self consistent energy bands, charge densities and effective masses

Wang C.S., B.M. Klein: Phys. Rev. B **24**, 3417 (1981). First principles electronic structure of Si, Ge, GaP, GaAs, ZnS and ZnSe: II. Optical properties

Welber B., M. Cardona, C.K. Kim, S. Rodriguez: Phys. Rev. B **12**, 5729 (1975). Dependence of the direct energy gap of GaAs on hydrostatic pressure

Welkowsky M., R. Braunstein: Phys. Rev. B **5**, 497 (1972). Interband transitions and exciton effects. Band structures of Ge, Si, GaAs, GaP, GaSb, InAs, InP, InSb and AlSb

Wells J.E., P. Handler: Phys. Rev. B **3**, 1315 (1971). Piezoreflectivity of gallium arsenide

Yu P.Y., M. Cardona: Solid State Commun. **9**, 1421 (1971). Spatial distribution in the dielectric constant of GaAs

Zucca R.R., Y.R. Shen: Phys. Rev. B **1**, 2668 (1970). Wavelength modulation of some semiconductors

Zucca R.R., J.P. Walter, Y.R. Shen, M.L. Cohen: Solid State Commun. **8**, 627 (1970). Wavelength modulation spectra of GaAs and silicon

B.4.15 Gallium Phosphide

Aspnes D.E., C.G. Olson: Phys. Rev. Lett. **33**, 1605 (1974). Electroreflectance of GaP to 27 eV

Aspnes D.E., C.G. Olson, D.W. Lynch: Phys. Rev. B **12** 2527 (1975). Electroreflectance of GaAs and GaP to 27 eV using synchrotron radiation

Aspnes D.E., C.G. Olson, D.W. Lynch: Phys. Rev. B **14**, 2534 (1976). Line shape and symmetry analysis of core level electroreflectance spectra of GaP

Aspnes D.E., C.G. Olson, D.W. Lynch: Phys. Rev. Lett. **36**, 1536 (1976). Temperature coefficients of energy separations between Ga 3d core levels and sp^3 valence-conduction bands in GaP

Aspnes D.E., M. Cardona, V. Saile, M. Skibowski, G. Spruessel: Solid State Commun. **31**, 99 (1979). Fine structure in optical transitions from 3d and 4d core levels to the lower conduction band in Ga-V and in-V compounds

Bergstresser T.K., M.L. Cohen, E.W. Williams: Phys. Rev. Lett. **15**, 662 (1965). Reflectivity and band structure of GaAs, GaP and Ga(As,P). alloys

Booth I.J., C.F. Schwardtfeger: Solid State Commun. **55**, 817 (1985). Optical detection of cyclotron resonance in GaP and ZnTe

Chelikowsky J.R., M.L. Cohen: Phys. Rev. B **14**, 556 (1976). Nonlocal pseudopotential calculations for the electronic structure of eleven diamond and zinc-blende semiconductors

Cohen M.L., T.K. Bergstresser: Phys. Rev. **141**, 789 (1966). Band structures and pseudopotential form factors for fourteen semiconductors of the diamond and zinc-blende structures

Dean P.J., G. Kaminsky, R.B. Zetterstrom: J. Appl. Phys. **38**, 3551 (1967). Intrinsic optical absorption of gallium phosphide between 2.33 eV and 3.12 eV

Eastman D.E., W.D. Grobman, J.L. Freeouf, M. Erbudak: Phys. Rev. B **9**, 3473 (1974). Photoemission spectroscopy using synchrotron radiation. I. overviews of valence band structure for Ge, GaAs, GaP, InSb, ZnSe, CdTe and AgI

Gray A.M.: Phys. Status Solidi **37**, 11 (1970). Evaluation of the electronic energy band structures of GaAs and GaP

Hornung D., R. von Blatz, Solid State Commun. **48**, 225 (1983). Band structure investigation of the bulk photovoltaic effect in n-GaP

Hu J.T., D.R. Black, I.L. Spain, Solid State Commun. **51**, 491 (1984). GaP at ultrahigh pressure

Lane T., C.J. Vesley, D.W. Langer: Phys. Rev. B. **6**, 3770 (1972). X-ray photoemission measurements of GaP, GaAs, InAs and InSb

Ley L., R.A. Pollak, F.R. McFeely, S.P. Kowalczyk, D.A. Shirley: Phys. Rev. B **9**, 600 (1974). Total valence band densities of states of III-V and II-VI compounds from x-ray photoemission spectroscopy

Onton A.: Phys. Rev. **186**, 786 (1969). Optical absorption due to excitation of electrons bound to Si and S in GaP

Onton A., R.C. Taylor: Phys. Rev. B **1**, 2587 (1970). Spectroscopic study of Te donors in GaP

Panish M.B., H.C. Casey: J. Appl. Phys. **40**, 163 (1969). Temperature dependence of the energy gap in GaAs and GaP

Rao M.N., D.P. Mohapatra, B.K. Panda, H.C. Pandi: Solid State Commun. **55**, 241 (1985). Directional compton profile study of GaP

Rodriguez C.O.: Solid State Commun. **46**, 11 (1983). Structural properties of Si and GaP

Scott J.F., T.C. Damen, R.C. Leite, W.T. Silfvast: Solid State Commun. **7**, 953 (1969). Resonant Raman effect in the indirect gap semiconductor gallium phosphide

Sell D.D., P. Lawaetz: Phys. Rev. Lett. **26**, 311 (1971). New analysis of direct exciton transitions: application to GaP

Solal F., G. Jezequel, F. Houzay, A. Barski, R. Pincheaux: Solid State Commun. **52**, 37 (1984). Angle resolved photoemission valence band dispersions E(k) for GaP

Stokowski S.E., D.D. Sell: Phys. Rev. B **5**, 1636 (1972). Reflectivity and 1/R (dR/dE). of GaP between 2.5 eV and 6.0 eV

Thomson A.G., J.C. Woolley, M. Rubenstein: Can. J. Phys. **44**, 2927 (1966). Reflectance of GaAs, GaP and $GaAs_{1-x}P_x$ alloys

Varea de Alvarez C., J.P. Walter, J. Stokes, Y.R. Shen, M.L. Cohen: Phys. Rev. B **6**, 1412 (1972). Wavelength modulation spectra and band structures of InP and GaP

Ves S., K. Strossner, C.K. Kim, M. Cardona: Solid State Commun. **55**, 327 (1985). Dependence of the direct energy gap of GaP on hydrostatic pressure

Walter J.P., M. L. Cohen: Phys. Rev. **183**, 763 (1969). Calculation of the reflectivity, modulated reflectivity and band structure of GaAs, GaP, ZnSe, and ZnS

Wang C.S., B.M. Klein: Phys. Rev. B **24**, 3393 (1981). First principles electronic structure of Si, Ge, GaP, GaAs, ZnS and ZnSe: I. Self-consistent energy bands, charge densities and effective masses

Wang C.S., B.M. Klein: Phys. Rev. B **24**, 3417 (1981). First principles electronic structure of Si, Ge, GaP, GaAs, ZnS and ZnSe: II. Optical properties

Weinstein B.A., G.J. Piemarial: Phys. Rev. B **12**, 1172 (1975). Raman scattering and phonon dispersion in Si and GaP at very high pressure

Welkowsky M., R. Braunstein: Phys. Rev. B **5**, 497 (1972). Interband transitions and exciton effects. Band structures of Ge, Si, GaAs, GaP, GaSb, InAs, InP, InSb and AlSb

B.4.16 Gallium Selenide

Baldereschi A., K. Maschke, M. Schlüter: Helv. Phys. Acta **47**, 434 (1974). Multi-center $k \cdot p$ expansion for the band structure of GaSe

Bassani F., G.P. Parravicini: Nuovo Cimento B **50**, 95 (1967). Band structure and optical properties of graphite and the layered compounds GaS and GaSe

Kowalczyk S.P., L. Ley, F.R. McFeely, D.A. Shirley: Solid State Commun. **17**, 463 (1975). A high resolution x-ray photoemission study of the total valence band densities of states of GaSe and BiI_3

Mooser E., M. Schlüter: Nuovo Cimento **18**, 164 (1973). Band gap excitons in gallium selenide

Mooser E., I.C. Schlüter, M. Schlüter: J. Phys. Chem. Sol. **35**, 1269 (1974). The electronic charge densities in semiconducting layer and chain structures

Ottaviani G., C. Canali, F. Nava, P. Schmid, E. Mooser, R. Minder, I. Zschokke: Solid State Commun. **14**, 933 (1974). GaSe: A layer compound with anomalous valence band anisotropy

Schlüter M.: Nuovo Cimento **33**, 313 (1972). Electronic structure of GaSe

Schlüter M., J. Camassel, S. Kohn, J.P, Voitchovsky, Y.R. Shen, M.L. Cohen: Phys. Rev. B **13**, 3534 (1976). Optical properties of GaSe and $GaS_x Se_{1-x}$

Schlüter M., M.L. Cohen: Phys. Rev. B **14**, 424 (1976). Valence band density of states and chemical bonding for several non-transition metal layer compounds: $SnSe_2$, PbI_2, BiI_3, GaSe

Shepherd F., P.M. Williams: Phys. Rev. B **12**, 5705 (1975). Photoelectron studies of the densities of states in the gallium chalcogenides

Thiry R., R. Pincheaux, D. Dagneaux, Y. Petroff: In *Proc. 12th Int'l Conf. on Physics of Semiconductors*, ed. by Pilkuhn (Teubner, Stuttgart 1974), p.1324. Photoemission and optical properties of GaSe

Williams R.H., G.P. Williams, C. Norris, M.R. Howell, I.H. Munro: J. Phys. C **7**, L29 (1974). Photoemission from gallium selenide using synchrotron radiation

Williams R.H., P.C. Kemeny, L. Ley: Solid State Commun. **19**, 495 (1976). Spatial symmetries of valence band structures by angularly resolved x-ray photoelectron spectroscopy

Williams R.H., I.T. McGovern, R.B. Murray, H. Howells: Phys. Status Solidi B **73**, 307 (1976). Investigation of the electronic structure of GaSe and GaTe by photoelectron spectroscopy using a synchrotron source and electron energy loss spectroscopy

B.4.17 Gallium Sulphide

Bassani F., G.P. Parravicini: Nuovo Cimento B **50**, 95 (1967). Band structure and optical properties of graphite and the layered compounds GaS and GaSe

Schlüter M., J. Camassel, S. Kohn, J.P. Voitchovsky, Y.R. Shen, M.L. Cohen: Phys. Rev. B **13**, 3534 (1976). Optical properties of GaSe and $GaS_x Se_{1-x}$

Shepherd F., P.M. Williams: Phys. Rev. B **12**, 5705 (1975). Photoelectron studies of the densities of states in the gallium chalcogenides

B.4.18 Gallium Telluride

Williams R.H., I.T. McGovern, R.B. Murray, H. Howells: Phys. Status Solidi **73**, 307 (1976). Investigation of the electronic structure of GaSe and GaTe by photo-electron spectroscopy using a synchrotron source and electron energy loss spectroscopy

B.4.19 Germanium

Allen P.B., M. Cardona: Phys. Rev. B **27**, 4760 (1983). Temperature dependence of the direct gap of Si and Ge

Allen P.B., M. Cardona: Phys. Rev. B **23**, 1495 (1981). Theory of the temperature dependence of the direct gap of germanium

Allen F.G., E.O. Kane: Phys. Rev. Lett **12**, 94 (1964). Polarization evidence for momentum conservation in photoelectric emission from germanium and silicon

Aspnes D.E.: Phys. Rev. Lett. **31**, 230 (1973). Interband masses of higher interband critical points in Ge

Aspnes D.E.: Phys. Rev. B **12**, 2297 (1975). Schottky-barrier electroreflectance of Ge: non-degenerate and orbitally degenerate critical points

Auvergne D., J. Camassel, H. Mathieu, M. Cardona: Phys. Rev. B **9**, 5168 (1974). Temperature dependence of the band structure of germanium and zinc-blende type semiconductors

Bachelet G.B., N.E. Christensen: Phys. Rev. B **31**, 879 (1985). Relativistic and core-relaxation effects on the energy bands of gallium arsenide and germanium

Batterman B.W., D.R. Chipman: Phys. Rev. **127**, 690 (1962). Vibrational amplitudes in germanium and silicon

Batz B.: Solid State Commun. **4**, 241 (1965). Reflectance modulation at a germanium surface

Batz B.: Solid State Commun. **5**, 985 (1967). Thermoreflectance in germanium

Brust D.: Phys. Rev. **134**, A1337 (1964). Electronic spectra of crystalline germanium and silicon

Brust D.: Phys. Rev. B **4**, 3497 (1971). Nonlocal corrections to the band structure of Si, Ge and α-SN

Camassel J., D. Auvergne: Phys. Rev. B **12**, 3258 (1975). Temperature dependence of the fundamental edge of germanium and zinc-blende type semiconductors

Cardona M., G. Harbeke: J. Appl. Phys. **34**, 813 (1963). Absorption spectrum of germanium and zinc-blende type materials at energies higher than the fundamental absorption edge

— Cardona M., F.H. Pollak: Phys. Rev. **142**, 530 (1966). Energy band structure of germanium and silicon: the k·p method

Cerdeira F., W. Dreybrodt, M. Cardona: Solid State Commun. **10**, 591 (1972). Resonant Raman scattering in germanium

Cerdeira F., N. Mestres, M. Cardona: Phys. Rev. B **29**, 3737 (1984). Light scattering by plasmons in germanium

Chadi D.J., R.M. Martin: Solid State Commun. **19**, 643 (1976). Calculation of lattice dynamical properties from electronic energies: application to C, Si and Ge

Chandrasekhar M., F.H. Pollak: Phys. Rev. B **15**, 2127 (1977). Effects of uniaxial stress on the electroreflectance spectrum of Ge and GaAs

Chelikowsky J.R., M.L. Cohen: Phys. Rev. Lett. **31**, 1582 (1973). High resolution band structure and the E_2 peak in Ge

Chelikowsky J.R., M.L. Cohen: Phys. Ref. Lett. **33**, 1339 (1974). Electronic charge densities and the temperature dependence of the forbidden (222). reflection in Si and Ge

Chelikowsky J.R., M.L. Cohen: Phys. Rev. B **14**, 556 (1976). Nonlocal pseudopotential calculations for the electronic structure of eleven diamond and zinc-blende semiconductors

Cohen M.L., J.C. Phillips: Phys. Rev. **139**, A912 (1965). Spectral analysis of photoemissive yields in Si, Ge, GaAs, GaSb, InAs and InSb

Cohen M.L., T.K. Bergstresser: Phys. Rev. **141**, 789 (1966). Band structures and pseudopotential form factors for fourteen semiconductors of the diamond and zinc-blende structures

Dawson B., B.T. Willis: Proc. R. Soc. Ser. A **298**, 307 (1966). Anaharmonic vibration and forbidden reflections in silicon and germanium

Donovan T.M., J.E. Fischer, J. Matsuzaki, W.E. Spicer: Phys. Rev. B **3**, 4292 (1971). Detailed study of the Γ_{15} conduction band minimum in germanium by photoemission and transverse electroreflectance

Dresselhaus G., A Kip, C. Kittel: Phys. Rev. **98**, 368 (1955). Cyclotron resonance of electrons and holes in silicon and germanium crystals

Dresselhaus G., M.S. Dresselhaus: Phys. Rev. **160**, 649 (1967). Fourier expansion for the electronic energy bands in silicon and germanium

Eastman D.E., W.D. Grobman, J.L. Freeouf, M. Erbudak: Phys. Rev. B **9**, 3473 (1974). Photoemission spectroscopy using synchrotron radiation: I. Overviews of valence band structure for Ge, GaAs, GaP, InSb, ZnSe, CdTe and AgI

Eastman D.E., J.L. Freeouf: Phys. Rev. Lett. **33**, 1601 (1974). Photoemission partial yield measurements of unoccupied intrinsic states for Ge(111). and GaAs(110).

Gerhardt U.: Phys. Rev. Lett. **15**, 401 (1965). Polarization dependence of the piezoreflectance in Si and Ge

Gerhardt U.: Phys. Status Solidi **11**, 801 (1965). Das Reflexionsvermögen von Germanium und Silizium Einkristallen bei elastischer Deformation

Gobeli G.W., F.G. Allen: Phys. Rev. **137**, A245 (1965). Photoelectric properties of cleaved GaAs, GaSb, InAs and InSb surfaces: Comparisons with Si and Ge

Grobman W.D., D.E. Eastman: Phys. Rev. Lett. **33**, 1034 (1974). Absolute conduction and valence band positions for Ge from an anisotropic model of photoemission

Grobman W.D., D.E. Eastman, J.L. Freeouf: Phys. Rev. B **12**, 4405 (1975). Photoemission spectroscopy using synchrotron radiation II. The electronic structure of germanium

Groves S.H., C.R. Pidgeon, J. Feinleib: Phys. Rev. Lett. **17**, 643 (1966). Infrared magnetoelectroreflectance in Ge, GaSb and InSb

Hensel J.C., K. Suzuki: Phys. Rev. B **9**, 4219 (1974). Quantum resonances in the valence bands of germanium. II. Cyclotron resonances in uniaxially stressed crystals

Herman F.: Phys. Rev. **93**, 1214 (1954). Calculation of the energy band structures of the diamond and germanium crystals by the method of orthogonalized plane waves

Higginbotham C.W., M. Cardona, F.H. Pollak: Phys. Rev. **184**, 821 (1969). Intrinsic piezobirefringence of Ge, Si and GaAs

Humlicek J., F. Lukes, E. Schmidt, M.G. Kekoua, E, Khoutsishvili: Solid State Commun. **47**, 387 (1983). Disorder broadening of E_2 optical spectra in Ge-Si alloys

Joannopoulos J.D., M.L. Cohen: Solid State Commun. **11**, 549 (1972). Comparison of the electronic structure of amorphous and crystalline polytypes of Ge

Joannopoulos J.D., M.L. Cohen: Solid State Commun. **13**, 1115 (1973). New insight into the optical properties of amorphous Ge and Si

Joannopoulos J.D., M.L. Cohen: Phys. Rev. B **7**, 2644 (1973). Electronic properties of complex crystalline and amorphous phases of Ge and Si I. Density of states and band structure

Joannopoulos J.D., M.L. Cohen: Phys. Rev. B **8**, 2733 (1973). Electronic properties of complex crystalline and amorphous phases of Ge and Si II. Band structure and optical properties

Kane E.O.: J. Phys. Chem. Solids 1, 82 (1956). Energy band structure in p-type germanium and silicon

Kelso S.M.: Phys. Rev. B 25, 1116 (1982). Energy- and stress-dependent hole masses in germanium and silicon

Klima J.: J. Phys. C 3, 70 (1970). Calculation of soft x-ray emission spectra of silicon and germanium

Kline J.S., F.H. Pollak, M. Cardona: Helv. Phys. Acta 41, 968 (1968). Electroreflectance in Ge-Si alloys

Lambrecht W.R.L., O.K. Anderson: Phys. Rev. B 34, 2439 (1986). Minimal basis sets in the linear muffin tin orbital method: Application to the diamond structure crystals: C, Si and Ge

Lautenschlager P., P.B. Allen, M. Cardona: Phys. Rev. B 31, 2163 (1985). Temperature dependence of band gaps in Si and Ge

Levinger B.W., D.R. Frankl: J. Phys. Chem. Solids 20, 281 (1963). Cyclotron resonance measurements on the energy band parameters of Ge

Ley L., S.P. Kowalczyk, R.A. Pollak, D.A. Shirley: Phys. Rev. Lett. 29, 1088 (1972). X-ray photoemission spectra of crystalline and amorphous Si and Ge valence bands

Marple D.T., H. Ehrenreich: Phys. Rev. Lett. 8, 87 (1962). Dielectric constant behaviour near band edges in CdTe and Ge

Melz P.: J. Phys. Chem. Solids 32, 209 (1971). Energy band structure of strained crystals: Pseudopotential calculations for Ge and Si with trial calculations for GaAs and CdTe

Minomura S., H.G. Drickamer: J. Phys. Chem. Solids 23, 451 (1962). Pressure induced phase transitions in silicon, germanium and some III-V compounds

MacFarlane G.G., T.P. McClean, J.E. Quarrington, V. Roberts: Proc. Phys. Soc. 71, 863 (1958). Direct optical transitions and further exciton effects in germanium

Pandey K.C., J.C. Phillips: Phys. Rev. B 9, 1552 (1974). Nonlocal pseudopotentials for Ge and GaAs

Papconstantopoulos D.A.: Phys. Rev. B 27, 2569 (1983). Self-consistent augmented plane wave band structure calculations of Si and Ge with overlapping spheres

Phillips J.C., K.C. Pandey: Phys. Rev. Lett 30, 787 (1973). Nonlocal pseudopotential for Ge

Pollak F.H., M. Cardona: Phys. Rev. 172, 816 (1968). Piezo-electroreflectance in Ge, GaAs and Si

Pollak R., L. Ley, S. Kowalcyzk, D.A. Shirley, J. Joannopoulos, D.J. Chadi, M.L. Cohen: Phys. Rev. Lett. 29, 1103 (1973). X-ray photoemission valence band spectra and theoretical valence band densities of states for Ge, GaAs and ZnSe

Raccah P.M., R.N. Euwema, D.J. Stuckel, T.C. Collins: Phys. Rev. B 1, 756 (1970). Comparison of theoretical and experimental charge densities for C, Si, Ge and ZnSe

Renucci J.B., M.A. Renucci, M. Cardona: Solid State Commun. 9, 1235 (1971). Resonant Raman scattering in germanium and zinc-blende type semiconductors temperature dependence

Roberto J.B., B.W. Batterman, D.J. Keating: Phys. Rev. B 9, 2590 (1974). Diffraction studies of the (222). reflection in Ge and Si: Anharmonicity and the bonding electrons

Roth L.M., B. Lax: Phys. Rev. Lett. 3, 217 (1959). g factor of electrons in germanium

Saravia L.R., D. Brust: Phys. Rev. 176, 915 (1968). Spin splitting and the ultra violet absorption of Ge

Sell D.D., E.O. Kane: Phys. Rev. 185, 1103 (1969). Piezoreflectance of Ge from 1.9 to 2.8 eV

Sell D.D., E.O. Kane: Phys. Rev. B **5**, 417 (1972). Identification of Γ transitions in the E_0 region of germanium by piezoreflectance measurements

Seraphin B.O., R.B. Hess: Phys. Rev. Lett. **14**, 138 (1965). Franz Keldysh effect above the fundamental edge in germanium

Sramek S.J., M.L. Cohen: Phys. Rev. B **6**, 3800 (1972). Frequency and wave-vector-dependent dielectric function for Ge, GaAs and ZnSe

Srivastava G.P.: Phys. Rev. B **25**, 2815 (1982). Self-consistent pseudopotential calculation for the electronic structure of Ge

Straub D., L. Ley, F.J. Himpsel: Phys. Rev. B **33**, 2607 (1986). Inversion Photoemission study of unoccupied electronic states in Ge and Si: Bulk energy bands

Suzuki K., J.C. Hensel: Phys. Rev. B **9**, 4184 (1974). Quantum resonances in the valence bands of germanium I. Theoretical considerations

Tubino R., L. Piseri, C. Zerbi: J. Chem. Phys. **56**, 1022 (1972). Lattice dynamics and spectroscopic properties by a valence force potential of diamond-like crystals: C, Si, Ge and Sn

Viña L., S. Logothetids, M. Cardona, Phys. Rev. B **30**, 1979 (1984). Temperature dependence of the dielectric function of germanium

Wanger J., M. Cardona: Phys. Rev. B **32**, 8071 (1985). Electronic Raman scattering in heavily doped p-type germanium

Walter J.P., M.L. Cohen: Phys. Rev. B **2**, 1821 (1970). Wave vector dependent dielectric function for Si, Ge, GaAs and ZnSe

Walter J.P., M.L. Cohen: Phys. Rev. B **4**, 1877 (1971). Pseudopotential calculations of electronic charge densities in seven semiconductors

Walton A.K., S.F. Metcalfe: J. Phys. C **9**, 3605 (1976). Free carrier absorption of low temperature uniaxially stressed n-type Ge, Si and GaAs

Wang C.S., B.M. Klein: Phys. Rev. B **24**, 3393 (1981). First principles electronic structure of Si, Ge, GaP, GaAs, ZnS and ZnSe: I. Self consistent energy bands, charge densities and effective masses

Wang C.S., B.M. Klein: Phys. Rev. B **24**, 3417 (1981). First principles electronic structure of Si, Ge, GaP, GaAs, ZnS and ZnSe. II. Optical properties

Weber W.: Phys. Rev. B **15**, 4789 (1977). Adiabatic bond charge model for phonons in diamond, Si, Ge and α-Sn

Welkowsky M., R. Braunstein: Phys. Rev. B **5**, 497 (1972). Interband transitions and exciton effects. Band structures of Ge, Si, GaAs, GaP, GaSb, InAs, InP, InSb and AlSb

Yin M.T., M.L. Cohen: Solid State Commun. **38**, 625 (1981). Microscopic theory of the static structural properties and phase transformations of Ge

Yin M.T., M.L. Cohen: Solid State Commun. **43**, 391 (1982). Calculation of the lattice dynamical properties of Ge

Zallen R., W. Paul: Phys. Rev. **155**, 703 (1967). Effect of pressure on interband reflectivity spectra of germanium and related semiconductors

Zucca R.R., Y.R. Shen: Phys. Rev. B **1**, 2668 (1970). Wavelength modulation of some semiconductors

B.4.20 Germanium Telluride

Tung Y., P.B. Allen, M.L. Cohen: J. de Phys. **29**, 163 (1968). Optical properties, band structure and superconductivity of SnTe and GeTe

Tung Y.W., M.L. Cohen: Phys. Rev. **180**, 823 (1969). Relativistic band structure and electronic properties of SnTe, GeTe and PbTe

B.4.21 Indium Antimonide

Aspnes D.E., M. Cardona, V. Saile, M. Skibowski, G. Spruessel: Solid State Commun. **31**, 99 (1979). Fine structure in optical transitions from 3d and 4d core levels to the lower conduction band in Ga-V and In-V compounds

Bilderback D.H., R. Colella: Phys. Rev. Lett. **35**, 858 (1975). Valence charge density in indium antimonide

Bloom S., T.K. Bergstresser: Solid State Commun. **6**, 465 (1968). Band Structure of α-Sn, InSb and CdTe including spin orbit effects

Cardona M., N.E. Christensen, M. Dobrowolska, J.K. Furyna, S. Rodriguez: Solid State Commun. **60**, 17 (1986). Spin splitting of the conduction band of InSb along [110]

Cardona M., C.M. Penchina, N. Shevchik, J. Tejeda: Solid State Commun. **11**, 1655 (1972). Photoemission of GaAs and InSb core levels

Chelikowsky J.R., M.L. Cohen: Phys. Rev. B **14**, 556 (1976). Nonlocal pseudopotential calculations for the electronic structure of eleven diamond and zinc-blende semiconductors

Cohen M.L., J.C. Phillips: Phys. Rev. **139**, A912 (1965). Spectral analysis of photoemissive yields in Si, Ge, GaAs, GaSb, InAs and InSb

Eastman D.E., W.D. Grobman, J.L. Freeouf, M. Erbudak: Phys. Rev. B **9**, 3473 (1974). Photoemission spectroscopy using synchrotron radiation. I. Overviews of valence band structure for Ge, GaAs, GaP, InSb, ZnSe, CdTe and AgI

Glosser R., B.O. Seraphin: Phys. Rev. **187**, 1021 (1969). Band population effects in the electroreflectance spectrum of InSb

Glosser R., J.E. Fischer, B.O. Seraphin: Phys. Rev. B **1**, 1607 (1970). Inter-conduction-band transitions in the electroreflectance spectrum of InSb

Gobeli G.W., F.G. Allen: Phys. Rev. **137**, A245 (1965). Photoelectric properties of cleaved GaAs, GaSb, InAs and InSb surfaces: Comparisons with Si and Ge

Groves S.H., C.R. Pidgeon, J. Feinleib: Phys. Rev. Lett. **17**, 643 (1966). Infrared magnetoelectroreflectance in Ge, GaSb and InSb

Kane E.O.: J. Phys. Chem. Solids **1**, 249 (1956). Band structure of indium antimonide

Lane T., C.J. Vesley, D.W. Langer: Phys. Rev. B **6**, 3770 (1972). X-ray photoemission measurements of GaP, GaAs, InAs and InSb

Ley L., R.A. Pollak, F.R. McFeely, S.P. Kowalczyk, D.A. Shirley: Phys. Rev. B **9**, 600 (1974). Total valence band densities of states of III-V and II-VI compounds from x-ray photoemission spectroscopy

Mele E.J., J.D. Joannopoulos: Phys. Rev. B **24**, 3145 (1981). Electronic structure of the zinc-blende and rocksalt phases of InSb

Middelman H.U., L. Sorba, V. Hinkel, K. Horn: Phys. Rev. B **34**, 957 (1986). Valence band structure determination of InSb by angle resolved photoemission

Muthukrishnan R., D.G Seiler: Phys. Status Solidi (b). **54**, K83 (1972). Deformation potential parameters of n-InSb

Pidgeon C.R., S.H. Groves: Phys. Rev. **186**, 824 (1969). Inversion-asymmetry and warping induced interband magneto-optical transitions in InSb

Singh D., Y.P. Varshni: Phys. Rev. B **31**, 8252 (1985). Valence charge in InSb

Tuomi T., M. Cardona, F.H. Pollak: Phys. Status Solidi **40**, 227 (1970). Stress dependence of E_1 and $E_1+\Delta_1$ transitions in InSb and GaSb

Varea de Alvarez C., J.P. Walter, R.W. Boyd, M.L. Cohen: J. Chem. Phys. Solids **34**, 337 (1973). Calculated band structures, optical constants and electronic charge densities in InAs and InSb

Walter J.P., M.L. Cohen: Phys. Rev. B **4**, 1877 (1971). Pseudopotential calculations of electronic charge densities in seven semiconductors

Welkowsky M., R. Braunstein: Phys. Rev. B 5, 497 (1972). Interband transitions and exciton effects. Band structures of Ge, Si, GaAs, GaP, GaSb, InAs, InP InSb and AlSb

Yu P.Y., M. Cardona, F.H. Pollak: Phys. Rev. B 3, 340 (1971). Intrinsic piezobire-fringence in GaSb, InAs and InSb

Zhukotynski S., N. Saleh: Phys. Status Solidi (B). 38, 571 (1970). Effective mass tensor in uniaxially stressed n-type InSb

Zucca R.R., Y.R. Shen: Phys. Rev. B 1, 2668 (1970). Wavelength modulation of some semiconductors

B.4.22 Indium Arsenide

Aspnes D.E., M. Cardona, V. Saile, M. Skibowski, G. Spruessel: Solid State Commun. 31, 99 (1979). Fine structure in optical transitions from 3d and 4d core levels to the lower conduction band in Ga-V and In-V compounds

Chelikowsky J.R., M.L. Cohen: Phys. Rev. B 14, 556 (1976). Nonlocal pseudopotential calculations for the electronic structure of eleven diamond and zinc-blende semiconductors

Cohen M.L., J.C. Phillips: Phys. Rev. 139, A912 (1965). Spectral analysis of photoemissive yields in Si, Ge, GaAs, GaSb, InAs and InSb

Gobeli G.W., F.G. Allen: Phys. Rev. 137, A245 (1965). Photoelectric properties of cleaved GaAs, GaSb, InAs and InSb surfaces: Comparisons with Si and Ge

Lane T., C.J. Vesley, D.W. Langer: Phys. Rev. B 6, 3770 (1972). X-ray photoemission measurements of GaP, GaAs, InAs and InSb

Ley L., R.A. Pollak, F.R. McFeely, S.P. Kowalczyk, D.A. Shirley: Phys. Rev. B 9, 600 (1974). Total valence band densities of states of III-V and II-VI compounds from x-ray photoemission spectroscopy

Varea de Alvarez C., J.P. Walter, R.W. Boyd, M.L. Cohen: J. Chem. Phys. Solids 34, 337 (1973). Calculated band structures, optical constants and electronic charge densities in InAs and InSb

Welkowsky M., R. Braunstein: Phys. Rev. B 5, 497 (1972). Interband transitions and exciton effects. Band structures of Ge, Si, GaAs, GaP, GaSb, InAs, InP, InSb and AlSb

Yu P.Y., M. Cardona, F.H. Pollak: Phys. Ref. B 3, 340 (1971). Intrinsic piezobire-fringence in GaSb, InAs and InSb

Zucca R.R., Y.R. Shen: Phys. Rev. B 1, 2668 (1970). Wavelength modulation of some semiconductors

B.4.23 Indium Phosphide

Aspnes D.E., M. Cardona, V. Saile, M. Skibowski, G. Spruessel: Solid State Commun. 31, 99 (1970). Fine structure in optical transitions from 3d and 4d core levels to the lower conduction band in Ga-V and In-V compounds

Chelikowsky J.R., M.L. Cohen: Phys. Rev. B 14, 556 (1976). Nonlocal pseudopotential calculations for the electronic structure of eleven diamond and zinc-blende semiconductors

Cohen M.L., T.K. Bergstresser: Phys. Rev. 141, 789 (1966). Band structures and pseudopotential form factors for fourteen semiconductors of the diamond and zinc-blende structures

Dzwig P., V. Crum, M.G. Burt, J.C. Inkson: Solid State Commun. 39, 407 (1981). Calculation of optical matrix elements in gallium arsenide

Fischer T.E.: Phys. Rev. 142, 519 (1966). Photoemission and work function of InP

James L.W., J.P. Van Dyke, F. Herman, D.M. Chang: Phys. Rev. B 1, 3998 (1970). Band structure and high field transport properties of InP

Ley L., R.A. Pollak, F.R. McFeely, S.P. Kowalczyk, D.A. Shirley: Phys. Rev. B **9**, 600 (1974). Total valence band densities of states of III-V and II-VI compounds from x-ray photoemission spectroscopy

McGinnity T.M., G.G. Roberts: Solid State Commun. **46**, 643 (1983). Electroabsorption in single crystal indium phosphide

Onton A., R.J. Chicotka, Y. Yacoby: *11th Int. Conf. on the Phys. of Semicond. Warsaw* (Warszawa 1972) p.1023. Subsidiary indirect conduction band minima and their donor levels in GaAs and InP

Pitt G.D.: Solid State Commun. **8**, 1119 (1970). The conduction band structure of InP from a high pressure experiment

Pitt G.D.: J. Phys. C **6**, 1586 (1973). Conduction band structures of GaAs and InP

Pitt G.D., J. Lees, R.A. Hoult, R.A. Stradling: J. Phys. C **6**, 3282 (1973). Magnetophonon effect in GaAs and InP to high pressures

Soma T., J. Satoh, H. Matsuo: Solid State Commun. **42**, 889 (1982). Thermal expansion coefficients of GaAs and InP

Varea de Alvarez C., J.P. Walter, J. Stokes, Y.R. Shen, M.L. Cohen: Phys. Rev B **6**, 1412 (1972). Wavelength modulation spectra and band structures of InP and GaP

Vaidyanathan A., A.H. Guenther, S.S. Mitra: Phys. Rev. B **24**, 2259 (1981). Bandstructure calculations of the two phonon absorption coefficients of GaAs, InP, CdTe and ZnSe

Welkowsky M., R. Braunstein: Phys. Rev. B **5**, 497 (1972). Interband transitions and exciton effects. Band structures of Ge, Si, GaAs, GaP, GaSb, InAs, InP, InSb and AlSb

B.4.24 Lead Diiodide

Schlüter I.C., M. Schlüter: Phys. Rev. B **9**, 1652 (1974). Electronic structure and optical properties of PbI_2

Schlüter M., M.L. Cohen: Phys. Rev. B **14**, 424 (1976). Valence band density of states and chemical bonding for several non-transition metal layer compounds: $SnSe_2$, PbI_2, BiI_3, GaSe

B.4.25 Lead Selenide

Dalven R.: Solid State Physics **28**, 179 (1973). Electronic Structure of PbS, PbSe, and PbTe

Gupta B.P.K., V. Kumar: Solid State Commun. **45**, 745 (1983). Analysis of effective compressibilities in PbS, PbSe, PbTe, and SnTe

Kohn S.E., P.Y. Yu, Y. Petroff, Y.R. Shen, Y. Tsang, M.L. Cohen: Phys. Rev. B **8**, 1477 (1973). Electronic band structure and optical properties of PbTe, PbSe and PbS

Leloup J.Y., B. Sapoval, G. Martinez: Phys. Rev. B **7**, 5276 (1973). Knight shift in multivalley semiconductors: II. Determination of the hyperfine coupling constants in n-type and p-type PbSe and PbTe

Martinez G., M. Schlüter, M.L. Cohen: Phys. Rev. B **11**, 651 (1975). Electronic structure of PbSe and PbTe: I. Band structures, densities of states and effective masses

Martinez G., M. Schlüter, M.L. Cohen: Phys. Rev. B **11**, 660 (1975). Electronic structure of PbSe, and PbTe II. Optical properties

McFeely F.R., S.P. Kowalczyk, L. Ley, R.A. Pollak, D.A. Shirley: Phys. Rev. B **7**, 5228 (1973). High resolution x-ray photoemission spectra of PbS, PbSe, and PbTe valence bands

Schlüter M., G. Martinez, M.L. Cohen: Phys. Rev. B **11**, 3808 (1975). Electronic charge densities in PbSe and PbTe

Schlüter M., G. Martinez, M.L. Cohen: Phys. Rev. B **12**, 650 (1975). Pressure and temperature dependence of electronic energy levels in PbSe and PbTe

B.4.26 Lead Sulphide

Dalven R.: Solid State Physics **28**, 179 (1973). Electronic structure of PbS, PbSe and PbTe

Gupta B.P.K., V. Kumar: Solid State Commun. **45**, 745 (1983). Analysis of effective compressibilities in PbS, PbSe, PbTe and SnTe

Kohn S.E., P.Y. Yu, Y. Petroff, Y.R. Shen, Y. Tsang, M.L. Cohen: Phys. Rev. B **8**, 1477 (1973). Electronic band structure and optical properties of PbTe, PbSe and PbS

McFeely F.R., S.P. Kowalczyk, L. Ley, R.A. Pollak, D.A. Shirley: Phys. Rev. B **7**, 5228 (1973). High resolution x-ray photoemission spectra of PbS, PbSe and PbTe valence bands

B.4.27 Lead Telluride

Chattopadhyag D., H. Aichmann, G. Nimtz: Solid State Commun. **51**, 151 (1984). Negative differential mobility in PbTe and PbSnTe at high electric field

Dalven R.: Solid State Physics **28**, 179 (1973). Electronic structure of PbS, PbSe and PbTe

Gelmont B.L., T.R. Globus, A.V. Matveenko: Solid State Commun. **38**, 931 (1981). Optical absorption and band structure of PbTe

Gungor A., H.D. Drew: Solid State Commun. **44**, 701 (1982). Observation of inter-valley optical transitions in PbTe by magneto-photo response

Gupta B.P.K., V. Kumar: Solid State Commun. **45**, 745 (1983). Analysis of effective compressibilities in PbS, PbSe, PbTe and SnTe

Keffer C., T.M. Hayes, A. Bienenstock: Phys. Rev. Lett. **21**, 1676 (1968). PbTe Debye-Waller factors and band gap temperature dependence

Kohn S.E., P.Y. Yu, Y. Petroff, Y.R. Shen, Y. Tsang, M.L. Cohen: Phys. Rev. B **8**, 1477 (1973). Electronic band structure and optical properties of PbTe, PbSe and PbS

Leloup J.Y, B. Sapoval, G. Martinez: Phys. Rev. B **7**, 5276 (1973). Knight shift in multivalley semiconductors. II. Determination of the hyperfine coupling constants in n-type and p-type PbSe and PbTe

Martinez G., M. Schlüter, M.L. Cohen: Phys. Rev. B **11**, 660 (1975). Electronic structure of PbSe and PbTe II. Optical properties

Martinez G., M. Schlüter, M.L. Cohen: Phys. Rev. B **11**, 651 (1975). Electronic structure of PbSe and PbTe I. Band structures, densities of states and effective masses

Martinez G., M. Schlüter, M.L. Cohen: Phys. Rev. Lett. **35**, 1746 (1975). Energy level parities at L in PbTe

McFeely F.R., S.P. Kowalczyk, L. Ley, R.A. Pollak, D.A. Shirley: Phys. Rev. B **7**, 5228 (1973). High resolution x-ray photoemission spectra of PbS, PbSe and PbTe valence bands

Schlüter M., G. Martinez, M.L. Cohen: Phys. Rev. B **11**, 3808 (1975). Electronic charge densities in PbSe and PbTe

Schlüter. M., G. Martinez, M.L. Cohen: Phys. Rev. B **12**, 650 (1975). Pressure and temperature dependence of electronic energy levels in PbSe and PbTe

Tauber R.N., A.A. Machonis, I.B. Cadoff: J. Appl. Phys. **37**, 4855 (1966). Thermal and optical energy gaps in PbTe

Tsang Y.W., M.L. Cohen: Solid State Commun. **9**, 261 (1971). Band ordering in PbTe

Tsang Y.W., M.L. Cohen: Phys. Rev. B **3**, 1254 (1971). Calculation of the temperature dependence of the energy gaps in PbTe and SnTe

Tsang Y.W., M.L. Cohen: Solid State Commun. **10**, 871 (1972). Electronic charge density in PbTe

Tung Y.W., M.L. Cohen: Phys. Rev. **180**, 823 (1969). Relativistic band structure and electronic properties of SnTe, GeTe and PbTe

Tung Y.W., M.L. Cohen: Phys. Lett. A **29**, 236 (1969). The fundamental energy gap in SnTe and PbTe

B.4.28 Magnesium Oxide

Cohen M.L., P.J. Lin, D.M. Roessler, W.C. Walker: Phys. Rev. **155**, 992 (1967). Ultraviolet optical properties and electronic band structure of magnesium oxide

Fong C.Y., W. Saslow, M.L. Cohen: Phys. Rev. **168**, 992 (1968). Pseudopotential calculation of the optical constants of MgO from 7-28 eV

Lin P.J., D.M. Roessler, W.C. Walker, M.L. Cohen: Phys. Rev. **155**, 992 (1967). Ultraviolet optical properties and electronic band structure of magnesium oxide

Roessler D.M., W.C. Walker: Phys. Rev. **159**, 733 (1967). Electronic spectrum and ultraviolet optical properties of crystalline MgO

Walker W.C., D.M. Roessler, E. Loh: Phys. Rev. Lett. **20**, 847 (1968). Phonon induced splitting of exciton lines in MgO and BeO

Whited R., C.J. Flaten, W.C. Walker: Solid State Commun. **13**, 1903 (1973). Exciton thermoreflectance of MgO and CaO

B.4.29 Magnesium Silicide

Au-Yang M.Y., M.L. Cohen: Solid State Commun. **6**, 855 (1968). Electronic structure and dielectric function of Mg_2Si

B.4.30 Mercury Selenide

Bloom S., T.K. Bergstresser: Phys. Status Solidi **42**, 191 (1971). Band structure of HgSe and HgTe

B.4.31 Mercury Sulphide

Shevchik N.J., J. Tejeda, D.W. Langer, M. Cardona: Phys. Status Solidi (B) **60**, 345 (1973). Photoemission and density of valence states of II-VI compounds II. ZnSe, CdS and HgS

B.4.32 Mercury Telluride

Bloom S., T.K. Bergstresser: Phys. Status Solidi **42**, 191 (1971). Band structure of HgSe and HgTe

Cade N.A., P.M. Lee: Solid State Commun. **56**, 673 (1985). Self-consistent energy band structures for HgTe and CdTe

Cardona M., D.L. Greenaway: Phys. Rev. **131**, 98 (1963). Fundamental reflectivity and band structure of ZnTe, CdTe and HgTe

Chadi D.J., J.P. Walter, Y. Petroff, M. Balkanski, M.L. Cohen: Phys. Rev. B **5**, 3058 (1972). Reflectivities and electronic band structures of CdTe and HgTe

Chadi D.J., M.L. Cohen: Phys. Rev. B 7, 692 (1973). Electronic structure of $Hg_{1-x}Cd_xTe$ alloys and charge density calculations using representative k-points

Gerlach E., P. Grosse (eds.): *The Physics of Selenium and Tellurium*, Springer Ser. Solid-State Sci., Vol.13 (Springer, Berlin, Heidelberg 1979)

Guenzer C.S., A. Bienenstock: Phys. Lett. A 34, 172 (1971). Temperature dependence of the HgTe band gap

Guenzer C.S., A. Bienenstock: Phys. Rev. B 8, 4655 (1973). Unsuccessful Brooks-Yu typecalculation of HgTe band gap temperature dependence

Ley L. R.A. Pollak, F.R. McFeely, S.P. Kowalczyk, D.A. Shirley: Phys. Rev. B 9, 600 (1974). Total valence band densities of states of III-V and II-VI compounds from x-ray photoemission spectroscopy

B.4.33 Selenium

Joannopoulos J.D., M. Schlüter, M.L. Cohen: *Proc. 12th Int. Conf. on the Phys. of Semicond.* (Stuttgart 1974). Electronic density of states of amorphous and trigonal Se and Te, p. 1304

Joannopoulos J.D., M. Schlüter, M.L. Cohen: Phys. Rev. B 11, 2186 (1976). Electronic structure of trigonal and amorphous Se and Te

Gerlach E., P. Grosse (eds.): *The Physics of Selenium and Tellurium*, Springer Ser. Solid-State Phys., Vol.13 (Springer, Berlin, Heidelberg 1979)

Schlüter M., J.D. Joannopoulos, M.L. Cohen: Phys. Rev. Lett. 33, 89 (1974). New interpretation of photoemission measurements on trigonal Se and Te

Schlüter M., J.D. Joannopoulos, L. Ley, S.P. Kowalczyk, R.A. Pollak, D.A. Shirley, M.L. Cohen: Solid State Commun. 15, 1007 (1974). The structural nature of amorphous Se and Te

von Boehm J., H.M. Isomaki: Solid State Commun. 40, 495 (1981). The relativistic valence and conduction band edges of trigonal Te and Se

B.4.34 Silicon

Aldred P.J., M. Hart: Proc. R. Soc. A 332, 223 (1973). The electron distribution in silicon: Experiment

Aldred P.J., M. Hart: Proc. R. Soc. A 332, 239 (1973). The electron distribution in silicon: Theory

Allen F.G., E.O. Kane: Phys. Rev. Lett. 12, 94 (1964). Polarization evidence for momentum conservation in photoelectric emission from germanium and silicon

Allen P.B., M. Cardona: Phys. Rev. B 27, 4760 (1983). Temperature dependence of the direct gap of Si and Ge

Appelbaum J.A., D.R. Hamann: Phys. Rev. Lett. 31, 106 (1973). Surface states and surface bonds of Si(111)

Appelbaum J.A., D.R. Hamann: Phys. Rev. B 8, 1777 (1973). Self-consistent pseudopotential for Si

Aspnes D.E., A.A. Studna: Solid State Commun. 11, 1375 (1972). Direct observation of the E_o and $E_o + \Delta_o$ transitions in silicon

Averkiev N.S., Y.V. Ilisavskiy, V.M. Sternin: Sol. State Commun. 52, 17 (1984). The free charge carrier effects on the elastic properties of silicon

Batterman B.W., D.R. Chipman: Phys. Rev. 127, 690 (1962). Vibrational amplitudes in germanium and silicon

Bertoni C.M., V. Bortolani, C. Calandra, E. Tosatti: Phys. Rev. Lett. 28, 1578 (1972). Dielectric matrix and phonon frequencies in silicon

Bertoni C.M., V. Bortolani, C. Calandra, E. Tosatti: Phys. Rev. B 9, 1710 (1974). Dielectric screening matrix and lattice dynamics of Si

Biswas R., R.M. Martin, R.J. Needs, O.H. Nielsen: Phys. Rev. B **30**, 3210 (1984). Complex tetrahedral structures of silicon and carbon under pressure

Brown F.C., O.P. Rustgi: Phys. Rev. Lett. **28**, 497 (1972). Extreme ultraviolet transmission of crystalline and amorphous silicon

Brust, D., M.L. Cohen, J.C. Phillips: Phys. Rev. Lett. **9**, 389 (1962). Reflectance and photoemission from Si

Brust D.: Phys. Rev. **134**, A1337 (1964). Electronic spectra of crystalline germanium and silicon

Brust D., Phys. Rev. B **4**, 3497 (1971). Nonlocal corrections to the band structure of Si, Ge and α-Sn

Bullet D.W.: J. Phys. C **8**, 2707 (1975). Chemical pseudopotential approach to covalent bonding: Bond lengths and bond energies in diamond, silicon and graphite

Car R., E. Tossatti, S. Bartoni, S. Leelapurte: Phys. Rev. B **24**, 985 (1981). Dielectric band structure of crystals: General properties and calculations for silicon

Cardona M., F.H. Pollak: Phys. Rev. **142**, 530 (1966). Energy band structure of germanium and silicon: The k·p method

Cardona M.: Phys. Rev. B **15**, 5999 (1977). Transverse reduced mass of the E_1 and $E_1 + \Delta_1$ transitions in silicon

Cerofolini G.F., L. Meda: *Physical Chemistry of, in and on Silicon*, Springer Ser. Mat. Sci., Vol.8 (Springer, Berlin, Heidelberg 1988)

Chadi D.J., R.M. Martin: Solid State Commun. **19**, 643 (1976). Calculation of lattice dynamical properties from electronic energies: Application to C, Si and Ge

Chaney R.C., C.C. Lin, E.E. Lafon: Phys. Rev. B **3**, 459 (1971). Application of the method of tight binding to the calculation of the energy band structures of diamond, silicon and sodium crystals

Camp P.E.Van, V.E. Van Doren, J.T. Devreese: Phys. Rev. B **24**, 1096 (1981). Dielectric screening theory in the local-density-functional formalism. Application to silicon using slater exchange

Camp P.E.Van, V.E. Van Doren, J.T. Devreese: Phys. Rev. B **34**, 1314 (1986). First principies calculation of the pressure coefficient of the charge density in C and Si

Chelikowsky J.R., M.L. Cohen: Phys. Rev. Lett. **33**, 1339 (1974). Electronic charge densities and the temperature dependence of the forbidden (222) reflection in Si and Ge

Chelikowsky J.R., M.L. Cohen: Phys. Rev. B **10**, 5095 (1974). Electronic structure of Si

Chelikowsky J.R., M.L. Cohen: Phys. Rev. B **14**, 556 (1976). Nonlocal pseudopotential calculations for the electronic structure of eleven diamond and zincblende semiconductors

Cohen M.L., J.C. Phillips: Phys. Rev. **139**, A912 (1965). Spectral analysis of photoemissive yields in Si, Ge, GaAs, GaSb, InAs and InSb

Cohen M.L., T.K. Bergstresser: Phys. Rev. **141**, 789 (1966). Band structures and pseudopotential form factors for fourteen semiconductors of the diamond and zincblende structures

Dawson B., B.T. Willis: Proc. R. Soc. Ser. A **298**, 307 (1966). Anaharmonic vibration and forbidden reflections in silicon and germanium

Dimigen H.: Z. Phys. **165**, 53 (1961). Energie Analyse im Elektronenstreudiagramm einer dünnen Silizium Folie

Dovesi R., M. Causa, G. Angonoa: Phys. Rev. B **24**, 4177 (1981). Exact exchange Hartree Fock calculations for periodic systems: Ground state properties of silicon

Dresselhaus G., A. Kip, C. Kittel: Phys. Rev. **98**, 368 (1955). Cyclotron resonance of electrons and holes in silicon and germanium crystals

Dresselhaus G., M.S. Dresselhaus: Phys. Rev. **160**, 649 (1967). Fourier expansion for the electronic energy bands in silicon and germanium

Falter C., W. Ludwig, M. Selmke: Solid State Commun. **54**, 497 (1985). A microscopic model for the phonon dispersion in silicon

Frova A., P. Handler: Phys. Rev. Lett. **14**, 178 (1965). Direct observation of phonons in silicon by electric field modulated optical absorption

Gahwiller C.G., F.C. Brown: *Proc. of the 10th Int. Conf. on the Phys. of semicond:* (Cambridge Mass, 1970). Photoabsorption near the LII,III edge of silicon, p. 213

Gerhardt U.: Phys. Rev. Lett. **15**, 401 (1965). Polarization dependence of the piezoreflectance in Si and Ge

Gerhardt U.: Phys. Status Solidi **11**, 801 (1965). Das Reflexionsvermögen von Germanium und Silizium Einkristallen bei elastischer Deformation

Gobeli G.W., F.G. Allen: Phys. Rev. **127**, 141 (1962). Direct and indirect excitation processes in the photoelectric emission from silicon

Gobeli G.W., F.G. Allen, Phys. Rev. **137**, A245 (1965). Photoelectric properties of cleaved GaAs, GaSb, InAs and InSb surfaces: Comparisons with Si and Ge

Goroff I., L. Kleinman: Phys. Rev. **132**, 1080 (1963). Deformation potentials in silicon. III. Effects of a general strain on conduction and valence levels

Grover J.W., P. Handler: Phys. Rev. B **9**, 2600 (1974). Electroreflectance of silicon

Gygi F., A. Baldereschi: Phys. Rev. B **34**, 4405 (1986). Self-consistent Hartree-Fock and screened exchange calculations in solids: Application to silicon

Hattori H., H. Kuriyama, T. Katayawa, M. Kato: J. Phys. Soc. Japan **20**, 988 (1965) Absolute measurement of structure factors of Si by means of x-ray pendelloesung fringes

Heine V., J.A. Van Vechten: Phys. Rev. B **13**, 1622 (1976). Effect of electron-hole pairs on phonon frequencies in Si related to temperature dependence of band gaps

Hensel J.C., H. Hasegawa, M. Nakagama: Phys. Rev. **138**, A225 (1965). Cyclotron resonance in uniaxially stressed silicon II. Nature of the covalent bond

Higginbotham C.W., M. Cardona, F.H. Pollak: Phys. Rev. **184**, 821 (1969). Intrinsic piezobirefringence of Ge, Si and GaAs

Humlicek J., F. Lukes, E. Schmidt, M.G. Kekoua, E. Khoutsishvili: Solid State Commun. **47**, 387 (1983). Disorder broadening of E_2 optical spectra in Ge-Si alloys

Ihm J., M.L. Cohen: Solid State Commun. **29**, 711 (1979). Self-consistent pseudopotential calculations of the equilibrium properties of bulk and surface Si

Joannopoulos J.D., M.L. Cohen: Phys. Lett. A **41**, 71 (1972). Electronic structure of crystalline polytypes and amorphous Si

Joannopoulos J.D., M.L. Cohen: Solid State Commun **13**, 1115 (1973). New insight into the optical properties of amorphous Ge and Si

Joannopoulos J.D., M.L. Cohen: Phys. Rev. B **7**, 2644 (1973). Electronic properties of complex crystalline and amorphous phases of Ge and Si I. Density of states and band structures

Joannopoulos J.D., M.L. Cohen: Phys. Rev. B **8**, 2733 (1973). Electronic properties of complex crystalline and amorphous phases of Ge and Si II. Band structure and optical properties

Joannopoulos J.D., G. Lucovsky (eds.): *The Physics of Hydrogenated Amorphous Silicon I and II*, Topics Appl. Phys., Vols.55 and 56 (Springer, Berlin, Heidelberg 1983,84)

Kane E.O.: J. Phys. Chem. Solids **1**, 82 (1956). Energy band structure in p-type germanium and silicon

Kane E.O., G.W. Gobeli: Phys. Rev. Lett **15**, 142 (1965). Dependence of the optical constants of silicon on uniaxial stress

Kane E.O.: Phys. Rev. **146**, 558 (1966). Band structure of silicon from an adjusted Heine-Abrarenkov calculation

Kane E.O., Phys. Rev. B **4**, 1910 (1971). Need for a nonlocal correlation potential in Si

Kane E.O., Phys. Rev. B **23**, 4054 (1981). Bond-bending force constant of silicon by an r-space method

Kato M., S. Tanemura: Acta Crystallogr. A **28**, 69 (1972). Absolute measurement of structure factors of silicon by using x-ray pendelloesung and interferometry

Kelso S.M.: Phys. Rev. B **25**, 1116 (1982). Energy- and stress-dependent hole masses in germanium and silicon

Klima J.: J. Phys. C **3**, 70 (1970). Calculation of soft x-ray emission spectra of silicon and germanium

Kline J.S., F.H. Pollak, M. Cardona: Helv. Phys. Acta **41**, 968 (1968). Electroreflectance in Ge-Si alloys

Koo J., Y.R. Shen, R.R. Zucca: Solid State Commun. **9**, 2229 (1971). Effects of uniaxial stress on the E_o peak of silicon

Kunz A.B.: Phys. Rev. Lett. **27**, 567 (1971). Energy bands and the soft x-ray absorption in Si

Lambrecht W.R.L., O.K. Anderson: Phys. Rev. B **34**, 2439 (1986). Minimal basis sets in the linear muffin tin orbital method: application to the diamond structure crystals: C, Si and Ge

Lautenschlager P., P.B. Allen, M. Cardona: Phys. Rev. B **31**, 2163 (1985). Temperature dependence of band gaps in Si and Ge

Ley L., S.P. Kowalczyk, R.A. Pollak, D.A. Shirley: Phys. Rev. Lett **29**, 1088 (1972). X-ray photoemission spectra of crystalline and amorphous Si and Ge valence bands

Louie S.G., J.R. Chelikowsky, M.L. Cohen: Phys. Rev. Lett. **34**, 155 (1975). Local field effects in the optical spectrum of Si

Louie S.G., M.L. Cohen: Phys. Rev. B **17**, 3174 (1978). Dielectric screening and zone center phonons in silicon

Manghi F., G. Reigler, C.M. Bertoni, G.B. Bachelet: Phys. Rev. B **31**, 3680 (1985). Band structure calculation for GaAs and Si beyond the local density approximation

Melz P.: J. Phys. Chem. Solids **32**, 209 (1971). Energy band structure of strained crystals: Pseudopotential calculations for Ge and Si with trial calculations for GaAs and CdTe

Minomura S., H.G. Drickamer: J. Phys. Chem. Solids **23**, 451 (1962). Pressure induced phase transitions in silicon, germanium, and some III-V compounds

Ohkashi I., K. Shindo: J. Phys. Soc. Japan **43**, 1879 (1977). A pseudopotential approach to the crystal energy of Si

Papconstantopoulos D.A.: Phys. Rev. B **27**, 2569 (1983). Self-consistent augmented plane wave band structure calculations of Si and Ge with overlapping spheres

Pasternak J., K. Verdam: Phys. Rev. B **3**, 2567 (1971). Optical anisotropy of silicon single crystals

Phillips J.C.: Phys. Lett. A **37**, 434 (1971). Anharmonicity and temperature dependence of the forbidden (222) reflection in silicon

Pietsch U., V.G. Tsirelson, R.P. Ozeror: Phys. Status Solids B **137**, 441 (1986). X-ray electron density of Si

Pollak F.H., M. Cardona: Phys. Rev. **172**, 816 (1968). Piezo-electroreflectance in Ge, GaAs and Si

Raccah P.M., R.N. Euwema, D.J. Stuckel, T.C. Collins: Phys. Rev. B **1**, 756 (1970). Comparison of theoretical and experimental charge densities for C, Si, Ge and ZnSe

Roberto J.B., B.W. Batterman: Phys. Rev. B **2**, 3220 (1970). Anharmonicity and the temperature dependence of the forbidden (222) reflection in silicon

Roberto J.B., B.W. Batterman, D.J. Keating: Phys. Rev. B **9**, 2590 (1974). Diffraction studies of the (222) reflection in Ge and Si: Anharmonicity and the bonding electrons.

Rodriguez C.O.: Solid State Commun. **46**, 11 (1983). Structural properties of Si and GaP

Saravia L.R., D. Brust: Phys. Rev. **171**, 916 (1968). High resolution study of the one electron spectrum of Si

Schlüter M., J.R. Chelikowsky, S.G. Louie, M.L. Cohen: Phys. Rev. B **12**, 4200 (1975). Self-consistent pseudopotential calculations for Si(111) surfaces: Unreconstructed (1x1) and reconstructed (2x1) model structures

Straub D., L. Ley, F.J. Himpsel: Phys. Rev. Lett. **54**, 142 (1985). Conduction-band and surface-state critical points in Si: An inversion photoemission study

Straub D., L. Ley, F.J. Himpsel: Phys. Rev. B **33**, 2607 (1986). Inversion photoemission study of unoccupied electronic states in Ge and Si: Bulk energy bands

→Stukel D.J., R.N. Euwema: Phys. Rev. B **1**, 1635 (1970). Self-consistent orthogonalized plane wave energy band study of silicon

Sy H.K., C.K. Ong: Solid State Commun. **52**, 881 (1984). Electron mobility in heavily doped silicon

Szmulowicz F.: Phys. Rev. B **23**, 1652 (1981). Self-consistent non-muffin-tin augmented-plan-wave calculation of the band structure of silicon

Trucano P., B.W. Batterman: Phys. Rev. B **6**, 3659 (1972). Bonding electron distributions, anharmonicity and the temperature dependence of the forbidden Si (442) reflection

Tubino R., L. Piseri C. Zerbi: J. Chem. Phys. **56**, 1022 (1972). Lattice dynamics and spectroscopic properties by a valence force potential of diamond-like crystals: C, Si Ge and Sn

Viña L., M. Cardona: Phys. Rev. B **29**, 6739 (1984). Effect of heavy doping on the optical properties and the band structure of silicon

von der Linden W., P. Fulde, K.P. Bohnen: Phys. Rev. B **34**, 1063 (1986). Efficient approach to the *ab initio* Hartree-Fock problem of solids with application to diamond and silicon

Wagner L.F., W.E. Spicer: Phys. Rev. Lett. **28**, 1381 (1972). Observation of a band of silicon surface states containing one electron per surface atom

Walter J.P., M.L. Cohen: Phys. Rev. B **2**, 1821 (1970). Wave vector dependent dielectric function for Si, Ge, GaAs and ZnSe

Walter J.P., M.L. Cohen: Phys. Rev. B **4**, 1877 (1971). Pseudopotential calculations of electronic charge densities in seven semiconductors

Walter J.P., M.L. Cohen: Phys. Rev. B **5**, 3101 (1972). Frequency and wave-vector-dependent dielectric function for silicon

Walton A.K., S.F. Metcalfe: J. Phys. C **9**, 3605 (1976). Free carrier absorption of low temperature uniaxially stressed n-type Ge, Si and GaAs

Wang C.S., B.M. Klein: Phys. Rev. B **24**, 3393 (1981). First principles electronic structure of Si, Ge, GaP, GaAs, ZnS, and ZnSe: I. Self-consistent energy bands, charge densities and effective masses

Wang C.S., B.M. Klein: Phys. Rev. B **24**, 3393 (1981). First principles electronic structure of Si, Ge, GaP. GaAs, ZnS, and ZnSe: II. Optical properties

Wang C.S., W.E. Pickett: Phys. Rev. Lett. **51**, 597 (1983). Density-functional theory of excitation spectra of semiconductors: Application to Si

Weber W: Phys. Rev. B **15**, 4789 (1977). Adiabatic bond charge model for phonons in diamond, Si, Ge and α-Sn

Weinstein B.A., G.J. Piemarial: Phys. Rev. B **12**, 1172 (1975). Raman scattering and phonon dispersion in Si and GaP at very high pressure

Welkowsky M., R. Braunstein: Phys. Rev. B **5**, 497 (1972). Interband transitions and exciton effects. Band structures of Ge, Si, GaAs, GaP, GaSb, InAs, InP, InSb, and AlSb

Yang L.W., P. Coppens: Solid State Commun. **15**, 1555 (1974). On the experimental electron distribution in silicon

Yin M.T., M.L. Cohen: Phys. Rev. Lett. **50**. 1172 (1983). Valence-electron density of silicon under high pressure

Zhao Y.-X., F. Buehler, J.R. Sites, I.L. Spain: Solid State Commun. **59**, 679 (1986). New metastable phases of silicon

Zucca R.R., Y.R. Shen: Phys. Rev. B **1**, 2668 (1970). Wavelength modulation of some semiconductors

Zucca R.R., J.P. Walter, Y.R. Shen, M.L. Cohen: Solid State Commun. **8**, 627 (1970). Wavelength modulation spectra of GaAs and silicon

B.4.35 Silver Chloride

Bassani F., R.S. Knox, W.B. Fowler: Phys. Rev. **137**, 1217 (1965). Band structure and electronic properties of AgCl and AgBr

Farberovich O.V., Y.K. Timoshenko, A.M. Bugakov, E.P. Domahevshaya: Solid State Commun. **40**, 559 (1981). APW-LCAO energy bands and fundamental absorption bands in silver chloride crystals

Kunz A.B.: Phys. Rev. B **26**, 2070 (1982). Electronic structure of AgF, AgCl and AgBr

Ves S., D. Glotzel, M. Cardona, H. Overhof: Phys. Rev. B **24**, 3073 (1981). Pressure dependence of the optical properties and band structures of the copper and silver halides

Wang J.S., M. Schlüter, M.L. Cohen: Phys. Status Solidi (b) **77**, 295 (1976). The electronic structure of AgCl

B.4.36 Silver Iodide

Eastman D.E., W.D. Grobman, J.L. Freeouf, M. Erbudak: Phys. Rev. B **9**, 3473 (1974). Photoemission spectroscopy using synchrotron radiation. I. Overviews of valence band structure for Ge, GaAs, GaP. InSb, ZnSe, CdTe and AgI

Kunz A.B: Phys. Rev. B **26**, 2070 (1982). Electronic structure of AgF, AgCl and AgBr

Ves S., D. Glotzel, M. Cardona, H. Overhof: Phys. Rev. B **24**, 3073 (1981). Pressure dependence of the optical properties and band structures of the copper and silver halides

B.4.37 Tellurium

Gerlach E., P. Grosse (eds.): *The Physics of Selenium and Tellurium*, Springer Ser. Solid-State Sci., Vol.13 (Springer, Berlin, Heidelberg 1979)

Joannopoulos J.D., M. Schlüter. M.L. Cohen: *Proc. 12th Int. Conf on the Phys. of Semicond.* (Stuttgart, 1974). Electronic density of states of amorphous and trigonal Se and Te, p. 1304

Joannopoulos J.D., M. Schlüter, M.L. Cohen: Phys. Rev. B **11**, 2186 (1976). Electronic structure of trigonal and amorphous Se and Te

Schlüter M., J.D. Joannopoulos, M.L. Cohen: Phys. Rev. Lett. **33**, 89 (1974). New interpretation of photoemission measurements on trigonal Se and Te

Schlüter M., J.D. Joannopoulos, L. Ley, S.P. Kowalczyk, R.A. Pollak, D.A. Shirley, M.L. Cohen: Solid State Commun. **15**, 1007 (1974). The structural nature of amorphouse Se and Te

von Boehm J., H.M. Isomaki: Solid State Commun. **40**, 495 (1981). The relativistic valence and conduction band edges of trigonal Te and Se

B.4.38 Tin

Bloom S., T.K. Bergstresser: Solid State Commun. **6**, 465 (1968). Band structure of α-Sn, InSb and CdTe including spin orbit effects

Brust D.: Phys. Rev. B **4**, 3497 (1971). Nonlocal corrections to the band structure of Si, Ge and α-SN

Cardona M., D.L. Greenaway: Phys. Rev. **125**, 1291 (1962). Reflectivity of gray tin single crystals in the fundamental absorption region

Cardona M., P. McElroy, F.H. Pollak, K.L. Shaklee: Solid State Commun **4**, 319 (1966). Electroreflectance and band structure of gray tin

Chelikowsky J.R., M.L. Cohen: Phys. Rev. B **14**, 556 (1976). Nonlocal pseudopotential calculations for the electronic structure of eleven diamond and zincblende semiconductors

Cohen M.L., T.K. Bergstresser: Phys. Rev. **141**, 789 (1966). Band structures and pseudopotential form factors for fourteen semiconductors of the diamond and zincblende structures

Groves S., W. Paul: Phys. Rev. Lett. **11**, 194 (1963). Band structures of gray tin

Middlemann H.U., L. Sorba, V. Hinkel, K. Horn: Phys. Rev. B **35**, 718 (1987). Valence band structure of α-Sn as determined by angle resolved photoemission

Pollak F.H., M. Cardona, C.W. Higginbotham, F. Herman, J.P. Van Dyke: Phys. Rev. B **2**, 352 (1970). Energy band structure and optical spectrum of gray tin

Tubino R., L. Piseri, C. Zerbi: J. Chem. Phys. **56**, 1022 (1972). Lattice dynamics and spectroscopic properties by a valence force potential of diamond-like crystals: C, Si, Ge and Sn

Viña L., H. Höchst, M. Cardona: Phys. Rev. B **31**, 958 (1985). Dielectric function of α-Sn and its temperature dependence

Walter J.P., M.L. Cohen: Phys. Rev. B **4**, 1877 (1971). Pseudopotential calculations of electronic charge densities in seven semiconductors

Weber W.: Phys. Rev. B **15**, 4789 (1977). Adiabatic bond charge model for phonons in diamond, Si, Ge and α-Sn

Weisz G.: Phys. Rev. **149**, 504 (1966). Band structure and fermi surface of white tin

B.4.39 Tin Diselenide

Au-Yang M.Y., M.L. Cohen: Phys. Rev. **178**,1358 (1969). Electronic structure and optical properties of SnS_2 and $SnSe_2$

Camassel J., M. Schlüter, S. Kohn, J.P. Voitchovsky, Y.R. Shen, M.L. Cohen: Phys. Status Solidi (B) **75**, 303 (1976). Wavelength modulation spectra and electronic structure of SnS_2 and $SnSe_2$

Fong C.Y., M.L. Cohen: Phys. Rev. B **5**, 3095 (1972). Electronic energy band structure of SnS_2 and $SnSe_2$

Fong C.Y., M.L. Cohen: J. Phys. C **7**, 107 (1974). Electronic charge densities for two layer semiconductors: SnS_2 and $SnSe_2$

Murray R.B., R.H. Williams: J. Phys. C **6**, 3643 (1973). Band structure and photoemission studies of SnS_2 and $SnSe_2$ 2. Theoretical

Schlüter I.C., M. Schlüter: Phys. Status Solidi **57**, 145 (1973). Electronic structure of SnS_2 and $SnSe_2$

Schlüter M., M.L. Cohen: Phys. Rev. B **14**, 424 (1976). Valence band density of states and chemical bonding for several non-transition metal layer compounds: $SnSe_2$, PbI_2, BiI_3, GaSe

Williams R.H., R.B. Murray, D.W. Govan, J.M. Thomas, E.L. Evans: J. Phys. C **6**, 3631 (1973). Band structure and photoemission studies of SnS_2 and $SnSe_2$: I. Experimental

B.4.40 Tin Disulphide

Au-Yang M.Y., M.L. Cohen: Phys. Rev. **178**, 1358 (1969). Electronic structure and optical properties of SnS_2 and $SnSe_2$

Bacewicz R., B. Palosz, W. Palosz, S. Gierlotka: Solid State Commun. **54**, 283 (1985). Absorption edge of SnS_2 polytypes

Camassel J., M. Schlüter, S. Kohn, J.P. Voitchovsky, Y.R. Shen, M.L. Cohen: Phys. Status Solidi (B) **75**, 303 (1976) Wavelength modulation spectra and electronic structure of SnS_2 and $SnSe_2$

Fong C.Y., M.L. Cohen: Phys. Rev. B **5**, 3095 (1972). Electronic energy band structures of SnS_2 and $SnSe_2$

Fong C.Y., M.L. Cohen: J. Phys. C **7**, 107 (1974). Electronic charge densities for two layer semiconductors: SnS_2 and $SnSe_2$

Mula G., F. Aymerich: Phys. Status Solidi (A) **51**, K35 (1972) Electronic structures of SnS_2

Murray R.B., R.H. Williams: J. Phys. C **6**, 3643 (1973). Band structure and photoemission studies of SnS_2 and $SnSe_2$ 2. Theoretical

Schlüter I.C., M. Schlüter: Phys. Status Solidi **57**, 145 (1973). Electronic structure of SnS_2 and $SnSe_2$

Williams R.H., R.B. Murray, D.W. Govan, J.M. Thomas, E.L. Evans: J. Phys. C **6**, 3631 (1973). Band structure and photoemission studies of SnS_2 and $SnSe_2$: I. Experimental

B.4.41 Tin Telluride

Bernick R.L., L. Kleinman: Solid State Commun. **8**, 569 (1970). Energy bands, effective masses and g-factors of the lead salts and SnTe

Gupta B.P.K., V. Kumar: Solid State Commun. **45**, 745 (1983). Analysis of effective compressibilities in PbS PbSe, PbTe and SnTe

Lin P.J., W. Saslow, M.L. Cohen: Solid State Commun. **5**, 893 (1967). Analysis of the optical properties and electronic structure of SnTe using the empirical pseudopotential method

Tsang Y.W., M.L. Cohen: Phys. Rev. B **3**, 1254 (1971). Calculation of the temperature dependence of the energy gaps in PbTe and SnTe

Tung Y., P.B. Allen, M.L. Cohen: J. de Phys. **29**, 163 (1968). Optical properties, band structure and superconductivity of SnTe and GeTe

Tung Y.W., M.L. Cohen: Phys. Rev. **180**, 823 (1969). Relativistic band structures and electronic properties of SnTe, GeTe and PbTe

Tung Y.W., M.L. Cohen: Phys. Lett. A **29**, 236 (1969). The fundamental energy gap in SnTe and PbTe

B.4.42 Zinc Germanium Phosphide

Varea de Alvarez C., M.L. Cohen: Phys. Rev. Lett. **30**, 979 (1973). Calculated band structures and reflectivity spectra of $ZnGeP_2$

Varea de Alvarez C., M.L. Cohen, S.E. Kohn, Y. Petroff, Y.R. Shen: Phys. Rev. B **10**, 5175 (1974). Calculated and measured reflectivity of $ZnGeP_2$

Varea de Alvarez C., M.L. Cohen, L. Ley, S.P. Kowalczyk, F.R. McFeely, D.A. Shirley, R.W. Grant: Phys. Rev. B **10**, 596 (1974). Electronic density of states and bonding in chalcopyrite-type semiconductors

B.4.43 Zinc Oxide

Bloom S., I. Ortenburger: Phys.Status Solidi (B) **58**, 561 (1973). Pseudopotential band calculation for ZnO

Catalano I.M., A. Cingolani: Solid State Commun. **52**, 539 (1984). Three photon absorption coefficient in ZnSe and ZnO

Chelikowsky J.R.: Solid State Commun. **22**, 351 (1977). An oxygen pseudopotential: Application to the electronic structure of ZnO

Hengehold R.L., R.J. Almasy, F.L. Pedrotti: Phys. Rev. B **1**, 4784 (1970). Electron energy loss and ultraviolet reflectivity spectra of crystalline ZnO

Klucker R., H. Nelkowski, Y.S. Park, M. Skibowski, T.S. Wagner: Phys. Status Solidi (B) **45**, 265 (1971). Optical anisotropy of ZnO in the ultraviolet region

Kobayashi A., O.F. Sankey, S.M. Volz, J.D. Dow: Phys. Rev. B **28**, 935 (1983). Semiempirical tight-binding band structures of wurtzite semiconductors: AlNb, CdS, ZnS and ZnO

Ley L., R.A.Pollak, F.R.McFeely, S.P. Kowalczyk, D.A. Shirley: Phys. Rev. B **9**, 600 (1974). Total valence band densities of states of III-V and II-VI compounds from x-ray photoemission spectroscopy

Liang W.Y., A.D. Yoffe: Phys. Rev. Lett. **20**, 59 (1968). Transmission spectra of ZnO single crystal

Park Y.S., J.R. Scheider: J. Appl.Phys. **39**, 3049 (1965). Index of refraction of ZnO

Powell R.A., W.E. Spicer, J.C. McMenamin: Phys. Rev. Lett. **27**, 97 (1971). Location of the Zn 3d-states in ZnO

Powell R.A., W.E. Spicer, J.C. McMenamin: Phys. Rev. B **6**, 3056 (1972). Photoemission studies of wurtzite zinc oxide

Zwicher G., K. Jacobi: Solid State Commun. **54**, 701 (1985). Experimental band structures of ZnO

B.4.44 Zinc Selenide

Aven M., D.T. Marple, B. Segall: J. Appl. Phys. Suppl. **32**, 2261 (1961). Some electrical and optical properties of ZnSe

Catalano I.M., A. Cingolani: Solid State Commun. **52**, 539 (1984). Three photon absorption coefficient in ZnSe and ZnO

Chelikowsky J.R., M.L. Cohen: Phys. Lett. A **47**, 7 (1974). Calculated valence band density of states and reflectivity for ZnSe

Chelikowsky J.R., M.L. Cohen: Phys. Rev. B **14**, 556 (1976). Nonlocal pseudopotential calculations for the electronic structure of eleven diamond and zincblende semiconductors

Cohen M.L., T.K. Bergstresser: Phys. Rev. **141**, 789 (1966). Band structures and pseudopotential form factors for fourteen semiconductors of the diamond and zincblende structures

Eastman D.E., W.D. Grobman, J.L. Freeouf, M. Erbudak: Phys. Rev. B **9**, 3473 (1974). Photoemission spectroscopy using synchrotron radiation. I. Overviews of valence band structure for Ge, GaAs, GaP. InSb, ZnSe, CdTe and AgI

Eckelt P.: Phys. Status Solidi **23**, 307 (1967): Energy band structures of cubic ZnS, ZnSe, ZnTe and CdTe

Ley L., R.A. Pollak, F.R. McFeely, S.P. Kowalczyk, D.A. Shirley: Phys. Rev. B **9**, 600 (1974). Total valence band densities of states of III-V and II-VI compounds from x-ray photoemission spectroscopy

Petroff Y., M. Balkanski, J.P. Walter, M.L. Cohen: Solid State Commun. **7**, 459 (1969). The optical properties and electronic band structure of zinc selenide

Pollak R., L. Ley, S. Kowalczyk, D.A. Shirley, J. Joannopoulos, D.J. Chadi, M.L.

Cohen: Phys. Rev. Lett. **29**, 1103 (1973). X-ray photoemission valence band spectra and theoretical valence band densities of states for Ge, GaAs, and ZnSe

Raccah P.M., R.N. Euwema, D.J. Stuckel, T.C. Collins: Phys. Rev. B **1**, 756 (1970). Comparison of theoretical and experimental charge densities for C, Si, Ge and ZnSe

Shevchik N.J., J. Tejeda, D.W. Langer, M. Cardona: Phys. Status Solidi (B) **60**, 345 (1973). Photoemission and density of valence states of II-VI compounds II. ZnSe, CdS and HgS

Sramek S.J., M.L. Cohen: Phys. Rev. B **6**, 3800 (1972). Frequency and wave-vector-dependent dielectric function for Ge, GaAs and ZnSe

Stukel D., R. Euwema, T.C.Collins, F. Herman, R. Kortum: Phys. Rev. **179**, 740 (1969). Self-consistent orthogonalized plane wave and empirically refined OPW energy band models for cubic ZnS, ZnSe, CdS and CdSe

Vaidyanathan A., A.H. Guenther, S.S. Mitra: Phys. Rev. B **24**, 2259 (1981). Band structure calculations of the two phonon absorption coefficients of GaAs, InP, CdTe and ZnSe

Ves S. K. Strossner, M. Cardona: Solid State Commun. **56**, 479 (1985). Pressure dependence of the lowest direct absorption edge in ZnSe

Walter J.P., M.L. Cohen: Phys. Rev. **183**, 763 (1969). Calculation of the reflectivity, modulated reflectivity and band structure of GaAs, GaP, ZnSe and ZnS

Walter J.P., Y. Petroff, M. Balkanski, M.L. Cohen: Phys. Rev. B **1**, 2661 (1970). Calculated and measured reflectivity of ZnTe and ZnSe

Walter J.P., M.L. Cohen: Phys. Rev. B **2**, 1821 (1970). Wave vector dependent dielectric function for Si, Ge, GaAs and ZnSe

Walter J.P., M.L. Cohen: Phys. Rev. B **4**, 1877 (1971). Pseudopotential calculations of electronic charge densities in seven semiconductors

Wang C.S., B.M. Klein: Phys. Rev. B **24**, 3393 (1981). First principles electronic structure of Si, Ge, GaP, GaAs, ZnS and ZnSe I. Self-consistent energy bands, charge densities and effective masses

Wang C.S., B.M. Klein: Phys. Rev. B **24**, 3393 (1981). First principles electronic structure of Si, Ge, GaP. GaAs, ZnS and ZnSe: II. Optical properties

B.4.45 Zinc Sulphide

Bergstresser T.K., M.L. Cohen: Phys. Lett. **23**, 8 (1966). Electronic structure of hexagonal zinc sulphide

Bergstresser T.K., M.L. Cohen: Phys. Rev. **164**, 1069 (1967).Electronic structure and optical properties of hexagonal CdSe, CdS and ZnS

Cohen M.L., T.K. Bergstresser: Phys. Rev. **141**, 789 (1966). Band structures and pseudopotential form factors for fourteen semiconductors of the diamond and zincblende structures

Drews R.E., E.A. Davis, A.G. Leign: Phys. Rev. Lett. **18**, 1194 (1967). Reflectivity spectra of $Cd_{1-x}Zn_xS$ single crystals

Eckelt P.: Phys. Status Solidi **23**, 307 (1967). Energy band structures of Cubic ZnS, ZnSe, ZnTe and CdTe

Joannopoulos J.D., M.L. Cohen: J. Phys. C **6**, 1572 (1973). Electronic charge densities for ZnS in the wurzite and zincblende structures

Kobayashi A., O.F. Sankey, S.M. Volz, J.D. Dow: Phys. Rev. B **28**, 935 (1983). Semiempirical tight-binding band structures of wurtzite semiconductors: AlNb, CdS, ZnS, and ZnO

Ley L., R.A. Pollak, F.R. McFeely, S.P. Kowalczyk, D.A. Shirley: Phys. Rev. B **9**, 600 (1974). Total valence band densities of states of III-V and II-VI compounds from x-ray photoemission spectroscopy

Paskov P.P., L.I. Pavlov, S.S. Dimor, I.J. Lalov: Solid State Commun. **59**, 491 (1986). Four photon spectroscopy of excitons in hexagonal zinc sulphide

Piper W.W., P.D. Johnson, D.T. Marple: J. Phys. Chem. Solids **8**, 457 (1959). Temperature dependence of the optical gap in ZnS

Rössler U., M. Lietz: Phys. Status Solidi **17**, 597 (1966). Band structure of cubic and hexagonal ZnS

Stukel D., R. Euwema, T.C. Collins, F. Herman, R. Kortum: Phys. Rev **179**, 740 (1969). Self-consistent orthogonalized plane wave and empirically refined OPW energy band models for cubic ZnS, ZnSe, CdS and CdSe

Vedam K., E.D. Schmidt: Phys. Rev **150**, 766 (1966). Non-linear piezo-optic behaviour of sphalerite

Walker W.C., J. Osantowski: J. Opt. Soc. Am. **53**, 399 (1963). Reflection spectrum of cubic zinc sulfide in the interband transition region

Walter J.P., M.L. Cohen: Phys. Rev. **183**, 763 (1969). Calculation of the reflectivity, modulated reflectivity and band structure of GaAs, GaP, ZnSe and ZnS

Wang C.S., B.M. Klein: Phys. Rev. B **24**, 3393 (1981). First principles electronic structure of Si, Ge, GaP. GaAs, ZnS and ZnSe: I. Self-consistent energy bands, charge densities and effective masses

Wang C.S., B.M. Klein: Phys. Rev. B **24**, 3393 (1981). First principles electronic structure of Si, Ge, GaP, GaAs, ZnS and ZnSe: II. Optical properties

Wheeler R.G., J.C, Miklosz: *Proc. of the Int. Conf. on Phys. of Semicon.* (Paris, 1964). Exciton structure and Zeeman effects in zinc sulfide, p.873

B.4.46 Zinc Telluride

Booth I.J., C.F. Schwardtfeger: Solid State Commun. **55**, 817 (1985). Optical detection of cyclotron resonance in GaP and ZnTe

Cardona M., D.L. Greenaway: Phys. Rev. **131**, 98 (1963). Fundamental reflectivity and band structure of ZnTe, CdTe and HgTe

Cohen M.L., T.K. Bergstresser: Phys. Rev. **141**, 789 (1966). Band structures and pseudopotential form factors for fourteen semiconductorsof the diamond and zincblende structures

Eckelt P.: Phys. Stat. Solidi **23**, 307 (1967). Energy band structures of cubic ZnS, ZnSe, ZnTe and CdTe

Ley L., R.A. Pollak, F.R. McFeely, S.P. Kowalczyk, D.A. Shirley: Phys. Rev. B **9**, 600 (1974). Total valence band densities of states of III-V and II-VI compounds from x-ray photoemission spectroscopy

Shay J.L., W.E. Spicer: Phys. Rev. **175**, 741 (1968). Photoemission study of the electronic structure of ZnTe

Shevchik N.J., J. Tejeda, D.W. Langer, M. Cardona: Phys. Status Solidi (B) **59**, 87 (1973). Photoemission and density of valence states of II-VI compounds I. ZnTe, CdSe, CdTe, HgSe and HgTe

Walter J.P., Y. Petroff, M.Balkanski, M.L. Cohen: Phys. Rev. B **1**, 2661 (1970). Calculated and measured reflectivity of ZnTe and ZnSe

Subject Index